JAPANESE INDUSTRIAL POLICY

A descriptive account of postwar
developments with case studies of
selected industries

Ira C. Magaziner

Thomas M. Hout

No. 585

ISBN 0 85374 176-X
Published by Policy Studies Institute, 1-2 Castle Lane, London SW1E 6DR
Printed by Dawson & Goodall Ltd., The Mendip Press, Bath

The Authors

Ira C. Magaziner is a founding partner of Telesis, a consulting company specialising in long term economic and industrial policy for governments and international strategy for corporations. He worked for six years with The Boston Consulting Group during which time he managed cases in a variety of industries for Western and Japanese clients. He was educated at Brown University and spent two years as a Rhodes Scholar at Balliol College, Oxford. He currently resides in Providence, Rhode Island.

Thomas M. Hout is a vice-president of The Boston Consulting Group and lives in Boston. He holds a Bachelor's degree in Economics from Yale University, an MBA from Stanford University, and he attended Manchester University. He has lived in Japan. His publications include *Japan in 1980,* co-author with James C. Abegglen, Financial Times, Ltd, London, 1974; case studies in *Japan — The Government — Business Relationship,* US Department of Commerce, Washington, DC, 1972; 'Facing Up to the Trade Gap with Japan', co-author with James C. Abegglen, *Foreign Affairs,* Autumn 1978. He has consulted on the Japanese business system for corporations and governments.

Acknowledgements

The authors share a common background with the Boston Consulting Group where they have worked for clients on confidential assignments in a variety of industries and on a range of policy issues. These clients have included major Japanese companies as well as major Western companies and governments. The analysis of particular industries is excerpted primarily from this work. Similarly, the authors' acquaintance with Japanese industrial policy comes from client work, particularly that with Japanese corporations. Specific data references and sources accordingly must remain proprietary.

The authors gratefully acknowledge the research of Michiko Kato and the editorial assistance of Nancy G. Jackson and Susan Chira. Finally, they acknowledge a large debt to James C. Abeglen for his guidance and encouragement over many years.

Contents

List of Tables and Figures

I Introduction

In order to understand Japan's success in international trade, it is necessary to have some appreciation of how Japanese companies compete internationally. It is interesting to see how many observers resort to special factors or uncommon mechanisms to explain Japan's success. These typically include a low priced and obedient labour force, producers' collusion at home, unfair trade practices, and government orchestration of the whole system. The implication is that these factors matter a great deal but are simply not available to other countries. These explanations are unsatisfactory less because they are untrue for, indeed, some of these factors at some time played a part, but more because they miss the crucial points about the competitive process.

Japanese companies enjoy good growth and profitability by becoming low cost producers. Where the Japanese succeed, they displace leading Western companies through a superior understanding of the competitive evolution of a business and a willingness to invest heavily for a sustained period of time. But they do not succeed in every industry. Japan has become the leader in steel but not in chemicals, in motorcycles but not in marine engines, and in consumer electronics but not in industrial electronics. In these less successful industries, the Japanese enjoy the same advantages of a well disciplined labour force, a supportive government, easy access to debt financing, etc. Yet the Japanese remain marginal producers. This is no accident. It largely reflects the more astute strategies of the Western competitors.

The purpose of this paper is to analyse Japan's industrial policy in the context of the basic competitive and economic forces which operate within all businesses. It is our view that industrial policy — which is defined here as the application of government resources and influence to industrial affairs — cannot be properly studied or prescribed without a thorough understanding of how competition varies by industry and how the economics of businesses change over time.[1] Industrial policy must be informed by more than national priorities and where the fast growth markets are. Industrial policy is an integral part of the international competitive business system and must be highly responsive to it. This is a major theme of this booklet.

---

[1]For a discussion of competitive business economics and its relation to industrial policy, see Ira C. Magaziner, et al.: *A Framework for Swedish Industrial Policy*. (Liberförelag, Stockholm, 1979)

Japan is a good subject because it illustrates this theme effectively. The Japanese have taken industrial policy seriously from their initial industrialisation only a century ago. They have also developed a complex set of institutions and mechanisms across both the public and private sectors of the economy for hammering out and exercising industrial policy. It should be emphasised that most of these institutions and mechanisms have been fashioned by the nation's modern history; they represent accomplishments, not cultural inheritance.

If the first strength of Japanese industrial policy is its competitive realism and economic logic, its second is the process which generates it. This policy by consensus approach is widely admired outside Japan and thinly understood. The Japanese, in the authors' experience, do not agree among themselves more readily nor subjugate one interest to another more easily than people in other countries. Policy making there, as everywhere, is conflict resolution, and it is neither easy nor benign. The Japanese do, however, share a remarkably common view on the legitimacy of national government as guide and mediator. The bureaucracy is small and highly competent. The policy process, in both its formal and informal operation, is carefully geared to explore and resolve issues before a decision is made. Often, decisions are made acceptable to all participants or they are not made at all. Policy is often slow to emerge but usually is sound and widely implemented when it does.

Japanese industrial policy has been, in general, effective in the context we have defined, and our treatment of it here is essentially positive. We should, however, emphasise the limits of our aims. Our purpose is not a comprehensive statement of the origins and operation of Japan's industrial policy itself. That would take us deep into domestic politics and personalities in both government and business, well beyond our competence. Nor is it our intention to suggest Japan as a model approach to industrial policy analysis. The Japanese have made mistakes and experienced failures as the text will show. This paper does not endorse Japan's approach.

Chapter II develops the context for industrial policy in Japan. It briefly describes the central long term economic issues of the country and tracks the logic of its industrial policy historically. Then it focuses on particular Japanese industries and how they have succeeded or failed through the strategies of the major companies. Steel, motorcycles, and colour television are briefly analysed in these terms.

Chapter III deals with the question of who makes and influences industrial policy, what form it takes and how the policy community interacts. This chapter describes not only the players in the process but analyses in some detail the range of measures the government employs in executing policy.

Chapters IV to VI offer three pairs of case studies of policy in particular industries. These demonstrate how the course of policy is influenced differently by, and changes with, the stage of an industry's competitive cycle — early development and growth, healthy maturity, and eventual decline. In Japan, industrial policy is particularly active in the first and third stages, and inactive in the middle stage. The policy history of two currently healthy, internationally strong industries — steel and motor cars — is reviewed. The current attempts to ease the decline of the aluminium and shipbuilding sectors are described. Finally, the national effort to assist advanced industrial machinery and information electronics, two rapid growth industries where Japan is not yet competitively strong, is described. These case studies do not attempt to give full histories but rather seek to illustrate the themes of the earlier chapters.

II Japan's Industrial Policy: The Economic Background

The economics of Japan's industrial policy are straightforward. The objective is to help raise the real income of the population by assisting the shift of resources to the applications in which they can be most productive. The guiding force and discipline in this policy is that of international competitive advantage. Simply stated, this means that in an open economy, a country's real industrial wage can rise sustainably over time only if its labour and capital flow toward increasingly higher value added, higher productivity (per employee) businesses; the country's industry is then likely to become internationally cost competitive in these businesses. The quality of Japanese industrial performance rests on the ability of both Japanese government and Japanese companies to operate successfully in this way. Broadly speaking, they have done so.

There are three main elements in Japanese industrial development:

   (i)   recognition of the country's need to develop a highly competitive manufacturing sector;
   (ii)   the deliberate restructuring of industry over time towards higher value added, higher productivity industries. (The Japanese call them 'knowledge intensive');
   (iii) aggressive domestic and international business strategies.

These are three fairly simple and obvious ideas. Individually, they are unremarkable. Together, however, they explain very effectively the dynamic of Japanese performance.

Japan's need to export manufactured goods

Japan is essentially without natural resources, has little arable land, and did not industrialise until late in the 19th century. Accordingly, Japan's economic growth and development has been and continues to be dependent on imports

4

of raw materials, energy sources, food, and technology. Japan is the world's largest importer of non-manufactured goods — roughly $60 billion in 1978 — and of technology — roughly 25,000 separate licenses since the end of the second world war. Japan cannot prosper without imports of these basic industrial inputs, and much of its modern political and military history grows from this single preoccupation.

Equally important, Japan needs to export to pay for the imports, and manufacturing has been and will continue to be the only means to obtain exports. Japan has little else to sell. It is not surprising, then, that the development and guidance of the producing sector — i.e., industrial policy — has been a central concern of its government and people since Japan came out of isolation and industrialised just over one hundred years ago.

This concern is carefully defined in the parliamentary authorisation of the government's industrial bureaucracy to include all major elements in the producing system — raw materials sources, foreign exchange balances, technology, financial flows, quality of labour force and management, capital formation, and distribution including ocean shipping. The need to export was a principal stimulus to policy, but the policy which has been developed addressed the more fundamental concern of the overall health of the producing system. Japan has no separate export policy in any meaningful sense of the term.

Table II.1   Exports of goods as per cent of gross national product

	1960	1970	1977
Belgium	33	45	47
Netherlands	36	37	41
Switzerland	22	24	28
Sweden	18	21	26
United Kingdom	15	16	24
Germany	16	19	23
Japan	9	9	12
USA	4	4	6

Source: OECD Trade Statistics, Series A and B.

For all its trade success, Japan's exports of goods are a relatively low proportion of its gross national product (GNP). Table II.1 shows that Japan exported 12 per cent of national output in 1977, well below most European economies. This reflects two important points. One, Japan has a large and a historically fast growing domestic market — now the second largest non-Communist economy. Two, Japan is less well integrated into its Asian regional economy than are the Western European nations. The Treaty of Rome is now twenty years old while Japan took the first major steps to opening its market only ten years ago. Further specialisation and increased regional trade can be expected in the future.

Restructuring of Japanese industry

Japan's government and business leaders have long shared the assumption that the composition of the country's output must continually shift if living standards are to rise. This shared attitude lies at the root of the industrial structure policy of the government and the very high investment rate of business. This belief was well stated in a speech by Mr. Y. Ojimi, Vice Minister of International Trade and Industry, to the OECD Industrial Committee in Tokyo on June 24, 1970:

> 'Industrialisation in developing countries will stimulate competitive relations in the markets of advanced nations in products with a low degree of processing. As a result, the confrontation between free trade and protectionism will become more intense.
>
> The solution of this problem is to be found according to economic logic, in progressively giving away industries to other countries much as a big brother gives his out-grown clothes to his younger brother. In this way, a country's own industries become more sophisticated.
>
> A solution of the North-South problem depends not only on internal development for developing nations but also on giving them fair opportunities in the area of trade. To do this, the advanced nations must plan for sophistication of their industrial structures and open their market for unsophisticated merchandise as well as offer aid in the form of funds and technology.'

There is evidence of this restructuring in the composition of Japanese exports over time. Figure II.1 depicts this in the form of a diamond of changing contour. The diamond plots Japan's mix of total exports among four different categories of industry, each fundamentally different in its requirements for competitive success. Each point of the diamond locates Japan's position on one of the four co-ordinates (or industry categories). The bottom point of the diamond locates the percentage share of Japan's total exports in unskilled labour intensive industries like clothing, light assembly, footwear, toys, etc. These industries require little capital investment or technology relative to the others. The right hand point locates the share of capital intensive processing industries such as steel and fibre. These require heavy capital investment and consume raw materials heavily. The left-hand point represents capital intensive industries which are machine, rather than process, oriented such as motor cars, shipbuilding, light machinery, etc. These require considerable investment in plant and equipment and considerable technology as well. The top of the diamond locates knowledge intensive industries such as computers, fine chemicals, sophisticated machine tools, etc. These industries require high research and development expenditures, applications engineering, and marketing; many investments here are often regarded as part of current operating costs.

The shape of the diamond represents Japan's export mix in successive periods. In 1959, Japan's exports were mainly unskilled labour intensive, and the diamond was skewed towards the bottom. Throughout the 1960s, Japan's

6

Figure II.1 Evolution of Japanese industrial structure

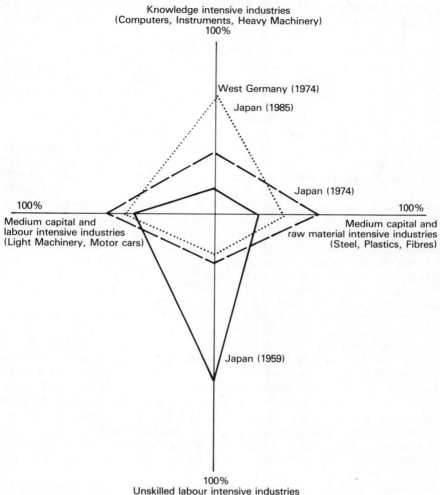

Knowledge intensive industries
(Computers, Instruments, Heavy Machinery)
100%

West Germany (1974)

Japan (1985)

Japan (1974)

100%
Medium capital and
labour intensive industries
(Light Machinery, Motor cars)

100%
Medium capital and
raw material intensive industries
(Steel, Plastics, Fibres)

Japan (1959)

100%
Unskilled labour intensive industries

Source: *Japan Economic Survey,* Economic Planning Agency, 1974-75.

exports became more capital intensive — steel, motorcycles, ships, etc. By the middle 1970s, more complex products in the middle to upper areas of the diamond such as motor cars and colour televisions became significant exports. This process is continuing as Japan's mix shifts towards high technology machinery and electronics industries. By 1985 the Japanese Economic Planning Agency hopes that Japan will have a structure similar to the structure of Germany's exports of manufactured goods in the mid-1970s (see dotted line in Figure II.1).

7

The evolution of Japan's industrial policy has led this shift in export mix. In the 1950s, labour-intensive products, such as textiles, were earning the foreign exchange for Japan. Policymakers recognized that increasing living standards required the development of capital intensive industries rather than reliance on those where competitive advantage depended on low wage rates.

In the early 1950s, the government began funding the steel, chemical fertiliser, and shipbuilding industries. An explicit and more comprehensive industrial policy was developed in the late 1950s and 1960s. Scarce capital was directed to targeted industries, sometimes directly by government but more typically through the private banking system responding to the ministries' cues. A tax policy highly favourable to capital intensive industries was developed, including protection for export earnings. Fragmented, undercapitalised industries such as motor car parts and sewing machines were consolidated at the government's initiative. Research and development in new industries like consumer electronics and downstream petrochemicals were publicly underwritten. Foreign investment into and out of Japan was sharply limited. Free trade was systematically rejected — manufactured imports were limited and exports were given a variety of incentives.

These policies and corresponding investments by industry had succeeded by the early 1970s. Japan had become the dominant supplier of steel, ships, motorcycles, and cameras to international markets. The trade balance swung into surplus, the yen became undervalued, foreign exchange accumulated, Japan was forced to open its borders to capital and products, and manufacturing wages and salaries rose annually by 10 per cent in real terms.

In the early 1970s, Japan's industrial policy began to shift in recognition of Japan's new competitive position. The new policy as it has emerged has several threads. One has been to end assistance to the successful capital intensive industries. Several like steel and motor cars are fully competitive and need no significant support. For heavy process industries like paper and pulp, aluminium, petrochemicals, and even steel, the policy has been to limit upstream[1] expansions to offshore sites only. This results from a desire to conserve energy, reduce pollution, spend foreign exchange, and, more fundamentally to accelerate the shift in industrial structure. Other countries have better plant sites and lower cost energy — Japan can then export the plants and technology.

A second thread has been to assist the shift in Japan's industrial structure towards higher value added, knowledge intensive areas and to import more of the less sophisticated, labour intensive manufactured goods. There were strong domestic reasons for this. Japanese producers were becoming uncompetitive in the latter area and imports were needed to keep prices down in the over protected domestic market. Moreover, Japan's industrial workplace had to learn to accommodate its people's rapidly increasing level of wages, skills, and aspirations.

---

[1]Upstream refers to early processing stages which usually are more capital and energy intensive than the finishing stages of production; the early processing stages are also potentially greater sources of pollution.

Industrial policy, as a result, shifted its emphasis in the 1970s to 'knowledge' intensive[2] industries where Japanese industry is, on average, still less advanced than its strongest Western competitors. (See Table II.2). Government support for research and development expenditure increased dramatically , and large joint government/industry development projects in computers and machine tools were started. Tax incentives for exports disappeared and were replaced by those for research and development, overseas investment and pollution abatement. Japan Development Bank, the government's largest lender to the business sector shifted new loans from large capital intensive plants to computer leasing. Low cost government export financing shifted from ships to entire plant exports where financing is a key competitive variable.

Table II.2   Japan's share of OECD exports, 1976 (selected examples)

Capital intensive products	Per cent
Motorcycles	90
Televisions and radios	70
Ships	43
Steel	29
Watches	23
Motor cars	20
Knowledge intensive products	
Electrical power machinery and switchgear	11
Heating and cooling equipment	10
Mechanical handling equipment equipment	9
Metalworking machine tools	8
Construction equipment	8
Telecommunications equipment	7
Power tools	6
Specialty chemicals	5
Medical instruments	5
Aircraft	2

Source: OECD Trade Statistics, Series C.

A third thread of industrial policy in the 1970s has been the need to help manage the decline of competitively troubled industries. Textiles and chemical fertilisers were in trouble before the 1970s, but others like aluminium, shipbuilding and synthetic textile fibres have become uncompetitive over the late 1970s as the yen rose in value and newly industrialising countries moved into these businesses. The major tasks are to consolidate these industries by scrapping high cost capacity and encouraging small producers to merge. This has proved to be the most difficult of the 1970s policy directions.

[2]See page 6.

Japan's industrial structure continues to change as international competitive forces operate, and the industrial policy has been a guiding factor. Over time, policy with respect to a particular industry has changed as its international competitive position has changed. On balance, Japan's industrial policy has been anticipating rather than reacting, to international competitive evolution.

Competitive strategies of Japanese companies

It takes more than rational industrial policy and evolution of industrial structure to establish international business leadership. Japan's export successes are the result of aggressive business strategies and competent management by Japanese companies in relation to their international competitors. Business competition is sustained conflict with an adversary. There are winners and losers. Although every competitive business confrontation has its own unique characteristics, a number of common principles determine success or failure.

The primary aim of any long term competitive strategy is to achieve the lowest cost in producing and distributing a product. Industries differ in their production and market characteristics and in the competitors who are active; hence, they require different strategies.

A common requirement for achieving a low cost position is the willingness to invest in physical capital. In most of Japan's successful industries, Japanese companies have invested more heavily and consistently than their Western competitors. Japanese companies typically evaluate investments differently from many Western companies. The latter usually isolate a project, grade it on a discounted cash flow (DCF) rate of return basis, and closely observe its effect on the current earnings of the individual profit centre.[3] This favours conservative, early return projects and penalises more risky, long term programmes which may attempt a fundamental alteration of the business. The advantages of this method are its clarity and its bias against compounding mistakes in risky long term programmes. Also in many Western companies, managers' salaries are often tied to the short term performance goals of their individual profit centre. In addition, managers are moved frequently from one branch to another. Projects which depress profitability even if they are expected to yield long term competitive advantage may thus be discouraged.

Effective Japanese companies, on the other hand, typically view a business not as a series of discrete projects but as an integrated business whose competitive position can be advanced or liquidated. Major investments are evaluated for their impact on competitive cost position and market share for the whole business over a several year period. Japanese companies do not usually employ the profit centre control system as often as Americans, and the

---

[3] The profit centre concept involves the assigning of individual profit goals and incentives to various sub-portions of a business. It is thought that this ensures more enthusiastic management at each level of the organisation and provides clear mechanisms to evaluate management at all levels of an organisation. In fact, in some cases it involves shortsightedness in strategic decision making. Maximising short term profitability at the profit centres may conflict with the long term profitability of the company as a whole.

compensation of management is less directly tied to this year's profit centre performance. Accordingly, the Japanese typically find it easier to initiate investments in projects with a long term payoff. Examples of such an investment might be a lower cost, higher volume plant which will require market share gains to fill to capacity or an extended research and development programme which aims at radically redesigning a product. The hazards of this approach are that more capital is put at risk, and continuing commitments may be made to a business that is fundamentally not viable. However, in high growth businesses where competition is still fluid and the outcome uncertain, the Japanese approach is usually superior.

Fixed capital investments are financed primarily by retained earnings and debt. By reputation, Japanese companies undertake large loans to finance their asset growth. This is an area, however, where generalisations can be misleading.

In Japan's most successful industries such as motorcycles, colour television, motor cars, office copiers, fork lift trucks, steel, shipbuilding, etc., companies did have a high debt/equity ratio in the growth years of the 1960s. Despite a closed home market, Japanese producers fought competitive battles with each other to build better products and bigger plants and to establish overseas distribution networks. The high Japanese market growth rates and intense competition helped the leaders who emerged to gain a strong position internationally.

In the 1970s, as cost advantage was secured against both marginal domestic competition and Western producers, loans were paid off and debt levels fell. With the exception of the capital intensive steel and shipbuilding industries, successful Japanese companies in other industries have balance sheets and income statements which are comparable to their American and European counterparts. Their reward for investing more heavily than their competitors over the long growth period has been a low cost position and a more durable cash flow.

Where Japanese investments have succeeded, they have usually reduced the costs of manufacturing products and increased product reliability. This comes from achieving high volume output which, depending upon the business allows for cost effective product design and large scale or long run production. The Japanese success in motorcycles and television, can be traced to the design of better components, the reduction in their number, and automated assembly.

In some businesses, the large scale plant or machine is essential to a low cost position. Japan has the largest scale facilities in the world in a range of products from carbon steel to major electronic components (Table II.3 and Table II.5).

In other businesses, achieving high volume without proliferating the product mix is crucial to a low cost position; it enables long production runs and highly mechanised processes. Table II.4 illustrates sales volume per bearing design offered among major international bearings producers which along with lower cost steel, explains Japan's strong cost position. A similar effect can be observed in motor cars and small diesel engines.

11

Table II.3 Relative scale of production facilities for selected components used in television sets (1977)

	Relative production scale EEC	Far East
Cathode ray tubes	1	2.5
Line output transformers	1	2
Speakers	1	4
Integrated circuits	1	1
Diodes	1	1
Transistors	1	4
Fixed resistors	1	20
Potentiometers	1	10
Ceramic capacitors	1	10
Film capacitors	1	2
Aluminium capacitors	1	8
Tantalum capacitors	1	7

Source: Client study.

The Japanese willingness to make investments which have a long payback period and their often superior production economics are related. Funds for product design and capital equipment, however, are only part of the necessary investment. Aggressive marketing and investment in distribution outlets are also required to enable full advantage to be taken of large scale production.

Table II.4 Production of ball bearings

	Average for major Japanese producers	Timken (USA)	SKF (Sweden)	Fag (Germany)
Number of variants	10,000	12,500	25,000	25,000
Sales (billions* US dollars)	1,417	820	1,492	671
Sales/variant	141.7	65.6	59.7	26.8

Source: Client assignment.
*Million million *not* thousand million.

Large scale production usually requires a strong market share in a large home market plus aggressive exporting. Japanese companies historically have had the advantage of a large domestic market which was either closed or very expensive for foreign manufacturers to enter. Some Western firms persevered and the Japanese market has been highly rewarding for them. Most, however, did not make the necessary investment in sales effort and have suffered the competitive consequences. Their Japanese competitors took advantage of a large home market which enabled them to produce on a large scale and become cost competitive. The Japanese companies could then use the uncontested home market profits for aggressive market entry elsewhere in the world.

Table II.5   Deepwater world scale steel plants (early 1980s) (excluding USSR)

Plant	Country	Projected capacity
		Million metric tons
Fukayama	Japan	16
Kashima	Japan	15
Kimitsu	Japan	14
Yawata	Japan	12
Oita	Japan	12
Chiba	Japan	10
Kagagawa	Japan	10
Mizushima	Japan	10
FOS	France	10
Taranto	Italy	10
Wakayama	Japan	9
Dunkirk	France	8
Nagoya	Japan	8
Hoogovens	Netherlands	6
Tabarao	Brazil	6
Pohang	Korea	6
Burns Harbor	USA	6

Source: Individual companies.

The market and product entry strategies of Japanese companies have often targeted the weak spots of competitors. Japanese companies commonly begin exporting to third world markets which are peripheral to their large US or European competitors. These markets represent a small portion of Western sales but can add significantly to the Japanese company's volume base. When entering these markets, Japanese companies generally cut prices.

Often the Western company's manager in these markets is concerned about his current profitability and does not look beyond a two or three year period after which he can return to the home office. He is likely to sacrifice market share to a new, aggressive Japanese competitor rather than see a decline in current profits. As market share is often taken from market growth and thus does not affect current sales level, this is safer than sacrificing profitability. In this way, Japanese competitors replace Western companies in these small but growing markets and gain a stronger overall volume base with which to enter European or American markets.

Similarly Japanese companies often enter a business at the simpler end of the product line, where the Western competitors often have lower profits. By aggressively pricing to gain market share, the Japanese company often causes its Western competitor to forfeit that part of the business. It was commonly thought that the Japanese might be hard to beat in the low end of the business, but would not be able to develop the products to threaten the main parts of the product range.

In fact, as the motorcycle, television, camera, and motor car industries, plus a long list of industrial products, demonstrate, Japanese competition rarely

13

stops with the 'low end' of the business. The extensive experience, production volume and distribution strength gained there can form a base for successful expansion.

When Japanese companies do enter the large markets and central parts of the product line which constitute the heart of a competitor's business, they tend to invest heavily in distribution, marketing and 'penetration pricing'. Usually they expect to wait many years before the cash flow from these products and markets turns positive. As with cost cutting capital investment, Japanese companies have shown a willingness to invest heavily in market penetration and to evaluate the investment with a long time horizon.

This brief tour of Japanese competitive behaviour runs the risk of caricature. The patterns described do not hold for all Japanese companies nor do they exclude Western companies. A number of Western companies from computers to construction equipment and from specialty chemicals to apparel have approached international competition in similar fashion — a long investment time horizon, a preoccupation with market share and cost position and an aggressive market by market focus, etc. This behaviour is by no means solely Japanese, but Japanese companies have provided some notable illustrations.

Steel

In 1950, the US produced over 70 per cent of total world steel, and imported virtually none. It had the world's largest steel producing facilities and thus, while it had the world's highest wage rates as well, was still the lowest cost producer. In 1958, the US steel industry was estimated to be three times more productive per manhour than Japanese producers. Modernisation of the Japanese steel industry proceeded rapidly during the 1950s and output increased at 15 per cent per year; nevertheless, Japanese companies remained high cost producers relative to the US and exported less than 5 per cent of their production.

During this period, the US industry invested far less in physical capital than the Japanese and had a higher profit margin. Increases in productivity in the US steel industry were less than one quarter of those of the Japanese industry. American companies were not as quick to take advantage of new technology offered by millmakers as were their Japanese counterparts.

By the early 1960s, Japanese total costs of production had reached US levels, though their productivity did not match that of the US steel industry until about 1970. Throughout the 1960s and early 1970s, although the rate of growth of domestic demand slowed down, the Japanese industry continued to expand production. This greater volume was absorbed by an increasingly aggressive export programme and allowed Japanese steelmakers to build large, modern, efficient mills. Eleven new facilities constructed between 1952 and 1978 now account for over 80 per cent of Japanese steel production (Table II.6). These mills are on average larger and more modern than their US and European counterparts, and give the Japanese industry a cost advantage. In many steel processes, the cost per unit declines systematically with increasing

Table II.6 Major Japanese steel plants

	Name of plant	Date of first operation	1973 Output	Projected capacity
			(Million metric tons)	
Nippon	Kimitsu	1965	9.0	14.0
	Yawata	1959	9.8	12.0
	Sakai	1961	4.4	4.3
	Nagoya	1958	6.2	7.3
	Oita	1971	3.5	12.0
NKK	Fukayama	1965	11.8	16.0
Kawasaki	Chiba	1952	6.1	6.5
	Mizushima	1961	7.9	10.0
Sumitomo	Wakayama	1960	7.2	9.5
	Kashima	1967	5.2	15.0
Kobe	Kogogawa	1968	4.4	10.0
Total			75.5	116.6

Source: Clients assignment.

volume. In blast furnaces, for example, this scale advantage amounts to a 30 per cent reduction in production cost for every doubling in scale. In 1977, Japan had twenty five blast furnaces capable of producing over two million annual tons in volume; the US had none and the EEC only seven (Table II.7).

Most expansion in the US during this period occurred in roundout[4] fashion in order to minimise investment and risk and to maintain current profitability and dividends. Only one greenfield[5] facility was constructed. Roundout investment tends to be highly inefficient, since a new strip mill or finishing mill is placed wherever there is space on the existing steel plant site. Materials handling, rework and internal transport costs become far greater than in a greenfield plant, which can be designed in line with the natural flow of the product. The more efficient product flow of the new Japanese plants represents a further advantage over American producers.

The Japanese industry, also invested to overcome inherent disadvantages in raw materials. By building ships that could carry large quantities of iron ore and coking coal, they were able to transport high quality ore and coal from Australia and Brazil to Japan at costs comparable to those required to bring lower quality ore from Minnesota to Ohio or Pennsylvania (Table II.8). Japanese companies also made heavy financial investments in these overseas mines in order to guarantee their sources of supply. Ultimately, the proximity of US mills to domestic sources of coal or iron ore became a drawback rather

---

[4]A roundout investment is one in which a new piece of equipment is placed at an already existing mill.

[5]A greenfield facility is one which is built completely from the ground upon a new site.

Table II.7   World's largest blast furnaces in 1977

Country	No. of furnaces over two million tons capacity In operation	Under construction
Japan	25	9
USSR	9	5
EEC	7	6
USA	0	3
Other:	0	5
Poland		1
Brazil		3
Austria		1

Source: Client study.

than an advantage. Japanese mills, constructed at sites with access to deep-water ports were better able to take advantage of newly developed higher quality lower cost sources of raw materials.

Thus, Japan built the world's most efficient steel industry. The venture required both massive capital investment and aggressive pursuit of export markets to support continued rapid growth despite decreases in the rate of growth of home consumption. In the crucial years when Japan gained its

Table II.8   Transport costs of Japanese iron ore (Average for all mills and mines)

	Constant (1973) dollars per ton
1964	8.00
1965	7.12
1966	6.20
1967	5.36
1968	4.87
1969	4.45
1970	4.52
1971	3.93
1972	3.45
1973	3.50
Upper Minnesota to Chicago (Great Lakes), 1973	3.50
Upper Minnesota to Pittsburgh, 1973	6.50

Source: Client study.

productivity advantage over the US, the Japanese steel industry increased its physical capital by over 23 per cent a year compared to only 4 per cent for the US, despite a lower average rate of return on capital (1.8 per cent for the Japanese big five companies and 3.8 per cent for the largest eight US companies). The Japanese incurred a marginal debt-to-equity ratio of almost 11 to 1[6] during these years, allowing a satisfactory return on equity and guaranteeing the continued improvement of their competitive productivity (Table II.9).

Table II.9   The financing of Japanese steel investment, 1966-72

Major Japanese steel companies	
Asset growth per year	23.6 per cent
Average return on assets 1966-72	1.8 per cent
Average return on equity 1966-72	20.0 per cent
Marginal debt to equity ratio, 1966-72	11:6.1
Debt to equity ratio, 1972	6:3.1
Cash sources for financing	*Per cent*
Debt	91.0
Retained earnings	1.1
New equity	7.9

Source: Annual Reports and Balance Sheets of the major steel companies.

The US steel industry's underlying assumptions about the business prevented it from making the aggressive investments in modernisation that would have been needed to match the pace of Japanese investment. From the US company's point of view, the discounted cash flow return from a new low cost greenfield steel mill could not justify its construction. Levels of debt as high as the Japanese industry's were unthinkable, and, since no attempts were made to export in large quantities, growth rates were too slow to justify the large additions to capacity. The limited modernisation investments which the companies made did not protect the US industry's leadership in world markets.

The increase in exports of the Japanese steel industry did not come easily. Japanese companies made large investments in more than 50 finishing facilities in developing countries in order to establish a base for steel exports. Penetrating the wary US and European markets, moreover, required large initial marketing investments. The Japanese industry was prepared to make these investments and to await a long term payback.

Although the success of the Japanese steel industry thus reflects a combination of valid assumptions, appropriate attitudes and intelligent decisions, it is also due in part to the sluggishness of its competition. In industries where US

[6]All short and long term debt is included.

and European producers have responded more alertly, the Japanese approach has been less successful.

In most commodity industries, costs (and prices) decline in real (inflation-adjusted) terms as production experience is gained.[7] Twenty to thirty per cent cost reductions with each doubling of accumulated production are fairly characteristic of most industries. Prices usually follow costs down a similar curve in the long term. In the US steel industry, however, prices actually increased in real terms during the late 1940s and 1950s. When the first Japanese imports entered the market in 1959, prices began to decline; in 1968, when the first voluntary restraint agreements on Japanese imports to the US were instituted, prices again began to climb (Figure II.2).

Figure II.2   Experience curve — United States steel industry

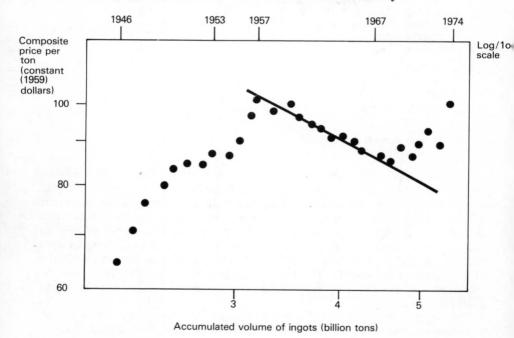

Source: Client study.

In the high-growth stainless steel sheet sector, the US industry prices remained constant in the late 1940s and 1950s while the Japanese prices declined along an 'experience curve' with a slope of 70 per cent i.e. prices dropped 30 per cent with each doubling of cumulative production (Figure II.3). Japanese

[7]This effect, is known as the 'experience curve'. For a detailed account of 'experience curves', see *Perspectives on Experience,* Boston Consulting Group, 1971.

prices fell below those of the US in the late 1950s. (Had the US industry achieved even modest decrease in costs and prices during this period, it could have pre-empted Japanese growth and ability to export).

Figure II.3   Comparative experience curve — stainless steel sheet

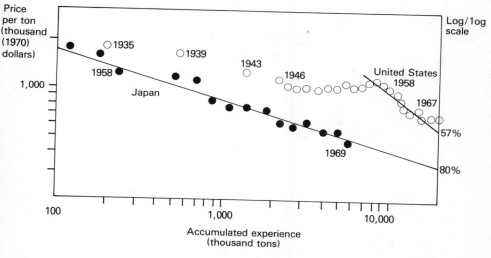

Source: Client study.

A look at other industries suggests that aggressive efforts to cut costs did protect the original leading position. In polyetheylene plastic resin, for instance, the US industry prices declined along a 25 per cent slope between 1950 and 1969 (Figure II.4). While a number of the strongest companies in Japan have entered this business, the Japanese industry generally lags behind strong US and European competitors in size of plant, technology, productivity and export success.

In low density polyethylene, Japanese producers operate on a smaller scale than their American and European counterparts and in high density polyethylene, where technology plays a big role, American and European competitors have kept a process technology lead over Japanese producers with the exception of Mitsui.

To reduce the difference between Japan's success in steel and its record in polyethylene industries to a single factor would be an over simplification. But there is little question that the sluggishness of the strategies of Western competitors in some industries has largely determined the success of Japan's post-war industrial growth.

19

Figure II.4 Experience curve — United States low density polyethylene film industry, 1959-1969

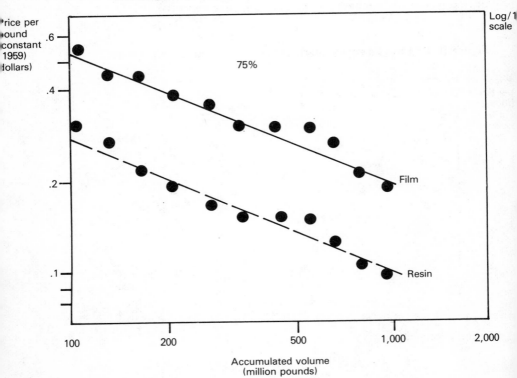

Source: Client study.

Motorcycles

The large size motorcycle industry provides another illustration of Japanese competitive success. The United States is easily the largest motorcycle market in the world, and leadership there is crucial in securing the top international position among producers. There is only one domestic producer in the US, Harley-Davidson. In 1968, the United Kingdom manufacturers, who have traditionally been world volume and style leaders in motorcycles over 450 cc in engine displacement, held 49 per cent of the US market (in units), and seven of the fifteen models sold were British. Japanese producers — including Honda, Yamaha, Kawasaki and Suzuki, who were very active in the small size motorcycle market — sold only 22 per cent of the large size units.

Between 1968 and 1974, the US market for motorcycles grew at 25 per cent a year; part of this growth was due to cyclists replacing smaller units with larger bikes. By 1974, Japanese producers had 77 per cent of the market while the UK share had fallen to roughly 10 per cent. The number of Japanese models rose from three to thirteen while the number of British models actually declined.

Japanese success in this industry again reflects a flagging effort on the part of its competitors. Investment in the UK industry was low; production levels had not grown, production methods remained unchanged, productivity was stagnant, innovation lagged, and the distribution network was not maintained. The Japanese, on the other hand, had established leadership in the smaller size market during the 1960's and extended their product line upward as the market shifted.

Competition among the four Japanese producers was central to the overall Japanese success. Selling more in the large US market was critical to remaining competitive in production efficiency at home, and it is not surprising that by the middle 1970s exports were over one half of total Japanese production (from four per cent in 1960). The Japanese producers competed for US dealerships and customers through new product introduction, better warehousing and spare parts services, image building campaigns, and price competition. Honda, the leader, was aggressively pursued, particularly by Yamaha. Each of the four gained a share of the US market over the period through quite independent business strategies.

This growth was accomplished without inherent advantages in wage rates or government assistance. Indeed, by 1970 wage rates in this industry were higher in Japan than in the UK. Japanese productivity levels, however, were dramatically higher as a result of highly specialised, large scale production facilities. The Japanese factories are far larger than their British counterparts (Table II.10). Once again, the high investment, high volume approach of the Japanese manufacturers allowed them to overtake their more sluggish Western competitors.

Table II.10   Motorcycle production and productivity, 1975

	Motorcycle output (000 Units)	Motorcycles per man year*
Honda (Japan):		
Suzuki	1,500	350
Hamamatsu	500	174
Kawasaki (Japan)		
Akashi	300	159
Norton-Villiers-Triumph (UK):		
Meriden	28	14
Wolverhampton	18	18
Harley-Davidson (USA)	38	11
BMW (Germany)	25	20

*Includes Japanese subcontracts.
Source: Client study.

Colour television

The Japanese consumer electronics industry grew up in the late 1950s and early 1960s around unskilled labour intensive component insertion. Using processes licensed from US and European companies, Japanese manufacturers based an overall competitive cost advantage on their relatively low wage rates. During the late 1960s, a strong group of independent Japanese companies emerged, although the Japanese industry was not yet a significant factor in world exports. Many felt that the rapid increase in wage rates and the appreciation of the yen that began in the early 1970s would spell the demise of the industry.

In 1970, productivity in television set manufacture was slightly lower in Japan than in Europe and the US, and Japanese capability in set design lagged behind that of their world competitors. Production volumes were relatively low and the industry exported only a small proportion of its output (17 per cent).

By 1978, Japanese productivity in set assembly was three to five times greater than that of its major world competitors (Figure II.5) and Japanese producers controlled over half of non-Comecon colour television sales (Table II.11). These advances occurred despite rapid increases in Japanese wage rates and the appreciation of the yen (Figure II.6).

Table II.11   Japanese colour television industry, 1977

Market	Market size	Japanese products made in Japan	Japanese local production	Controlled by Japan	Share
	Millions		*Million units*		*Per cent*
Japan	5.3	5.3	—	5.3	100
USA	9.1	2.1	1.4	3.5	39
Europe	9.0	.6	.3	.9	10
Other countries	5.4	1.6	1.0	2.6	48
Total	28.8	9.6	2.7	12.3	43

Source: Client study.

Japanese success in this industry is due once again to rapid growth and investment — in this case directed towards process engineering and product engineering to obtain lower production costs and to improve set reliability.

Since 1972, the Japanese producers have lowered the time required to assemble a colour television from approximately six man-hours to about one and a half man-hours. Three factors determined this increase in productivity: a reduced number of components in a set; an increased use of automation in insertion and materials handling; and a reduced number of circuit boards in a set.

Figure II.5   Average number of hours required to assemble twenty-inch colour television set, 1977

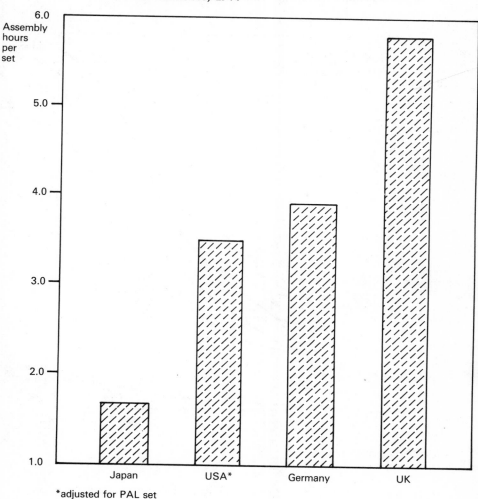

*adjusted for PAL set

Source: Client assignment.

Fewer components means less assembly time and a lower materials cost in a set. While the average PAL system television set made in Europe had about 600-650 components in 1978, the comparable Japanese set had less than 500. This results primarily from the use of integrated circuits with a higher level of integration than those used by European setmakers, and the use of preconverged picture tubes.

Figure II.6 Comparative total employment costs per hour — television set assembly (moving exchange rate basis)

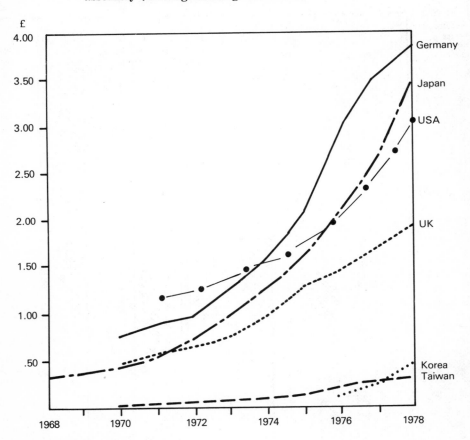

Source: Client assignment.

In 1978, roughly 70 to 80 per cent of all electrical components in a Japanese television set were automatically inserted. European producers average somewhere between 15 and 30 per cent. In addition, Japanese sets are designed to minimise insertion times by the machines and to allow a high degree of automation in testing during the insertion process. Many Japanese factories have also achieved high degrees of automation in inventory control and final set assembly, including the use of robots in certain functions.

Japanese sets have also achieved significantly higher reliability both in the factory and in the the field than Western produced sets (Figure II.7). This superiority results from a higher degree of preproduction component testing,

Figure II.7   Colour television sets — field call rate and production fall-off

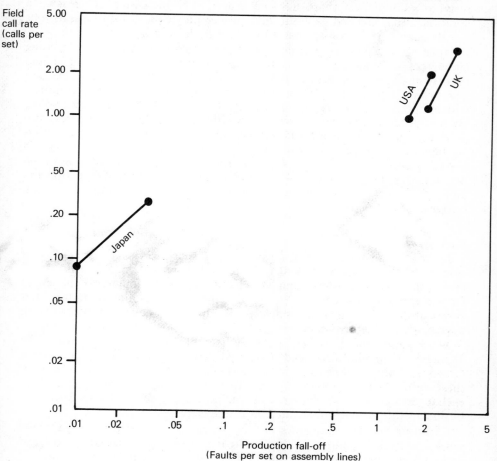

Note: The dots in the diagram represent the range for surveyed sets.
Source: Client study.

greater automatic testing of insertion and longer production runs of each chassis design allowing superior design 'debugging'.

All of these improvements depend to some extent on scale. Preproduction testing is feasible when producing over half a million sets a year as do Japanese factories, but more difficult when producing only one hundred thousand as in the UK. Japanese producers have surpassed their Western competitors both in average factory volume (700,000 in Japan, 150,000 in the UK for example) and in cumulative volume per chassis type (1.2 million in Japan; 400,000 in

Europe). The Japanese strategy of investing heavily and marketing aggressively to gain market share has encouraged ever increasing efficiency. In addition, it has enabled Japan to minimise employment dislocations, as jobs lost through automation are partially offset by jobs created by growth.

Japanese and Western producers have also responded differently to rising labour costs. While Japanese manufacturers concentrated on product and process engineering to reduce the labour content of the set, many US and European competitors have opted to move production offshore to countries with low wage rates. As late as the early 1970s, if companies in Europe and the US had pursued more aggressive export strategies together with process and product engineering, they could have maintained a leadership position *vis-a-vis* Japanese producers. They did not choose that course.

As in steel and motorcycles, Japanese success in colour television has been due both to strategic initiatives — aggressive investment for cost reduction and an increase in exports when home growth was slowing down and to the weak response of competitors.

Some Western successes

Japanese industry does not always achieve success in overtaking Western companies. As mentioned earlier, in polyethylene and many parts of the chemical industry, Western companies have successfully fought off challenges from major Japanese companies. In other industries, such as aluminium and forest products, Japan's raw materials disadvantages have prevented it from developing competitive industries.

More significant, however, are a number of industries where aggressive Japanese companies attempted but failed to overtake Western leaders with strategies similar to those used in the consumer electronics or car industries. In these cases, in industries as diverse as construction equipment, plate heat exchangers, chain saws and marine engines, aggressive US and European business strategies have frustrated Japanese efforts.

European and US companies in these businesses moved into the Japanese market early, sustaining the losses and high investment necessary to build secure market positions. This strategy prevented the Japanese from taking full advantage of their home market base. The operations in Japan of IBM, Caterpillar, Eastman Kodak, Omark, and others are examples. In addition, the astute competitor has blunted early the Japanese thrust into third markets, either preventing gains in the Japanese share of the market or at least making any gains extremely costly.

Competing against a competent Japanese company requires extraordinary perspective and determination. In the future, we are likely to see some high powered competition between strong Western leaders and aggressive Japanese challengers in a number of knowledge intensive businesses. Many Western companies in these industries have learned from the past and will not display the weaknesses characteristic of Western companies in steel, televisions and motorcycles.

26

Myths about Japanese competition

After the foregoing review of Japan's record in three major international industries, we are in a position to reconsider some frequent claims about Japanese competitive behaviour.

Japan's low wage rates during the 1960s and early 1970s are often cited as a reason for success. Wages were lower than major Western competitors, and for this reason Japan was able to compete even when its product design, production technology, and plant scale, i.e., factors that determine productivity, were inferior. As Japanese productivity achieved parity in a number of industries by the early and mid 1970's, the value of the yen was slow to respond and the Japanese cost advantage increased. This situation tended to correct itself as Japan's wages and salaries rose rapidly relative to those in Western Countries and as the value of the yen eventually rose as well.

Even though low wages did provide some initial advantage, this was not an essential cause of industrial success. Had Japanese wages been significantly higher in the 1960s and early 1970s, gains in the share of the international market by Japan would have occurred but might have taken longer. The rate of Japanese productivity increase would have been the same or even higher. Japanese capital investment was largely intended to reduce labour costs and to increase reliability. A higher wage rate would have provided greater incentive to invest so that labour would be used more efficiently. The fact is that Western competitors underestimated the Japanese ability to continue to increase productivity. They believed that rising Japanese wages would solve their competitive problems. It is interesting to speculate whether a higher wage rate (more respectable in Western eyes) would have caused competitors to take the Japanese more seriously.

Another claim sometimes made about Japanese competitive behaviour is that the Japanese used export markets to achieve their initial growth. This is not the case. In steel, motor cars and motorcycles and television sets exports took a relatively small share of total output until the home market was large and saturated (Table II.12). Only then did the export ratio begin to increase significantly. Strong export positions were built only when domestic markets were approaching saturation.

Table II.12   Exports as per cent of output (Selected products)

	Colour Television	Motor cars	Steel	Motorcycles
1966	14	14	27	40
1968	18	15	26	46
1970	17	23	25	60
1972	22	35	30	70
1974	33	43	37	75
1976	51	49	44	72

Source: Ministry of International Trade and Industry (Japan).

Another claim is that Japanese competitors often sell products into foreign markets at unfairly low prices. In a number of cases, charges of Japanese dumping have been upheld by US and European government investigation. But the volume of total Japanese exports covered by these findings is modest. It is often entirely reasonable for any competitor seeking to penetrate a well developed market, to price very aggressively and, if necessary, challenge the anti-dumping statute. The Japanese in a number of industries have done this.

The problem is that most dumping allegations are simply wrong or badly timed. Dumping is a highly technical finding, requiring many adjustments to be made to export and domestic prices before comparing them. Most investigations disappoint the party bringing the charge, for what appeared to be unfairly low pricing turns out to be based on a competitor's superior cost position. Even the charges with merit usually are made too late to matter. When the Japanese dump, they will usually do it when newly entering a market — before their product is known and acceptable on attributes other than price. Once established, the product typically commands a higher and higher price. In fact, in a large number of highly accepted Japanese products such as steel, motorcycles, colour television, and motor cars, Japanese export prices to the US during lengthy periods in the middle and late 1970s have been significantly higher than prices to the Japanese domestic market.

A final issue is the Japan Inc. allegation, whereby government and business collude to further Japan's exports, often at the expense of the domestic consumer. The view asserts a commanding industrial role for govenment. The next chapter discusses the industrial role of government at length.

III Japanese Industrial Policy: The Implementation Process

The previous chapter discussed production and distribution possibilities (valid for most industrialised countries) underlying Japanese industrial policy. More distinctly Japanese is the process by which industrial policy is determined and carried through. In this chapter we consider some key aspects of the industrial policy process in Japan. We begin with attitudes which create a favourable climate for successful industrial policy. We then explore the roots of industrial policy in Japanese history and describe the major institutions involved in policy formulation and implementation. Finally, we describe policy objectives and instruments and try to counter some false impressions often voiced in the West about how Japanese industrial policy operates.

The underlying attitudes

Many business leaders in the US and in Europe view any government initiatives towards industrial policy with suspicion and hostility. Not surprisingly, many conservative political leaders identified with the business community in these countries tend to oppose national industrial policy on ideological grounds. On the other side, progressive political parties tend to distrust big business and the motives of its leaders. Historically, the State assumed an active economic role in Western economies in order to correct what were considered to be the private sector's economic and social failures.

Japanese historical tradition, on the other hand, grants to government a legitimate role in shaping and helping to carry out industrial policy. Japanese businessmen share with government leaders and officials a sense of the importance of co-ordinated national development and are generally amenable to and, in fact, expect government intervention to advance this goal. Senior businessmen view government guidance of industry as a normal state of affairs. They may not always enjoy the process or approve the specific actions, but they see the process as legitimate and, in the main, useful. While business leaders are of course primarily concerned with the success of their individual firms, many actually identify the success of their companies with the greater good of Japan. This is somewhat less true of the younger generation of management, but it remains a very strong thread of the Japanese mentality.

In Japan, there is a strong tradition of bureaucrats overseeing industrial affairs. The Diet's Acts enunciate only essential policy, and give broad charter

29

to the ministries. The ministries are staffed by a competent core of career officials, many of whom enter politics when they retire from the ministry. This pattern has provided good working relations between the Diet and the ministries.

Diet members do have considerable influence, particularly in the appointment of staff to ministries and in tax and expenditure policies. To the ministries, however, belongs the responsibility for developing coherent programmes, drafting legislation, and carrying it out with broad discretion. Changes in the Diet's composition and mood do not greatly move the boundaries of the ministries' authority and effectiveness in industrial policy matters.

Historical roots of industrial policy

Although the substance of Japan's industrial policy has changed significantly during the postwar period, the process has remained relatively stable, retaining characteristics of the policy that accompanied Japan into the modern world with the Meiji Restoration a century ago.

In 1868, Japan was abruptly opened to world trade after centuries of economic isolation. The density of the population and the mountainous landscape ruled out large scale agriculture and dictated industrialisation as the path to higher income and trade. The government's response to this challenge set the tone for Japanese industrial policy to follow. Japan's new leaders recruited an elite, central bureacracy from the able clan samurai whose interests were nationalist and whose perspective was modern. Isolated from the Western debate on political economy (socialism versus capitalism), they were pragmatic rather than ideological in their thinking. They did not fear concentration of industrial or financial power, and, in fact, encouraged such concentration as a point of contact and co-ordination with the central ministries. Rapid capital accumulation had to be encouraged. After some limited early experiments in State entrepreneurship, the government played only a small direct or regulatory role in the nineteenth century's rapid industrialisation of Japan, but the State, as an architect, catalyst and co-ordinator of industrial policy, dominated the policymaking process.[1]

Westerners puzzled by the centripetal nature of this process should bear in mind that the origins and rationale of the State's authority are remarkably different from those of our own tradition. Japanese statism is rooted in familism.

'In the traditional view, the whole nation is a family; what the house is to a biological family, the state is to the national family. The state is not merely a part of the system, but the very framework of it. The Japanese feel that in the beginning there was the nation house called Japan and the people were born into it . . . The state bureaucrats exercise authority not in the name of the people, but in the name of the House of Japan. To the

---

[1]For further discussion, see William W. Lockwood, *The Economic Development of Japan*, Princeton University Press, N.J. (1954).

Japanese way of thinking, then, the state does not 'interfere' with the affairs of private business. It merely manages itself, exercising authority and control of its constituencies. The productive activities of private businesses is very much a part of the business of the whole nation-state.'[2]

Of course, familism does not fully describe the relations between the private sector and the government in Japan. Conflicts of interest do exist between the business community and the State as in the West, but there is a clear sense of common purpose — born probably of Japan's long isolation — and more importantly, a commonly accepted and extremely well developed process to resolve conflict.

Policy making institutions

To understand the ways in which this interaction occurs, it is necessary to know something of the various agencies and groups involved. In addition to government agencies, a wide variety of public institutions such as publicly funded banks play a key role in industrial policy, as well as a wide variety of private institutions such as business management associations, trade associations and the city banks. These private institutions serve as intermediaries between the ministries and companies and typically assist in research into policy initiatives and also help to implement policies.

The intricate web of interaction among the ministries, the public companies, the private associations and the city banks forms the core of what is normally called the informal consensus building in Japanese industrial policy. Though complex and informal, these processes do form regular patterns.

Key government agencies

Two agencies of government — the Ministry of Finance (MOF) and the Ministry of International Trade and Industry (MITI) — deserve extended discussion. The Economic Planning Agency, while it puts together indicative long-term economic plans and studies the economy's interdependencies, plays a lesser role in industrial policymaking.

Ministry of Finance. The MOF sets monetary and fiscal policies and controls the government's budgeting and tax collection operations. Because the principal instruments of industrial policy are direct budget and revenue items, any policy requires MOF approval. Japanese industrial policy uses such tools as selective tax measures, access to low-cost government lending, expenditure subsidies, tariff and customs policies, and foreign exchange rate changes. Since every ministry has a corresponding set of programme objectives and expenditures, MOF's budgeting sets the limits on the scope of industrial policy and approves its financial particulars. Its perspective is broad but its scrutiny can be very narrow; accordingly, MOF senior officials examine industrial policy proposals at several levels. They are concerned with the

---

[2]K. Haitani, *The Japanese Economic System,* Lexington Books, Lexington, Mass. (1976).

soundness of the national currency as well as with specific loans to business and with adequate govenment revenue generation as well as with tax subsidies to particular sectors.

The MOF has seven bureaus — Budget, Tax, Financial, Banking, International Finance, Customs and Tariffs, and Securities — and all can figure prominently in industrial policymaking. Budget and Tax are self-explanatory. The Financial Bureau manages the Fiscal Investment and Loan Plan (FILP), which channels government trust funds into industrial sectors via public corporations that offer loans and grants. These public corporations include the Japan Development Bank, Japan Highway Corporation, and the Export Import Bank among others, equal to one half the government's general account budget.[3] The FILP is a major government lever on cash flow in the economy.

The Banking Bureau exercises extraordinary control over both the Bank of Japan and the commercial banking system; together with the Securities Bureau, it gives the Ministry considerable influence over investment behaviour in the high debt sectors of the economy.

The International Finance Bureau is responsible for international payments and currency exchange. The Japanese have learned from the West Germans how to use exchange rate appreciation as an instrument of industrial policy, forcing industry restructuring and holding down inflation.

Customs and Tariffs is the most conservative bureau in a generally conservative ministry. Over the last ten years, Japan has dismantled its once elaborate tariff and quota system until protection is now at a level comparable to that in the USA and in Western European nations; within Customs and Tariffs, however, the execution of this more liberal policy can be reluctant or even obstructionist.

In preparing the budget for Diet approval, the Ministry of Finance must match funds to priorities across the whole economy, not just the industrial sector. This constraint is often overlooked by the ardent critics of Japan, Inc., who see the various ministries in conspiracy to promote Japanese manufactures. In fact, for a number of reasons, it has become increasingly difficult to persuade MOF of the merits of programmes which favour the business sector. Since the 1975 depression, the budget deficit has grown intolerably large, making tax reliefs and subsidies to industry harder to justify. Other priorities like social insurance and the environment are taking larger shares of budget expenditures and tax relief measures.

Ministry of International Trade and Industry. MITI is the most important institution in Japan's industrial policy making process. Formed in 1949 by the combination of the Ministry of Commerce and Industry and the Board of Trade, it includes all but a few major industries in its jurisdiction. MITI is notable for the variety of roles it plays — broad policy architect, *ad hoc* working level problem solver, formal regulator, regional policy arbiter, and

---

[3]See Chalmers Johnson, *Japan's Public Policy Companies,* American Enterprise Institute for Public Policy Research, Washington, D.C. (1978).

informal administrative guide. In some industries it has a strong statutory authority, in others only a broad and sometimes weak influence.

Other ministries play roles similar to MITI's in some major industries. Telecommunications producers and Nippon Telephone and Telegraph Corporation are supervised by the Ministry of Posts and Telecommunications. The Ministry of Transport oversees railway equipment producers and operating companies. Pharmaceuticals, one of Japan's developing industries, responds to the Ministry of Health and Welfare. These industrial ministries are in general more conservative and protective internationally of their constituents than MITI is today.

But MITI's influence is pervasive in shaping overall Japanese industrial policy. The Ministry has been assigned responsibility for:

(i)   shaping the structure of industry and adjusting dislocations that arise in transition;

(ii) guiding the healthy development of industries and their production and distribution activities;

(iii) managing Japan's foreign trade and its commercial relations;

(iv) ensuring adequate raw materials and energy flows to industry; and

(v)   managing particular areas such as small business, patents, industrial technology, etc.

The breadth of this charter, in both function and spirit, gives MITI a comprehensive perspective across industries and policy areas.

MITI has responsibility for developing industries as well as regulating their excesses. Difficult trade-offs are made and various policies integrated informally within one ministry culture. Thus, it considers the whole range of potential government measures — tax, anti-trust, special lending, price and capacity controls, export and import measures, environmental regulations, raw material price setting and procurement, technology subsidy, dislocation subsidy, regional policy — which influence an industrial sector's performance and its effect on other sectors.

MITI does not employ all these tools in every industry nor does it act independently of other agencies. In fact, the treatment of various industries differs enormously; many experience little or no special 'policy intervention' for long periods while a few (like petroleum refining and computers) are highly co-ordinated or subsidised. Moreover, MITI is neither autonomous in determining policy nor can it directly finance its own programme. The Fair Trade Commission limits MITI's structural initiatives, the Diet and Prime Minister's office circumscribe MITI politically, and MOF passes judgment on its budgets. MITI, nevertheless, remains the focal point in industrial policy determination, lending it continuity and consistency. There is no pretension of zero-base budgeting,[4] no sudden upheavals after elections. Policy changes are usually a long time coming (which is sometimes a weakness) but well rooted when they emerge.

---

[4] A budgetary revaluation process which assumes that all items must be rejustified each accounting period.

Much of the leverage MITI and other agencies exert over industry stems from the pervasive practice of administrative guidance. Administrative guidance occurs when government officials guide industries and firms in desired directions by informal means and without statutory authority. Ministries justify the practice by invoking the broad statutory mandate of laws under which they were established, which call on the ministries to promote, regulate and guide those industries under their jurisdiction. Japanese academic thinking leans toward the view that specific statutory authority is not required for administrative guidance.[5] Ministerial officials summon representatives of a firm, an industry, or the industry association, to their offices and express their wishes or expectations. These may be expressed in the form of a request, a recommendation, or occasionally, an admonition. Compliance is technically voluntary, but the officials do not hesitate to use the various carrots and sticks available to them — which are often totally unrelated to the issue at hand — to assert their will.

Administrative guidance is a fundamental part of the government-business relationship in Japan. Businessmen generally understand that in the long term it is in their best interest, even though on particular occasions the issue being pressed by the ministry is an unpopular one. MITI, for example, will suggest that a company participate in an unappealing foreign investment project or delay a capacity addition to accomplish a broader end. Firms vary in their rate and spirit of compliance, but all regard administrative guidance as justifiable and part of the price business pays for the valuable services of an economic bureaucracy that in general guides the economy well.

MITI's structure is well suited to its broad policy role. The Minister's Secretariat and four bureaus — Industrial Policy, International Trade Policy, International Trade Administration and Industrial Location and Environmental Protection — develop and co-ordinate policy across industries. Three bureaus — Basic Industries (steel, chemicals, fertiliser, etc.), Machinery and Information Industries, and Consumer Products Industries — develop programmes, implement general policy and solve problems at the individual industry level. Finally, there are nine regional bureaus that reconcile policy to local issues and develop MITI's extraordinary data base on its industries. The acuteness and soundness of MITI policy are attributable to the interplay among these horizontal policy bureaus and vertical industry bureaus, with their broad powers, comprehensive data base, and firstrate career staff. Japan has thus far avoided the proliferation of layered agencies that single issue politics has brought to America's industrial policy.

The Industrial Policy Bureau has played the major role in guiding overall industrial development. It is this Bureau that has emphasized the shift toward more knowledge intensive businesses. Within the Bureau general divisions work out actual policy details: the Industrial Structure Division projects the desired future structure of industrial output and designs broad measures toward achieving it; the Business Behaviour Division studies tax measures and

[5]See Dan Fenno Henderson, *Foreign Enterprise in Japan, Law and Politics*, Chapel Hill, University of North Carolina Press (1973).

labour issues; the Price Policy Division is responsible for seeing that appropriate industries are adequately financed. This last division makes recommendations on which businesses and projects gain access to low interest funds through MOF's Fiscal Investment and Loan Plan (FILP).

The Industrial Structure Division does the staff work on basic structure policy. The five explicit criteria used in their deliberations are:

(i) the rate of growth the industrial sector is capable of sustaining, given financial, labour and other direct constraints;

(ii) the desirable structure of the industrial sector in terms of input-output balance, socio-economic limits like regional balance and environmental protection, the need for productivity increases, etc.;

(iii) international competitiveness;

(iv) corporate vitality, particularly adequate profitability and reinvestment rates;

(v) the optimal rate of structural change which would meet economic targets while keeping dislocations tolerable.

A number of advantages accrue to MITI's organisation. MITI officials can negotiate solutions to a problem intramurally, where there is 'give and take' on both sides. An example is MITI's adjustment in the metal flatware industry, hit hard by yen revaluation in the late 1970s. Steel is a major cost element to this industry, but flatware is a small customer to steel producers. MITI was able to negotiate raw material price relief for the flatware industry and make it up to the steel companies somewhere else. The more issues under a ministry's jurisdiction, the greater potential for consistent and rational policy, but also a higher quality of staff will be demanded. The staff of MITI based in Tokyo itself is remarkably small — fewer than 2,500 professionals. The small ministry size and its broad range of responsibilities give its professionals a breadth of experience and close relations with one another.

Private institutions

The MOF and MITI are the centre of a web of organisations that influence industrial policy; many of these are not part of government, but include associations of senior businessmen, large trade associations and large commercial banks.

Business management associations. There are four major associations of senior businessmen that seek to influence policy. The Keidanren (Federation of Economic Organisation) is the major political voice for big business interests in Japan. Its membership includes some 700 large corporations, a number of important public corporations and the major industry associations. Keizai Doyukai (Committee for Economic Development) is a somewhat more progressive group, focusing on the role of business in broader issues. Shoko Kaigisho (Chamber of Commerce and Industry) speaks for small businesses in Japan. Its membership includes hundreds of thousands of companies in manufacturing, finance, distribution, etc. Nikkeiren (Japanese Federation of

Employers Association) attempts to develop a common labour policy for big business. Its membership is similar to that of Keidanren. The influence of these four federations stems from their comprehensive membership, their skilled permanent staff and their connection with politicians. Their leadership — known as the Zaikai — communicates directly and effectively with Diet members, taking advantage of the 'old school tie' network and the permissive laws governing political contributions. Keidanren acts as a major funnel of campaign contributions to the Liberal Democratic Party, a coalition of small business (tradesmen and farmers) and corporate interests.

Business retains influence in Japan (apart from the fact that its opponents are not yet well organized and financed) partly because it recognises the importance of being able to influence government policy; it preserves its influence by keeping issues within the traditional channels. Ezra F. Vogel notes, 'Perhaps the most important factor in influencing industrial policy is the framing of questions about a particular issue within Keidanren as well as MITI. The issues raised thus become the focus of official and unofficial concern and debate. Keidanren has a sizable staff doing research for committee sessions in which business leaders study, debate, and reach decisions about important issues. Government bureaucrats, scholars, and other knowledgeable persons frequently testify before these committees. Formal votes on important issues are almost never taken. Perhaps there is no better phrase to describe this process than consensus building.'[6]

Industry associations. Unlike the business organizations, industry associations are concerned with policy toward individual sectors; they maintain a working relationship with MITI's industry bureaus and divisions. These organisations are far more than data collecting and lobbying groups. They put forward proposals for MITI policy toward an industry and typically implement the policies that are adopted. Japan's Antimonopoly Law, for instance, permits MITI to authorise and supervise cartels that operate through these associations. These cartels are limited in duration and must serve specific purposes such as:

(i) long-term rationalisation of production (used effectively in bearings and car parts industries);

(ii) orderly reduction of excess capacity (currently being tried in some heavy process industries such as aluminium);

(iii) promotion of vertical integration (currently being tried in small downstream textile companies);

(iv) short-term production allocation (used frequently in recessions in the heavy process sector such as chemicals and steel);

(v) export price floors during trade crises (historically used in textiles, steel and other industries).

---

[6]Ezra F. Vogel, Guided Free Enterprise in Japan, *Harvard Business Review,* May/June, 1978. (Harvard Business School, Boston, Mass.)

The tradition of strong trade associations dates from the prewar period when government essentially ran industry through this mechanism. The structure remains much the same today but the functioning is less one sided. Officers of the associations sit on formal MITI advisory councils attached to the industry bureaus. Considerable data are passed to MITI through informal contact in Tokyo and in regional offices. It is because MITI is exceptionally well informed at the working level that the much discussed government-business communication can work so well. Once again, government prefers to deal with organisations which can focus constituents' interests, speak conclusively for them, and implement policy once it is reached. Splinter interest groups fighting for support through the media are anathema to the ministry.

City banks. The thirteen large commercial banks ('city banks') extend one quarter of all loans and discounts made by financial institutions, public and private, in Japan. Their principal borrowers are large corporations. City banks have more interest today in industrial policy than ever before, since it is Japan's more troubled businesses — the heavy process sector, marginal producers in mature manufacturing industries, and a number of trading companies — that are their largest borrowers. Japanese business has traditionally used loans rather than equity to finance its high growth rate. But today, it is the competitively vulnerable businesses which have large loans outstanding and not the strong, self-financing companies. The ministries and the banks discuss and study issues together closely, often setting up *ad hoc* committees to examine specific problems.

Moreover, the large banks are linked with the government through the Bank of Japan. The Bank, supervised by MOF, lends money to the thirteen city banks that in turn lend to major Japanese industries. MOF can exert considerable leverage over the banks, and on occasion will suggest which projects to support. The banks, although privately owned, rarely resist. Such a relationship helps both parties: the ministries occasionally need the assurance of funds for their client industries, and the Bank's portfolio sometimes needs government assistance to remain sound.

Thus a number of common interests, as well as more direct financial or political ties, link these quasi-public institutions to the government policy making bodies. Considerable tensions, of course, exist between the government agencies whose concern is Japan's overall international competitiveness and business associations organised to protect their own interests. But there is a process to resolve them.

Policy objectives

The process of selecting structural objectives and reconciling them to limited resources is enormously complex and, if not grounded in good data and real understanding of industry competition and producers' behaviour, can generate absurd policies. The Japanese approach reconciles relatively well the macroeconomic aspects of sector shifts, as well as productivity and output targets with the microeconomic questions of whether company cash flow will be high enough to finance necessary growth and whether Japan can compete internationally in certain business areas given the industry structure. This, of course, is where the central economic planner can often fail.

Japan's industrial policy process is often misunderstood. In sectors of policy interest, MITI collects a good deal of market and competitive data, gives administrative guidance to firms, and issues a lot of paper in support of a policy. Communication between MITI and individual producers takes place frequently and at several levels. Some observers of this process have mistakenly concluded that MITI is dictating investment rates in the industry. This is not MITI's intention. Market prospects, not ministries, stimulate investment in growth businesses and ultimately discourage investment in declining ones. MITI understands that it would be counter-productive to force wary producers to invest. Nor can a ministry know any particular business sector well enough to design or direct a specific series of investments. Instead, MITI tries to develop a shared perception of a business's future and designs incentives and subsidies to accelerate the desired course.

Nor does MITI normally have the power to dictate investment choices to business. Indeed, the autonomy of the individual firm sharply limits the government's ability to change industrial structure. What is industry development for MITI is risky capital investment for the firm, which although interested in sector structure is more directly interested in its competitive position. Unless its survival is at stake, a company will accept the incentives and subsidies available to the industry but balk at measures that threaten its autonomy. For example, in the 1960s, Japan's motor car companies welcomed the government's import protection, low cost lending and tax deferrals, but rejected MITI's attempts to merge producers and keep minority foreign capital investment out of the industry. In the 1970s the key mainframe computer producers — Hitachi, Fujitsu and Nippon Electric — remained independent competitors despite MITI attempts to consolidate the industry. In electronic calculators, Sharp and others successfully deflected MITI's attempt to shut off US integrated circuit imports, which threatened Japan's fledgling high cost production. While serving MITI's longer term structural aims, this import ban would have seriously damaged calculator producers' cost position. More recently, aluminium producers have resisted MITI's plan for permanent capacity retirement by formula allocation. The producers want short term relief only in order to preserve long term strategy flexibility.

Although conflicts do arise between MITI and reluctant companies, the ministry has many tools of persuasion. It has carrots — it can provide access to funds for investment — and it has sticks — it can hold up building permits, regulate raw material imports and provide material incentives to competitors. However, MITI's greatest strength appears to be its understanding of the competitive stages through which an industry moves and its ability to fashion appropriate policy.

MITI's policy objectives vary according to the competitive position of a business. For businesses in the early, rapid growth phases of development such as computers and machinery, policy calls for protection from foreign competition, concentration among producers, government support of the industry's cash flow, and stimulation of new technology. Today, real protection is available only to a few industries but MITI remains aggressive on the other fronts. For businesses which are already internationally competitive — motor cars, steel, consumer electronics — government assistance recedes[7] as it is no longer necessary. Finally, for businesses in competitive decline, MITI becomes active again, this time trying to bring about capacity reduction and rationalisation.

The process of discussion and debate between MITI and the companies in response to developments in the market place creates a dynamic decision-making process. MITI aptly refers to Japan as a 'plan-oriented market economy'.

Policy concerns and policy instruments

There are three broad industrial policy concerns of MITI and the other industrial ministries — investment rate and structure of producers, technology development, and export-import measures. A general survey of measures brought to bear on these concerns is now presented.

Investment rate and structure of producers

Japan has adopted policies generally favourable to capital investment: no capital gains tax on securities, central bank permanent control of interest rates, a strong anti-inflation commitment, and a minimum of administrative barriers. A relatively high growth rate in the economy as a whole also helps sustain high investment.

MITI, however, does not always favour investment by all competitors. In the rapid growth development stage of an industry MITI prods an industry to concentrate; conversely, in no-growth, declining sectors, MITI promotes capacity retirement. In both cases, MITI's objective is to accelerate market forces and bring about more stable competition among a few relatively low cost producers. In Japan, the key concern has been putting capital together, not splitting it apart.

Historically, the government has protected rapid growth industries from imports with formal barriers at the same time that it has sought to eliminate marginal producers. The success of these consolidation efforts was mixed. MITI exercised strong authority in the most fragmented industries, like sewing machines and car parts, where concentration brought unquestioned benefits in larger scale and lower costs. But in industries where marginal producers were still large companies — motor cars, petroleum refining, and chemicals — MITI failed to bring about mergers and absorptions. Group banks provided easy access to low cost capital while high growth concealed weaknesses and postponed the shakeout. MITI has usually managed to enforce a capacity expansion queue in the capital intensive, heavy process industries, in part

---

[7]With the significant exception of occasional officially sanctioned recession and export cartels co-ordinated by the industry associations.

through foreign exchange control of their raw materials. Even here, however, mavericks like Idemitsu in refining and Sumitomo in steel have been able to elude control.

Today, only a handful of fast growth, high technology industries such as computers, telecommunications, and railway equipment are protected from imports, and primarily through closed procurement rather than duties and quotas. In telecommunications and railway equipment, investment is stimulated and competition allocated directly by operating public corporations that buy the equipment.

There is open competition, however, among Japanese computer producers, and government has done its utmost to support investment in this business. It finances most leasing and software to preserve the producers' capital. The Japan Development Bank grants low interest loans to producers to finance the generation of new equipment. And the tax laws generously cushion producers from the loss on the trading in of old machines; accelerated depreciation of capital investment is also given. MITI has tried for years to consolidate the mainframe industry into two or three equipment-compatible groups but centrifugal forces have prevailed. Six Japanese mainframe manufacturers remain, and even given the increased rationalisation among them, they divide the market very thinly. Fujitsu and Hitachi, the two leaders after IBM, together have less than 40 per cent of the total market.

As it encourages investment and formally or informally protects knowledge intensive growth industries, MITI discourages investment in and protection of declining industries. Today, some large declining industries — aluminium smelting, shipbuilding, synthetic textile fibres, etc. — pose major structural problems. These industries are high cost internationally, have excess capacity, and have large outstanding loans.

In May 1978, the Diet passed the Structurally Depressed Industries Law, enabling MITI to develop a stabilisation plan using government funds. The procedure specified by the Law is typically Japanese. Industries become eligible for assistance only if two-thirds of the producers petition MITI, which then decides whether to grant their request. This condition helps the ministry to bring about a working agreement among the producers, whose cost positions and proposed solutions usually differ significantly. The major creditors like the Industrial Bank of Japan sit on *ad hoc* committees with MITI to study the nature of the problem in a particular industry and ways to solve it. The Law establishes a government loan guarantee fund when the producers borrow heavily because of massive scrapping or mothballing of capacity.

Concerns for industry structure and investment will occur in growth and decline phases only. In both cases, industry consolidation at optimal scale is the major goal. Currently competitive industries receive little attention.

Technology development

A second concern of Japanese industrial policy is technology development. This concern has grown as Japan has moved toward more knowledge intensive industries and as it has approached the frontiers of technology. There are some major government financing efforts — notably in energy and semiconductors — but the government mainly uses a variety of incentives for private development.

The government's own research and development effort is small, in part because the Japanese have been so successful in exploiting the basic research of American and European government and university laboratories, and in part because large national applied research projects are managed by government laboratories but performed on contract by working groups of corporations. MITI's Agency of Industrial Technology has sixteen associated research institutes that organise and manage long term large scale projects to develop system technologies for commercial use. Some current examples are VLSI semiconductors, high performance jet engines, water desalination and natural resource recycling. These projects run for five to eight years, can cost hundreds of millions of dollars, and are typically performed and co-funded by *ad hoc* associations of several large corporate and university laboratories. They are exempt from the Anti-Monopoly Law.

For industry in general, government uses a variety of more modest incentives and supporting tools for corporate research and development. These include tax credits, grants, loans, and sponsorship of associations. Some are available to all corporations while others are tied to particular MITI objectives.

There are three principal corporate tax incentives for technology development. One stipulates that 25 per cent of any year-to-year increase in research and development expenditures over the previous year is a tax credit, up to a limit of 10 per cent of total corporate tax. In 1978, manufacturing companies realised a 15 billion yen benefit through this credit. The second is accelerated depreciation on research and development facilities and hardware, which can often mean a 60 per cent write-off of the original purchase price in the first year. The provisions try to conserve the cash flow of high technology businesses. As growth of an industry slows, these incentives, appropriately enough, become ineffective and more cash flow is exposed to tax. The third is a lower tax rate on income received from technology licensed overseas — worth 10 billion yen to the manufacturing sector in 1978.

The government, in co-operation with other institutions, also directly funds research and development. Such grants can take one of several forms. Most common is a matching grant. Ministries receive applications in designated research and development areas from either companies or associations formed for that purpose. Many associations are groups of small companies that could not finance new technologies on their own. Often the technology issue is straightforward: for example, developing a continuous textile operation to replace a vertically fragmented one. For small business, MITI or the trade association sponsors these arrangements. Matching programmes are not, however, a major funding source of Japanese corporate research and development; they typically account for less than one per cent of the total. A parallel matching grant programme is run separately for small business.

Motor car and boat racing tax proceeds also benefit research and development. MITI guides the direction of these funds to various industry associations, which then distribute the money to specific projects in rationalisation, research and export promotion. They are separate from the government's official budgets and help to finance sectors and products that are not household words in Japan. In 1978, racing subsidies to the machinery industries, for example, were 7.3 billion yen.

Loans for technology development form a traditional element of Japanese industrial policy. The Japan Development Bank makes loans under various programme headings — commercialisation of new technology, developments of prototypes, and commercialisation of new technology for small enterprise. These loans are project related and represent simply low cost funds, hence, they are a marginal incentive. Loans are provided primarily to manufacturers and sometimes to users of the qualifying machinery. These programmes have grown throughout the 1970s. The government lent a total of 30 billion yen to all Japanese industry in 1976.

Overall, the government has increased its commitment to research and development over the decade rather substantially, mainly in the form of a few large high priority projects. This is consistent with the restructuring toward more knowledge intensive industries.

Export-import measures

The third major concern of Japanese industrial policy has been international trade. Through the early 1970s, the Japanese government stimulated exports, restricted manufactured imports, and assisted large scale raw material imports — classical behaviour for an island economy poor in natural resources and prone to experience trade deficits. The tax system, through special reserves and accelerated depreciation, effectively shielded significant portions of export revenue from taxation. The Bank of Japan discounted short-term export bills at less than market interest rates, and cheap long term credit for export-related investment was available from the Japan Development Bank and the Long Term Credit Bank of Japan. High duties and quotas blocked imported manufacturers where Japan thought itself uncompetitive. Assistance was given to overseas projects in mining, forestry and the like with financial guarantees and government-to-government assurances in order to strengthen supply security in basic materials.

The story is quite different now. Broad export incentives are gone. The tax system retains incentives only for exports by small and medium-size companies and for overseas investment. Export-related accelerated depreciation — worth 55 billion yen to the manufacturing sector in 1970 — was eliminated in 1972. Export bills now carry only a quarter of one per cent discount off domestic bill rates, and this subsidy works primarily to bolster Japan's declining exporters of textiles, plywood, flatware, etc.

Although MITI no longer directly assists exports, certain government policies and practices do aid selected knowledge intensive industries. Japan's Export-Import Bank aggressively finances and insures exports of plant systems — a rapidly growing part of trade. Large Third World development projects that Japan finances and supplies enjoy top priority and receive official economic aid. The country's utility monopolies in power generation and telecommunications protect and support designated key products and provide a large production volume on which to base an export effort.

The Japanese home market for manufactures is now essentially open, and foreign producers' market penetration depends on marketing effort and the suitability of the product far more than government approved barriers. There are three major exceptions to this pattern. One is government operated monopolies such as telecommunications, railway, cigarettes, and some computers. Closed procurement is the tool. Ministries other than MITI typically oversee these barriers and are under considerable international pressure to liberalise them. The second relates to machinery imports where the structure of Japanese industry keeps imports to a minimum, heavy industry companies are often part of large Zaibatsu[8] containing chemical, steel, electrical equipment and other companies which exercise closed buying.

The other exception is Japan's political wards like agriculture, retailing, and unskilled labour intensive manufacturing, where large, competitively vulnerable constituencies command protection. This residual protection is similar to that in other advanced countries. By and large, however, the appreciation of the yen and the migration of labour intensive production to developing countries is opening the door to imports. A large number of Japanese industries — textiles, aluminium, chemicals, and metal working — are under increasing pressure as international product specialisation shapes trade patterns.[9]

Some mythology

Any summary description of the Japanese approach to industrial policy runs the risk of becoming a caricature; it is easy to exaggerate the regularity of the processes, the unanimity of decisions, and the economic rationality of policies. The Japanese government is not a monolith in industrial matters. Even in Japan, budgetary politics and open rivalry among ministries can make policy consensus difficult to achieve and sometimes impossible. And here, as elsewhere, excessive zeal sometimes induces short sightedness.

When a policy issue cuts across the ties that bind the policy making groups together, consensus is difficult — sometimes impossible — to achieve. A vigorous debate on the introduction of a value-added tax has pitted big business, which favours it, against low profit small business, which prefers the income tax. The ruling Liberal Democratic Party (LDP), with both groups as major constituents, is thus divided on the matter. The net effect has been to delay the introduction of the new tax. Similarly, the crisis in the shipbuilding industry has posed the issue of rescuing some significant shipbuilders, a course favoured by some senior elected officials, but opposed by the ministries and many bankers. Despite the passage of the Depressed Industry Law, the

---

[8]Large industrial groups or conglomerates are known as Zaibatsu.
[9]See James C. Abegglen and Thomas M. Hout, Facing up to the Trade Gap with Japan, *Foreign Affairs* (Autumn, 1978).

industry's structural problems remain unresolved. The consensus building process here is a slow one, but because opposing bodies characteristically overlap on a broad range of issues, eventual orderly compromise is possible.

Moreover, ministries often disagree with one another about policy priorities. MITI has accused the Ministry of Forestry and Agriculture of prolonging unnecessarily its support of food subsidies and import barriers, causing the government to throttle back on expansionist fiscal policies toward the manufacturing sector. MITI opposes the Ministry of Posts and Telecommunications' extremely protectionist attitude toward the domestic telephone exchange equipment industry. Indeed, MITI has for some time argued against what it sees as excessive protectionism in other agencies. Finally, in the early postwar period, the Bank of Japan and MITI disagreed on whether Japan should develop its own passenger car industry. MITI, looking ahead to higher value added industries, favoured such a development while the Bank, seeking to conserve the scarce foreign exchange that would be needed for imported technology and capital goods in the short run, opposed it. We are daily reminded who won that battle.

Finally, it is easy to credit the industrial policy process with too much of the responsibility for the country's economic success. MITI has not always. been right. For too long, for instance, it doubted the sound basis for Sony's fascination with the transistor and instead defended investments in vacuum tubes. No analysis of government's various interventions should overshadow the competence and energy of Japanese corporations and the intense level of competition in most domestic markets. In fact, many of Japan's very successful, internationally dominant industries, such as consumer electronics, motorcycles, and copiers, are ones in which domestic competition has been especially high — without a significant government role.

The following three chapters present six case studies illustrating Japanese industrial policy and its evolution from the issues of the 1950s through those of the present day. We examine the history of industry development and government-business interaction in two generally successful industries — steel and motor cars; in two troubled, declining industries — aluminium and shipbuilding and in two industries which are just coming into international prominence — industrial machinery and information electronics.

IV Japanese Steel and Motor Car Industries

The first two case studies concern Japanese industries which are currently international leaders in the products they manufacture — steel and motor cars.[1] The studies document the government policies which helped these industries to develop, through both crisis and expansion. It also demonstrates how, once the ability to compete internationally was achieved, the government's role receded sharply. Particularly interesting is the ability of MITI to apply a precise, light touch to a problem. MITI's policy initiatives generally recognise the varying economic requirements for success in different businesses. Interesting, too, are the conflicts among the ministries and between a particular ministry and the industry. Most conflicts are resolved through an orderly process and are eventually translated into effective action. A few problems — like MITI's attempt to consolidate the motor car industry — remain unsolved.

The Steel Industry

The Japanese steel industry is the world's third largest in tonnage output behind the USSR and the USA. It is, however, the world's most efficient. Several major studies, public and private, over the last few years have indicated that the Japanese are significantly lower cost producers of the normal range of basic carbon steel products than any other major producer. Even the American Iron and Steel Institute has acknowledged that the Japanese have a 15 per cent productivity advantage over US producers.

Steel is traditionally the *sine qua non* of industrial development and military strength. Accordingly, governments have always kept a close watch over their steel industries. Some countries, including many in Europe and the Third World, have fully nationalised their steel industries while others, like the United States, have limited the government role to a careful monitoring of the industry's pricing.

The Japanese government has played a supportive role in its steel industry and has derived a great deal of influence from its actions. Steel in Japan is not government owned, and competition is considerable among major producers. But the results have been very much in the public interest — low cost steel

---

[1] The discussion in this chapter draws significantly on earlier published Boston Consulting Group case studies in *Japan: The Government — Business Relationship*, (U.S. Department of Commerce, Washington DC, 1972).

inputs to other manufacturing industries, a major source of foreign exchange, and reasonably viable steelmaking companies.

Japan's policy toward the industry over the last thirty years illustrates the characteristic flexibility and attention to competitive business economics of its industrial policy in general. In the late 1940s, the government identified steel as crucial to Japanese re-industrialisation and took immediate measures to restore pre-war production capability. Beginning in the late 1950s and 1960s, steel received special priority as a key feeder industry to shipbuilding, motor cars, domestic appliances and other capital intensive industries. By the early 1970s, Japan's steel industry had achieved world dominance and could be considered self-sustaining. Government assistance to the industry therefore virtually disappeared. Today, despite its continued pre-eminence worldwide, the industry is understood to be entering its declining phase, and MITI is discouraging domestic investment, promoting rationalisation in the industry, and supporting steel investment abroad.

Throughout this evolutionary process, three basic forms of assistance have been at the heart of Japanese policy: financing to build new plants, assistance in procurement of scarce raw materials necessary for growth, and assistance with cash flow during recessions.

Capacity expansion

Financing
Steel is an extremely capital intensive industry, with an assets-to-sales ratio exceeding 1.5 to 1. Over time, as the optimum scale of steel plants and of individual mills has risen, the cost of building new greenfield plants has increased enormously. As discussed in Chapter II, US steel companies have not been able to justify the construction of new greenfield plants on a return-on-investment basis, and instead have tended to add capacity and make modernisation investments in a less efficient, roundout fashion. The Japanese pursued a very different course. In a climate of rapid domestic demand growth, companies incurred extremely high debt-to-equity ratios and made the investments needed to build the new greenfield plants.

Immediately after the war the Reconstruction Finance Bank, a government financial institution, provided most of the capital for rehabilitating the industry. The government subsidised the steel price level to help the relatively inefficient industry begin to rebuild its markets. In the early 1950s, MITI developed the first rationalisation plan for the industry; industry growth was to be promoted through both tax incentives and financing assistance.

The tax measures applicable to the steel industry were proposed by a study group within the Ministry of Finance after examination of the tax systems of other nations. Five tax and duty exemptions were enacted in 1951-1952:

  (i)   import duty exemption on designated steel-making equipment (60 per cent of such equipment was imported at the time);
  (ii) 50 per cent increase in depreciation base allowed on designated equipment;

(iii) tax exemption for reserves meant to cover price changes in inventories and securities;

(iv) tax exemption for revaluation of assets, which effectively increased the depreciation base;

(v) tax exemption for additional bad debt reserves.

These measures increased the funds available for reinvestment and, in particular, for investment in optimum scale facilities embodying 'state-of-the-art' technology. Between 1951 and 1955, about one quarter of all capital investment originated internally, primarily through these tax exemptions.

The greater part of investment capital — roughly 65 per cent — was financed by debt, primarily through government financial institutions although supplemented by private financial institutions. Loans from the Japan Development Bank, and the Long Term Credit Bank — both government owned and the Industrial Bank of Japan — government influenced — accounted for roughly half of the $95 million in debt incurred by the steel industries during the period. The government encouraged commerical banks to finance steel expansion, and the Ministry of Finance permitted $11 million of foreign exchange loans to the industry.

The first rationalisation plan (1951-1954) doubled Japanese crude steel production from 4.8 to 9.5 million tons. Equally noteworthy was the nature of the government's involvement in this process. MITI avoided the role of direct central planner and concentrated instead on mobilising financial resources and creating financial incentives for growth. Government banks and private financial institutions were persuaded to provide funds to the industry, but final judgments on specific borrowers and amounts were left to the banks, particularly among the commerical banks. The tax measures also helped direct investment appropriately without overt government dictation. The reserve and special depreciation measures favoured growing firms at the expense of stagnant firms, and steered investment toward designated types of equipment.

Between 1955 and 1960, a second rationalisation plan, embodying similar measures, produced another doubling of capacity. This pattern continued throughout the 1960s. Japan's capital/output ratio in steel production (stock of physical capital per ton of steel produced) consistently remained the highest in the world and nearly twice that of the US during the latter part of the 1960s. In addition, because of the willingness to build greenfield plants, capital could be used more efficiently. Greenfield plants constructed after 1952 produced over 80 per cent of Japanese carbon steel production compared to less than 5 per cent in the US.

Throughout the 1960s, the role of direct government financing declined, although the government informally encouraged and, in some cases, insured private bank loans to the industry. Since the banks are important stockholders in the companies, they had incentives to continue to lend money. Between 1966 and 1972, the assets of the five largest producers grew at a formidable annual rate of 23 per cent, representing a huge amount of capital expenditure. During this critical period, when crude steel production grew from 41 million tons to

100 million tons, the industry sustained a debt-to-equity ratio of almost 12 to
1. By this time, the government did not need to provide much of the funding
directly, but it did guarantee much of the lending and in some cases subsidised
low interest rates.

Co-ordination

In addition to assisting in the financing of capacity expansions, the government played a co-ordinating role in approval of expansion plans. Both government and steelmakers had long recognised that a joint determination of the
rate of capacity additions was in both their interests. The impact of steel
expansion on the economy, the massive financial requirements and the
difficulties of imbalance in steel demand and supply dictated that the
government should influence the rate of growth of capacity. Steelmakers, in
turn, were generally willing to co-operate among themselves and with MITI
because of the cash flow crises and price instability that follow over expansion.

The capacity expansion approval process has changed somewhat over time,
but it operates roughly as follows. Representatives of the privately owned steel
producing firms gather under the umbrella of the Japan Iron and Steel Federation to present and discuss tentative investment plans for the coming year.
(Often these representatives, usually managing directors, are MITI alumni.)
The producers' plans are evaluated in relation to the demand outlook for the
industry and the existing pattern of market shares. After these meetings and
informal discussions among these managers and the officials of the Iron and
Steel Section of MITI's Heavy Industries Bureau, the presidents of the steel
companies try to reach a consensus on the rate and timing of the major
investments of individual producers. MITI participates *ex officio* in these
meetings. The frequency of consensus meetings varies with the complexity of
the problem; in times of crisis, meetings are continuous.

After consensus has been reached, MITI issues a report recommending a
course of action to the industry. In recent years, this report has been prepared
by the Iron and Steel Sub-committee of MITI's Industrial Structure Council, a
policy advisory group which reports at the vice-ministerial level. The council's
membership includes officials from several ministries including Finance,
prominent businessmen, and leading academics.

This process should not be viewed in terms of the Western dichotomy
between public and private forces. The government neither plans nor dictates
the rate of capacity expansion. The Industrial Structure Council does not
unilaterally accept or reject the industry's consensus, but rather evaluates it in
view of Japan's wider economic objectives. It has been said that no application
from a major firm for a capacity increment has ever been flatly rejected,
although some have been delayed. This, of course, is the mechanism of the
consensus process: the expanding firm is persuaded either to delay its application or to accept a delayed approval. When this persuasion fails, consensus is
frustrated.

The government can draw on both official and unofficial sources of
authority to facilitate consensus. MITI's control over imported raw materials

is one crucial policy instrument. Through foreign exchange import quotas, MITI directly controlled the importation and allocation among producers of both ore and coal until 1965, and still retains control over the import of coking coal. Since Japan currently imports 98 per cent of its iron ore requirements and 90 per cent of its coal needs, this tool gives MITI reasonably effective control over the rate of production, and hence the rate of expansion. Foreign exchange control also permits the Bank of Japan to limit steel producers' foreign borrowing, which has been a source of finance for the Japanese steel industry.

The Bank of Japan and the Ministry of Finance bring another perspective to the discussions regarding steel expansion. While MITI focuses on the relative competitiveness and growth of the Japanese steel industry, the financial authorities share a broader concern with macro economic effects and international payments balances. Hence, in 1970, the Bank denied requests for increased foreign borrowings in order to avoid undermining its domestic deflationary policy and depressing the rate of increase in dollar reserves. This forced the delay of capacity additions in the early 1970s.

The steel industry's good relationship with the bureaucracy, and with the broader economic policymaking community in and out of government (described in Chapter II) has made these negotiations generally successful. Harmony between MITI and the industry, however, is not universal. A case in point is Sumitomo's recalcitrance in the middle 1960s.

Sumitomo is perhaps Japan's most aggressive steelmaker. Since the middle 1950s, the company has achieved better results in profitability, modernity of facilities, export sales, and market share than any of its competitors in the industry. In 1965, Sumitomo challenged the industry consensus recommendation that steelmakers should delay all new investments in rolling facilities except those which replaced existing capacity. It went ahead with a new installation which, while technically a replacement, substantially improved productivity; at the same time, Sumitomo stepped up production while the majority of producers were trying to keep prices stable by moderating production levels. Fuji Steel vigorously protested against Sumitomo's action and comparable aggressive behaviour on the part of smaller steelmakers, and argued that only special legislation governing steel investment could resolve the industry's fundamental problem of overcapacity.

Response within MITI was mixed. Many, including the outgoing vice-minister, defended the traditional system of industrial consensus reached under MITI's watchful eye — an arrangement which Sumitomo felt put the fast-growing, efficient steelmakers who were responsible for Japan's international success at a disadvantage. It may be inferred that Sumitomo's view was echoed by the Fair Trade Commission, as it reiterated its disapproval of existing production cartels as anti-competitive. At the other extreme, a study committee of the Industrial Structure Council used this occasion to argue that the problems of capacity regulation and price stability could best be solved by a thorough consolidation of the steel industry.

The upshot of these confontations was continuation of the status quo.

Sumitomo continued to build its new facilities and produce aggressively. MITI disciplined the company by limiting its allocation of imported coking coal to what it considered appropriate levels. Before Sumitomo really felt the effect of this action, however, demand for steel recovered sharply and by 1967 Sumitomo's additional capacity was needed to meet domestic requirements.

The Sumitomo incident clearly indicates the limitations of the consensus system. But the majority of industry or government leaders would not have tolerated a more radical form of control. The consensus system struck an acceptable balance between autonomy and control, though this might have been more difficult had demand not recovered.

More recently, as steel has come to be regarded as less important in Japan's future, MITI has begun to discourage major investments at home, and to call for further industry rationalisation. As early as 1974, MITI was reluctant to support continued general expansion in the industry in Japan, despite the then current steel boom. Since, then, a long-term recession and worldwide overcapacity in steel have confirmed them in this view. Japan's remaining small local open hearth furnace producers have been designated as a troubled industry and are being encouraged to come up with a long term plan to reduce capacity.

MITI has, however, favoured foreign investment by Japanese firms in overseas steel mills, particularly in developing countries, as a way of maintaining Japanese dominance in steel while promoting the growth of the Japanese steelmaking machinery and whole plant export industries. MITI has encouraged Japanese participation in steel projects in Qatar, Iraq and Saudi Arabia among others.

In general, then, MITI helped industry growth very directly in the beginning, and more indirectly and informally during the 1960s and early 1970s. Its actions stemmed from a belief that having the largest, most efficient steel industry in the world would be a valuable national asset for many years to come, benefiting many other Japanese industries using steel. Means were found to spread the risk inherent in the commitment of vast financial resources to the industry while still providing a good return on equity for investors in the steel companies.

Raw material acquisition

Scale plants alone cannot guarantee a competitive steel industry; low-cost, high-quality raw materials are also essential. Because Japan produces only about 10 per cent of its total coking coal needs and almost none of its iron ore needs, ensuring a steady supply of good quality raw materials at a reasonable cost has been a major preoccupation of government policy. Long-term contracts arranged by the steel industry account for roughly four-fifths of the resources consumed in steelmaking itself. The Japanese government has provided a good deal of financial help. Government institutions such as the Export-Import Bank and the Overseas Economic Co-operation Fund directly finance imports. These institutions provide the assurance of long-term financing which is necessary in order to enter into supply agreements with overseas mining operations, many of whose total output and hence total investment, is targeted for Japan. In addition to providing a long term source of funds, the government designates iron ore and coal as priority import categories and ensures that foreign exchange is allocated to purchase them.

The government has also assisted steelmakers in undertaking direct overseas resource development investment. The Ministry of Finance once designated special sources in its annual budget in accordance with a standing policy to favour such overseas investment. During the 1950s and 1960s, when Japan's currently productive resource development projects were undertaken, capital exports of scarce foreign exchange were authorised first for ore, coal and petroleum exploration and mining ventures. Resource development accounted for 30 per cent of total cumulative Japanese foreign investment in 1970.

Just as important as the formal availability of loan funds for development has been the priority the government has given this type of investment and the resulting diverse forms of support. On several occasions MITI's alacrity in directing funds to a Japanese development co-ordinator, usually a large trading company, has proved critical to the project's success. Similarly, the government can ensure that funds are available for the export of Japanese equipment and technology that usually attends the overseas development project. MITI and the steel companies have dispatched teams of exploration experts to investigate possible coal development sites in Canada and Australia and to advise the developer. The Japan Overseas Development Corporation, a public corporation and a counterpart to the Japan Petroleum Development Corporation, assists in the organisation and financing of development projects abroad. The government has unequivocally demonstrated its commitment to develop foreign sources of ore and coal supply.

A third, more minor form of government financial assistance has been tax incentives and insurance against development losses. A contingency reserve for possible losses and thorough development loss insurance facilities are available to overseas ventures.

The government is also supporting basic geological exploration in prospective supply areas. In addition, public funds have established a resource development college to provide professional training in exploration and mining. However, the State has not directly invested in resource development on a significant scale nor does it direct the efforts of manufacturers and trading companies in exploration or mining.

While government's role in assisting capacity addition in the steel industry has declined in recent years, its interest in raw materials acquisition has increased. In the past, although Japanese companies and the government would agree to enter into long term purchasing contracts for Australian and Brazilian iron ore and US, Canadian and Australian coal, actual Japanese investment in these developments was minimal. Since the 1973 energy and raw material shortages demonstrated that availability (not just the cost) of supply was an issue, Japanese companies, with government assistance, have invested in new mining projects. The increasing strength of the yen and the existence of dollar surpluses have also spurred overseas investment.

In general, the government has not itself invested in these projects nor directly provided the funds for investment, but rather has helped to convene consortia and, through MITI's and MOF's involvement in discussions and negotiations, has influenced the direction taken. Government has also contributed to the success of development projects by relaxing antitrust regulations to allow cartels to invest and import raw materials; in some cases, the government has guaranteed financing.

Cartels

A final kind of government assistance to the steel industry has been the formation of recession cartels and export restraint cartels. Steel production is capital intensive both in the form of fixed and working capital. Reductions in steel production, leading to under-utilisation of capacity, can be extremely damaging, and the cyclical nature of the worldwide steel production has often caused severe cash flow problems for producers. Most American companies, for instance, show great swings in profitability and usually only have funds to invest during boom periods. It requires a few years to build new capacity, which then may come into use at the time of the next recession, thus exacerbating cash flow problems. As a result, producers are often tempted to cut prices in order to maintain capacity utilisation; this can compound the industry's problems, and distort its long term growth potential.

This problem first appeared in Japan during the mild recession of 1957, when the country's economic growth faltered in the midst of the steel industry's expansion, creating over-capacity. Because Japan's steelmakers operate with exceptionally high fixed financial and labour costs, and because capacity additions were accelerating, a severe cash flow crisis resulted from substantial under-utilisation. Prices dropped as producers tried to restore normal levels of capacity utilisation. As the crisis deepened, individual firms began to cut prices drastically.

Self-motivated collusion among firms to restrict production and stabilise prices would have violated the anti-monopoly Act. In this impasse, MITI led informal consultations with industry management and developed a public sales system to ameliorate the problem. Under this arrangement, steel producers agreed upon and reported their scheduled monthly production levels to MITI along with price schedules. Prices were made public and the industry's entire monthly output was to be sold at the announced prices. Thus, without unilaterally setting production limits and price levels, MITI was able to bring producers to an enforceable consensus.

Since the late 1950s, similar means have been used during major recessions to promote an orderly cutback in production and to manage pricing. In normal economic conditions, however, there is no price fixing or price control, and Japanese steel prices have steadily fallen as the industry's productivity and raw material supply have improved.

MITI has also co-ordinated voluntary export restraint cartels. The Export-Import Transaction Law of 1952 allows exporters to 'enter into an agreement with respect to price, quantity, grade, design, and other items in the export business of a designated category of goods to be exported to a specified destination by reporting to MITI,' and gives MITI the authority to alter or suspend the agreement if it cannot function effectively or if it fails to serve legitimate purposes. Such export restraint cartels were organised in the late 1960s in response to pressure from the US government to limit exports of Japanese steel products to the US.

Specialty steels

The most significant government cartel intervention in the industry came in response to the special steels crisis brought about by the recession of 1964-65. Specialty steel production — stainless, tool, etc. — grew rapidly from 1960 to 1965, but capacity grew even faster. By 1965, significant over investment had occurred. The major source of over investment was the entry of additional carbon steel producers into the stainless, tool and structural alloy fields.

In February 1964, the Japanese government initiated a deflationary monetary policy. As economic growth began to slow down, machinery and motor car producers reduced their steel orders. Specialty steel producers cut prices sharply to maintain market share and plant operating levels, but specialty steel production actually declined from 1964 to 1965.

The industry and MITI responded quickly. MITI suggested guidelines for voluntary production cutbacks as early as April, 1964. Demand fell faster than production, however, and by the end of 1964 production cuts of 10 to 15 per cent from previous-year levels were necessary. A formal production cartel was organised by MITI in January, 1965 for structural alloy steel. In March, of the same year a more stringent measure, a price cartel, followed as prices continued to deteriorate. March, 1965, also marked the financial collapse of Sanyo Specialty Steel, the largest bankruptcy of the postwar period. In December, MITI organised a production cartel for stainless and bearing steel. The economy recovered in 1966, and by September all cartels were abolished.

During the crisis, MITI took the initiative to push for a reorganisation of the industry. The Specialty Steel Policy Subcommittee of the Ministry's powerful Industry Structure Deliberation Council recommended a programme for reform. In November, 1965, the Subcommittee issued a report calling for co-operative efforts between MITI and the industry in three areas: vertical rationalisation of production among carbon steel and specialty producers, specialisation within steelmaking groups of particular products, and formal mergers of competing or complementary producers. Some significant changes were made over the next five years.

The government also acted to rescue individual firms from bankruptcy. Two major producers, Sanyo and Nippon Specialty, slid toward bankruptcy in 1965. Under the Corporate Rehabilitation Act, the government sponsored the reorganisation and refinancing of these two firms. MITI, the Ministry of Finance, the Bank of Japan, and the commercial banks all played important roles. In the case of Nippon Specialty Steel, the rehabilitation plan was drawn up in December, 1966 by the major creditors and shareholders under the supervision of the Ministry of Finance. In short, the method of rehabilitation was to reduce by large amounts the unsecured debt and paid-in capital without compensation to creditors and shareholders. Under the guidance of the Ministry of Finance, new shares were issued to creditors holding the cancelled debt instruments, mortgaged debt was frozen, and new management was installed. New debt was arranged through the intervention of the Bank of Japan.

In the commodity steel industry, such extensive government intervention has not been needed. Since the early 1970s, government has been working to rationalise existing capacity in commodity steel by enforcing agreements to close the least efficient furnaces during recessions as new ones came onstream and, more recently, by strongly encouraging the rationalisation of the small weak competitors. These actions, like those in special steels, have come in response to industry crisis and at the request of the companies involved, rather than as an imposition from government.

Summary

As discussed in Chapter II, Japan's success in steel can be largely attributed to aggressive investment strategies which allowed the country to build the world's lowest cost steel industry.

The value of government support to the industry cannot be measured in terms of cash expenditures. By the judicious application of support in the areas where it could be most effective, government has done a great deal for the industry. Selective measures — help through the insurance of debt for building greenfield plants, assistance in procuring raw materials and forming anti-recession cartels — have provided support without extinguishing competition or stifling initiative in individual companies. Even capacity expansion co-operation has been carried out in such a way as to allow substantial continued internal competition and even greater market share changes than occurred in the US. The actual flow of funds from government to the industry represented by loans, grants and tax allowances has been minimal, at least since the late 1950s. Per ton of steel, such assistance has been substantially less than that supplied by many European governments (often to subsidise the losses of uncompetitive plants).

The Motor Car Industry

The Japanese motor car industry, with two of the world's four largest companies in terms of output, is now second only to the US in total production, and is the largest exporter of automobiles in the world. The top three foreign cars sold in the United States are Japanese. This success has come in a comparatively short period of time. In 1965, Japan exported only 100,000 cars, primarily to other Asian countries, and even in 1970 fewer than 700,000 cars were exported. By 1978 exports had risen to more than 3 million units.

The Japanese car manufacturers have remained strong despite the revaluations of the yen and the rapid rise in relative Japanese labour costs over the past decade. In fact, the true potential of the industry has not yet been realised, primarily because of formal and informal import restrictions on Japanese-produced cars, particularly in Europe.

The success of Japan's major car firms — Toyota, Nissan, and Honda — stems mainly from their accomplishments in product design and production process. They have focused on a relatively limited range of chassis and engine types. They have achieved significantly higher levels of product reliability through greater discipline in tolerances and extensive pre-production testing. They designed and built high volume automated facilities which, when operating near capacity, are low cost, and they have gained high volume through the growth of their domestic market and a major effort in marketing abroad.

As in other industries,[2] the lethargy of American and European competitors contributed to Japan's success in the sales of motor cars. Except for Volkswagen, none of the European car manufacturers was willing to parallel Japan's heavy investment in marketing, distribution and service for the large US market; Detroit was slow to develop a true subcompact alternative car to those being imported and Volkswagen lagged in replacing 'the Beetle'. Thus, Japanese producers were able to capture a large part of the rapidly growing US small car market.

Finally, the large home market was an important asset to the Japanese car industry, providing rapid initial growth and a proving ground for domestic producers. European producers have recently begun co-operative efforts that have consolidated their own market base and made it possible to amortise investment in research and development and automation over greater volume. Had they taken such steps earlier, they might have posed a more effective deterrent to Japanese producers.

Postwar reconstruction

The Japanese government's role in the motor car industry began in the 1930s, when for military and for foreign exchange reasons, the government passed a law that forced the market leaders, General Motors and Ford, out of Japan. After failing to encourage Zaibatsu to enter the industry, the government provided incentives for Toyota and Nissan to do so.

In the immediate postwar period, the car industry was in disarray. Toyota, the largest producer, had to be saved from bankruptcy in 1949 by the Bank of Japan. The Bank opposed development of the industry, but MITI was in favour. The Korean War resolved the issue by creating an export market for Japanese-produced motor cars. Thus, in 1952, MITI developed a policy to protect and help fund development of the industry and to help it acquire needed technology.

The government played a significant role in the industry in the 1950s and 1960s. Government intervention in the car industry was characterised by three major policy goals; discouragement of foreign capital in the Japanese industry and protection against car imports; attempts to bring about rationalisation of

---

[2]See Chapter II.

production, and assistance with overseas marketing and distribution expenditure. Recently, the Japanese government has played only a minor role to assist in arranging voluntary European export cutbacks and in the industry's research and development programme to develop an electrically powered car.

Protection

The government devised a comprehensive and imposing set of protection measures which discouraged foreign investment in the car industry. These laws specified that no repatriation of earnings or capital would be guaranteed from foreign investment in marketing facilities. Repatriation would be guaranteed for investment in production facilities only if it 'contributes to the development of the domestic industry.'

MITI's purpose was to discourage import marketing investments while leaving the door open for selected joint ventures with foreign producers who had superior car parts technology. Admission of large American and European motor car assemblers was ruled out. Two instruments — quota and tariff — were used to protect the industry. Quotas were applied throughout the mid-1960s, and prohibitively high tariffs through the mid-1970s.

The imposition of import quotas and tariffs created for Japanese producers a market opportunity which they were not technologically prepared to exploit. Domestic producers turned out only 4,317 passenger cars in 1951, and these were uncompetitive in price and quality with Western imports. Parts technology and production methods were undeveloped. Most manufacturers agreed with MITI on the necessity of importing foreign technology.

MITI controlled all foreign licensing agreements. To make technology agreements more attractive to the licensor it guaranteed the remittance of royalties from Japan. The policy stipulated, however, that continued remittance would be guaranteed only if 90 per cent of the licenced parts were produced in Japan within five years.

MITI had struck a compromise. Obtaining operational foreign technology required substantial imports of foreign 'value-added' in the form of parts and sub-assemblies. By making remittance conditional on the transfer of parts manufacture to Japan, however, MITI served notice that knock-down imports would be permitted only for a limited period. Domestic manufacturers were thus given additional incentive to develop manufacturing capability for their licensors' parts. Import controls were not, however, relinquished; quotas and tariffs on parts were retained.

A year after the policy was agreed, six domestic manufacturers had negotiated agreements for knock-down assembly of foreign cars in Japan under licence. Of the six, Nissan was the only one then producing passenger cars. Hino, Mitsubishi and Isuzu were traditional truck manufacturers. MITI approved the applications of these four, while rejecting those of two others, Fuji Auto (no relation to Fuji Heavy Industries now producing cars) and Nichiei. MITI considered those firms too financially weak to survive, and did not want a fragmented industry. Nissan and Isuzu co-operated with Austin

(UK) and Rootes (UK) respectively. Hino cooperated with Renault and Mitsubishi with Willys (USA). Toyota and Prince, two of the three major passenger car producers of the period, used domestic know-how exclusively. The four licensees rapidly developed their own technology, with the result that assembly of European cars in Japan did not last very long. The Isuzu-Rootes agreement was the longest, running until 1964 but producing less than one million dollars in royalties over twelve years.

Government role in industry rationalisation

In the past two decades, the government has used a variety of financial assistance programmes to aid the car industry. The Japan Development Bank extended reconstruction loans to car producers from 1951 to 1955, financing roughly nine per cent of their total investment. Special accelerated depreciation rates were extended to car producers, permitting rates of up to 50 per cent depreciation in the first year. Finally, during the 1950s, direct subsidies amounting to roughly one million dollars were awarded to the Automobile Technology Association, representing manufacturers. After this initial financial assistance, the major investment role played by the government (primarily MITI) was to encourage rationalisation, both of the parts industry and of the motor car industry itself.

The car industry has from its inception been highly competitive internally. As a result, MITI has often met opposition from producers when it advocated mergers and associations within the industry. Particularly in the 1960s and 1970s, the limits of MITI's control can be seen clearly.

MITI's attempts at industry rationalisation have been most effective in the parts industry, where they had the co-operation of the major car producers; MITI has been least effective among the producers themselves, where competitive rivalries and the unwillingness of inefficient producers to go out of the business have frustrated the Ministry's plans.

The car parts industry

The structure of the motor car producing sector in the Japanese economy resembles a series of pyramids, with the products flowing from the bottom to the top. At the top are the vehicle producers — Toyota, Nissan, etc. — which manufacture engines and design and assemble vehicles. Each assembler is supplied by an affiliated group of primary parts manufacturers. These firms, roughly 300 in number, usually sell exclusively to one assembler.[3] The bottom layer comprises the small parts sub-contractors who supply, both exclusively and non-exclusively, the primary parts firms. There are several thousand small sub-contractors, many of whom are affiliated through ownership, technology agreements or simply captive arrangements with primary parts manufacturers or the assemblers themselves.

This system gave the assembler a stable yet elastic source of supply, as demand fluctuations were felt by the marginal sub-contractor. Labour costs at

---

[3]It should be noted, however, that several large independent parts manufacturers have now emerged.

the sub-contract level were usually lower than in the large firm. As design improvements required more advanced parts technologies, however, the system proved to have some serious drawbacks.

The chief problem was the large number and small size of the primary parts manufacturers and sub-contractors. A low production scale precluded economies of scale and modern production technologies. The firms were financially weak. Both MITI and the major car producers recognised that the production efficiency and technological progress of the industry would be inhibited if this structure remained.

MITI had taken a serious policy interest in the parts industry since the early 1950s. In 1952 MITI directed budget monies originally allocated to the car assemblers' development to immediate subsidies for specific parts producers. Over the next few years, it recommended that the Japan Development Bank extend long term credit to large, viable parts suppliers of the four major car producers. At least ten parts manufacturers participated.

In 1956, MITI used a major piece of new legislation to implement a more thorough financial assistance and rationalisation programme in the parts industry. An Auto Parts Committee including MITI Heavy Industry Bureau officials, presidents of various part manufacturers' trade associations, and senior officers of the Automobile Industry Association, representing the car manufacturers, was formed to co-ordinate the programme.

This ad hoc Committee was responsible for taking the initiative to develop operational programmes acceptable to all its constituents and formally proposing them to MITI. The car parts programme was planned in five year intervals and formally lasted until 1971.

The Committee worked between 1956 and 1966 to modernise facilities and concentrate production among fewer producers in 45 of 95 parts categories. Mergers, although encouraged, were not explicitly directed. Using criteria heavily influenced by MITI, the Committee approved borrowing for large, specialised exporting firms. Within the constraints of the affiliated system, MITI wanted to develop a small group of large, specialised parts firms capable of competing with American suppliers. (At one time, MITI reportedly suggested that the number of primary parts manufacturers could be reduced to 45. There presently remain over 300.)

The ten year programme from 1956-1966 was reasonably successful. Nearly $50 million in low interest long term loans were extended by the Japan Development Bank and the Small Business Finance Corporation over the period. Market share concentration occurred and costs were reduced.

Price reductions over this period were critically important to Japan's subsequent export penetration of the United States market. Annual percentage price reductions from 1960 to 1965 averaged roughly 30 per cent.

Despite gains in industry concentration and efficiency, however, the primary parts manufacturers in 1966 remained largely one or two product companies. (The criteria used for the advancement of loans had in fact encouraged specialisation.) In addition, Japanese parts manufacturers were smaller than their American counterparts. MITI thought that larger, horizontally integrated parts manufacturers would improve Japan's competitive position and would reduce the need for domestic firms to seek foreign technology through joint equity ventures.

Consequently, the rationalisation programme which MITI approved for the third five year period (1966-1971) emphasised horizontal combination, even across affiliated group lines. The government offered financial assistance either to mergers or to jointly established research efforts by parts producers. MITI hoped to create large 'unit system' sub-assembly producers. The programme was not successful. Despite annual production growth rates of 25 to 40 per cent during this period which made low cost, long term lending sources extremely attractive to these capital constrained single product companies, borrowings were not heavy and government programme budgets were not fully utilised.

Nor was the horizontal consolidation phase of the programme successful. A number of sub-contractors merged into primary parts manufacturers. For example, two large Nissan affiliates in the lighting equipment area merged, and a three-way clutch venture including Toyota and Nissan affiliates was considered. But there was little impact on the primary parts manufacturers who were the real targets of the programme.

The major reason for the relative failure of MITI's efforts was that the car producers themselves, especially Nissan, were reorganising their affiliates during this period. This inevitably caused some tensions. The vertical nature of the affiliate system did not easily accommodate the horizontal, total market orientation of the government's programme.

Overall, the consolidation and modernisation of parts suppliers during the 1950s and 1960s was essential to the emergence of a world competitive industry. It is clear that government played a crucial role in this effort, although its wishes did not always prevail. By the early 1970s, the industry had attained competitiveness and MITI moved to a 'hands-off' policy vis-à-vis the parts industry.

Consolidation efforts

MITI's attempts to rationalise the manufacture of motor cars failed, although they did exert some influence on producers. The history of this interaction gives a good picture of the tensions within Japanese industrial policy formulation.

During the 1950s and 1960s, MITI attempted to consolidate the industry into fewer and larger 'groups' of car producers. Although MITI introduced various consolidation plans, the government and the manufacturers never achieved consensus. A number of business combinations (in the form of mergers and co-operative production arrangements) did occur after 1965. These were largely self-motivated, however, and usually consummated by the producers without direct Ministry influence. The consolidations were clearly not responses to MITI's several 'grouping' plans enunciated during the decade.

To understand MITI's ambitions requires an appreciation of the circumstances of the motor industry. From the introduction of foreign technology in 1952 until 1960, the number of conventional passenger car producers had remained stable, with Nissan and Toyota the dominant firms. In 1960, three more firms — Mitsubishi, Fuji and Toyo — entered the passenger car business. The combined car market share of Toyota and Nissan dropped from three-quarters to less than one half between 1960 and 1962.

Rapid market entry, was, of course, to be expected as passenger car demand soared. Annual passenger car output more than tripled between 1959 and 1961. During 1961, for example, while Toyota and Nissan together lost 11 per cent of their market share, their combined sales revenue grew by 38 per cent.

MITI viewed this increase in the number of producers with anxiety. In 1953, the Ministry had rejected two of six applications for the import of foreign technology. Two years later, MITI suggested that all car producers should develop a prototype People's Car, and then permit MITI to select one design and subsidise its production by the single privileged manufacturer. The hope was that a single popular car which could dominate the market would be developed. The car manufacturers quietly but strongly objected to the single company subsidy concept, and the plan never reached the Diet. This was perhaps the manufacturers' first major resistance to MITI policy.

MITI's interest in the structure of the industry reflected its concern not only for the efficiency of domestic production but also for international competitiveness. Because liberalisation of passenger car import quotas was clearly inevitable, Japanese cars quickly had to become competitive in Japanese markets. Resisting imports was also important for developing the export opportunity. Japanese producers had to pre-empt all domestic market growth in order to gain sufficient production scale and experience to compete in American, and, it was hoped, European markets.

Either slow domestic growth, excessive product fragmentation or premature import liberalisation could keep the country's motor car producers from reaching competitive parity. MITI viewed this possibility with great concern, and made a series of efforts to consolidate the industry.

Proposed reorganisation of the industry. At a 1961 meeting of the Industry Structure Advisory Council, MITI proposed that passenger car producers be organised into groups based on the car's basic design type. Three groups — regular passenger cars, minicars, and specialty cars including sports-cars — were defined. A firm's entire production would be limited to one group, and minimum volumes would have to be met within three years. The objective was to force a concentration of product line and eventually eliminate small producers.

Toyota and Nissan — neither of whom produced minicars — reportedly did not voice strong opposition to the plan, which would have reduced competition in conventional passenger cars. Toyo Kogyo, Mitsubishi, Daihatsu, and Fuji, on the other hand, all produced both conventional and minicars, and together had roughly 30 per cent of the total car market by 1962. These producers reacted with hostility to MITI's proposal and after a series of unsuccessful discussions, it was dropped.

MITI, it should be noted, did not try to force consolidation upon reluctant car manufacturers. Industry attitudes and the limitations of MITI's direct power kept it from ordering formal combinations of producers.

Development Law for Specific Industries. In 1962, MITI was concerned with structure in several major industries including motor cars, petrochemicals, and tyres. It sought a comprehensive legislative charter to undertake, in co-operation with industry, major programmes for producer specialisation, establishing appropriate investment levels, and promoting mergers and groupings. Toward this end, MITI drafted the Development Law for Specific Industries. (The law conferred major financial advantages on the motor car industry and on other industries, if they chose to participate. The programmes themselves would be jointly conceived by the manufacturers, the commerical banks, and MITI.)

The wide scope of this ambitious proposal attracted attention from many elements of government. The leadership of the ruling Liberal Democratic Party strongly favoured enactment. The Fair Trade Commission (FTC) and the car producers themselves generally opposed the legislation. The FTC complained that the law would extend the government's intimacy with industry beyond desirable limits. Motor car manufacturers did not want to put their autonomy at risk. More importantly, even the secondary producers did not yet feel any financial necessity to seek consolidation. While the industry was exceptionally competitive, it was uniformly profitable during the early 1960s for major producers, all of whom earned a sufficient return on their investment to finance the required growth. Five secondary producers — Toyo, Kogyo, Mitsubishi, Fuji, Daihatsu, and Honda — gained or maintained their market share between 1963 and 1965 while following relatively conservative financial policies.

Other Measures. The draft law failed because of the opposition of producers in the motor car and other designated industries. The government, however, did not give up its effort to make mergers financially attractive should the occasion arise. Motor car manufacturers qualified for the existing government Investment and Loan Programme; the Japan Development Bank would help to finance any bona fide formal merger or co-operative production affiliation. In addition, the two Ministries devised and secured approval of a special tax deductible allowance which rewarded mergers. It reduced tax liability for a limited period in proportion to the increase in a firm's capital through a merger.

MITI did not limit its techniques of persuasion to the financial area. The Ministry was discriminating in its approval of foreign technology introduction by domestic producers. In 1968, for instance, Toyo Kogyo, the third ranking car producer, and a staunch opponent of consolidation, was denied permission to import radiator technology from Renault. Only later, in conjunction with the approval of an application from Nissan to import essentially the same technology, was Toyo's request granted.

By the middle 1960s, MITI's concern with structure was acute. Two facts were clear by 1965. First, the fragmentation of market share was pronounced: eight firms each held at least five per cent of total vehicle production. Only Toyota and Nissan were internationally viable.

Second, the prospect for continued protection from foreign competition was limited. In October 1965, quantitative restrictions on passenger car imports were removed. During the preceding year, Japan had become a member of the Organisation for Economic Co-operation and Development (OECD) and had given a commitment to liberalise restrictions on foreign capital investment. To defuse the inevitable liberalisation of investment in the motor car industry became MITI's dominant objective for the remainder of the 1960s. Quite apart from the fact that consolidation would strengthen the domestic industry competitively against American capital, merger and affiliation of Japanese producers were the only effective ways to deny foreign manufacturers domestic partners. A marginal, independent domestic car producer would be the naturally desirable partner for foreign companies trying to enter the Japanese market.

Nissan/Prince merger. The first major consolidation in the industry occurred in 1966 with the merger of Nissan and Prince. Although financial needs prompted the merger, MITI seized the opportunity when it arose and took steps to encourage it. The merger was consummated in May 1966. The negotiations principally involved the two companies and their banks, although the chief executive of the Japan Development Bank also entered the discussions and promised financial assistance to the merger.

The merger served many interests. MITI accomplished its strategic aim — the merger of a secondary producer with one of the two dominant companies. Nissan, which had struggled with inadequate passenger car capacity, acquired Prince's modern and under-utilised plant. Prince's technical staff was highly regarded, and its dealer network gave Nissan improved distribution coverage. Prince, of course, was financially extricated, and the bankruptcy of one of the country's major firms was avoided.

The Japan Development Bank extended roughly $15 million in credit to the merged company. This was the Bank's first loan to the motor car industry since MITI announced the new criteria for loans three years earlier. Only one other government sponsored loan to the industry was made subsequently, when Hino became affiliated with Toyota later in 1966.

Producer affiliations. The Nissan-Prince merger apparently stimulated other manufacturers to pursue consolidation. Within two years of the merger, six separate car producer affiliation arrangements were negotiated, though only two were consummated. These six were not formal merger proposals but rather 'groupings,' or limited bilateral arrangements by which minority shares were exchanged, overlapping production was rationalised, parts were standardised and dealerships were shared. The six negotiations are summarised below:

Year	Companies	Outcome
1966	Toyota-Hino	Success
1966	Fuji-Isuzu	Failure
1967	Toyota-Daihatsu	Success
1967	Mitisubishi-Fuji-Isuzu	Failure
1967	Mitisubishi-Isuzu	Failure
1968	Nissan-Isuzu	Failure

The only successes involve Toyota. In both cases, the product lines were complementary: Hino's trucks and Daihatsu's minicars with Toyota's conventional passenger cars. Both affiliations were arranged by Mitsui Bank, which was the primary creditor for all three firms. At the request of the manufacturers, MITI did not intervene in the discussions.

MITI's effort to bring Nissan and Isuzu together was one of several attempts in the late 1960s to consolidate the industry around Toyota and Nissan. Merger efforts focused on grouping secondary producers around the two dominant ones, but MITI failed to push through these mergers. An effort to merge Nissan and Toyo Kogyo met with similar resistance. Eventually, Nissan and Fuji did merge but MITI did not play a significant role.

At the end of the decade, it was clear that MITI's attempts to consolidate the industry had failed. Neither the three-group nor the two-group concept had materialised. MITI's legislative programmes for consolidation had not been enacted, and its financial incentives for affiliation had drawn limited response.

The effect of this failure can be seen in the accelerated flow of foreign capital into the industry after the liberalisation of restrictions which occurred in the early 1970s. Issuzu and General Motors joined forces, as did Chrysler and Mitsubishi. Toyo Kogyo and Ford also formed many agreements.

On the other hand, it is the indigenous and wholly Japanese producers which continue to dominate the Japanese market. Nissan, Toyota and Honda have been the most successful companies and Toyo Kogyo, despite its unsuccessful wankel engine gamble, remains in fourth place.

Export assistance

A further way in which the Japanese government has aided the automobile industry is through export assistance, including some financial support and direct functional assistance. Such aid was directed toward the development of overseas marketing and distribution capability for Japanese car producers.

Financial support

In 1949, six motor car manufacturers established an Export Promotion Association to perform basic overseas market research. The Ministry of Commerce and Industry subsidised the research and the preparation of catalogues written in English — perhaps Japan's first car export marketing step.

Long-term export credit offered by the Export-Import Bank of Japan dates from 1950. The Bank historically emphasised heavy equipment industries with large export financing requirements, including cars, ships and locomotives. Its lending was typically supplemented by commercial bank credit, with terms advantageous to the borrower. Since the early 1970s, however, preferential export borrowing terms have been disappearing.

The first tax assistance came in the form of an export income deduction provision in 1953. This system, which provided a maximum deduction of eight per cent of net export income, was initiated by MITI and approved by the Ministry of Finance. Less than 150,000 passenger cars were exported under this tax exemption, and the Japanese discontinued the practice in 1964 in compliance with GATT regulations.

In the same year, a series of more indirect financial incentives was established, including measures that permitted exporting firms to establish tax-free reserves for overseas marketing development and investment. Most notable among these income reserves was that for 'overseas market cultivation', which allowed a firm to shield 0.5 per cent of its export sales from tax. In addition, an accelerated depreciation schedule tied to export performance was instituted. A manufacturer who increased his export business relative to competitors or to the previous year's performance qualified for special accelerated schedules on export-related capital investment. For the rapidly growing firm these reserve and depreciation measures become a permanent and not insignificant source of funds. Suspension of these special provisions was announced in 1972.

Functional assistance

Since the early postwar years, the Japanese government has made an effort to improve the quality of the country's exports, required that exports of specific products be inspected either by government or by industry association authorities. In addition, since the Export Insurance Law of 1950, government has provided Japanese exporters with default insurance. Through the Heavy Machinery Export Council, manufacturers played an important role in developing the insurance programme, insisting on lower premiums and extended coverage.

In 1965, Japan's official export promotion agency — Japan External Trade Rehabilitation Organisation — established the Chicago Automobile Parts Centre to promote Japanese car exports to help solve the logistical problems of the overseas car part business, and to undertake market research. MITI partially subsidised the Auto Parts Centre.

Like other forms of government assistance to the industry, however, overseas investment and export assistance declined in the early 1970s and is now virtually non-existent.

64

V Aluminium and Shipbuilding Industries

This next study discusses two industries in decline — aluminium and shipbuilding.

Industries in serious trouble are not new to Japan. Japan's biggest manufacturing employer, the textile industry, has been in decline for 20 years. It has uncompetitively high wages, too many small and inefficient producers, and no advantage in raw material costs or market access against its Asian competitors. Today, the industry employs 300,000 fewer people than in 1965, and the loss has been concentrated in a few regions. Still, the rapid growth of the economy during the late 1960s and early 1970s has absorbed these workers, and serious political repercussions have been avoided. Japan's major capital-intensive industries — steel, aluminium, synthetic textile fibres — have undergone serious recessions in the past, but these were cyclical in nature. Recession cartels and countercyclical monetary and fiscal policy always brought recovery.

In the late 1970s, however, a number of major industries are basically uncompetitive internationally and unlikely ever to recover fully. They include aluminium smelting, chemical fertilisers, ferro-alloys, plywood, sugar refining, and synthetic textile fibres among others. The source of their structural problems vary: some have uncompetitive energy costs; others have too high priced raw materials. Some have been poorly managed; others are simply natural casualties of the industrialisation of the Third World. The solution to the serious problems posed by these declining industries has not yet been found. The Structurally Depressed Industry Law referred to in Chapter II was drafted by MITI and passed by the Diet but consensus has not yet developed to enable it to be used effectively. Major producers have been unwilling either to merge to trim permanently their operations and the national political leadership has already, in one notable shipbuilding case, shown itself unwilling to allow an uncompetitive firm to become bankrupt.

The Law designates several industries — aluminium smelting and shipbuilding among them — as structurally depressed and it sets forth criteria to cover others. To be eligible for reconstruction measures, an industry must have severe overcapacity, more than one half of the firms must be in serious financial difficulty, and two-thirds of the firms must sign a petition seeking designation as a depressed industry. Once designated, the responsible Ministry may develop a stabilisation plan for the industry wherein the Ministry forecasts supply and demand, measures excess capacity, and identifies plants to be closed or cut back. Where scrapping capacity brings real financial stress, the Law authorises a loan guarantee trust fund to encourage private banks to extend further credit to their ailing debtors. Most of this loan guarantee fund is subscribed by the Japan Development Bank and other public banks. To mitigate the employment effects of a reduction in physical capacity, two additional laws were passed in 1978. The first of these provides for an extension of unemployment benefits by 90 days and retraining allowances both for retained and dismissed employees. The second provides a variety of financial relief measures to small and medium size firms in the depressed regions.

The Law is typically Japanese in its intended operation. MITI is obliged to consult with those inside the industry. Labour unions are given an advisory voice. The Law empowers MITI to restrict new investment in the industry. The FTC is able to review the stabilisation plan to ensure that it is not anti-competitive. Finally, the companies in trouble and MITI have to agree on a workable plan. Despite its good lineage, to date, the Law has been applied neither to aluminium smelting nor to shipbuilding — two of the most protracted problem industries.

Aluminium

Japan has never been a world competitive producer of aluminium. The industry has grown at the same rate as the economy, but the volume of imports of aluminium was two or three times as great as exports in the period 1970 to 1976. Since 1974, the industry has been in especially difficult shape. Electricity is a key cost element in the smelting of aluminium. (About 15,000 kilowatt hours are required to refine one ton.) Since the oil shock in 1973, electricity prices for Japanese aluminium smelters have been about twice those in Europe and about four to five times those in North America. Japan's price for electricity is about 8 to 9 yen per kWh as against 1 to 2 yen in Canada. As a result, Japanese domestic aluminium costs in early 1978 were 320,000 yen per ton (of which one-third is electricity) compared with an import price of about 280,000 yen per ton-c.i.f. price).

In 1977, domestic capacity in the industry was about 1.1 million tons with production at 650,000 million tons; over 500 thousand tons were imported. In that year, operating losses in the industry amounted to about 20 billion yen. Results in 1978 were even worse. Two major public policy issues face the industry. How much capacity reduction should occur and should it be scrapping or mothballing? What should be the rate of allowable imports?

The producers disagree among themselves on these issues, but the firms in the industry would prefer short-term reversible measures, such as a production cartel, rather than permanent capacity reduction. They want a very limited scrapping of capacity, no more than 25 per cent; they claim that Japan cannot afford to let imports supply too large a share of consumption for economic security reasons. Finally, the industry wants to maintain corporate autonomy with no mergers or groupings.

MITI, on the other hand, wants at least a one-third reduction of capacity with a higher proportion of scrapping rather than mothballing of facilities. One idea current in MITI today is to combine the current fourteen plants and seven producers into two large groups with important operating and investment decisions made at the group level. MITI also would like to rely more on imports which are far lower in cost; it claims that Japanese overseas aluminium projects such as Sumitomo (Indonesia), Nippon Light Metal (Canada), and Mitsui (Brazil) will add about 25 per cent to Japanese owned capacity and will guarantee sources of supply.

MITI and the industry also disagree on the question of rate of import flow. Currently, the volume of imports is about four times that of exports; imports account for about one-third of the total market. Imports come in two ways: via trading companies, which average low price imports with high price-affiliated domestic product to sell to all users, and via independent importers who do not average and sell low priced imports directly to large users.

One producer wants the government to set up a public company to buy all aluminium, both imported and domestically produced, and sell to users. This step would allow the state to enforce a limit on imports by permitting only captive flows to enter. The producers also want an electricity rate subsidy so that they can supply competitively priced aluminium to the home market.

MITI regards protectionism via a state trading company as politically unacceptable inside and outside Japan, nor in any event would it solve the industry's cost problems. The electricity subsidy is ruled out as being too costly given the differential between Japanese rates and the rates of Canada, Norway and other producing countries. MITI proposed instead the use of a tariff quota device whereby duty would be cut on a specified import volume but the user price would stay the same. The difference would go to a restructuring loan fund for the industry. MITI has estimated that about three billion yen could be available from this fund in the first year.

Thus, MITI and the industry are at an impasse. A committee consisting of independent mediators is searching for appropriate means of rationalising the industry, but so far has not succeeded. Although the Law has been in effect for a year, still no solution is in sight. MITI is essentially market conscious and is looking for a permanent structure solution, resisting protection and agreeing to subsidise only when there is some rationalisation. The companies do not want to surrender their autonomy, or to regroup or cut a significant amount of capacity permanently. The stronger companies seem willing to wait for a survival of the fittest solution, and many of the companies in the industry are part of larger multi-business companies which can absorb financial losses for a while, enabling them to resist pressures.

Shipbuilding

The shipbuilding industry provides an example of an industry that has gone through all three phases of development in Japan. In the 1950s and early

1960s, shipbuilding was a priority industry that received substantial government assistance in its attempt to gain international competitive dominance. In the late 1960s and early 1970s, government involvement in the industry waned, as the industry became the world leader. Now, in the late 1970s, the industry is declining with the rise of new developing country competitors (hastened by the collapse of the tanker market over the past few years).

The history of the industry reflects the full cycle of Japanese industrial policy. Shipbuilding was covered in the initial machinery reconstruction Acts passed in 1956, and companies received considerable aid in modernising capital equipment. The government gave shipbuilding priority because of the need for a strong shipping industry in an island nation like Japan and because steel and labour are the major costs of ship construction. In the 1950s, Japan had an abundance of low cost labour, and steel was an investment priority.

Shipbuilding developed through Zaibatsu around sister trading companies and shipping companies. Some of the steel mills also formed their own shipbuilding companies. Thus, the industry included a significant number of large powerful companies. Because of the steel and labour advantages, a number of smaller companies also grew up during the 1960s; these companies tended to specialise around particular types of ships.

During the initial phase of industry development, the Ministry of Transport (which has jurisdiction over the industry) and the Ministry of Finance used various means to assist the introduction of new technology and also to encourage rationalisation. The government formed an industry development association to share techniques and to assist in overseas marketing. A key factor in the development of export markets in this period was the use of the sugar import measures (which will be described in Chapter VI) to allow Japanese shipbuilders to supply ships for export below their costs; shipbuilders received a compensating subsidy in the form of lucrative profits from the licensed import of raw sugar.

In 1959, an advisory council on Shipbuilding and Shipping was established and authorised interest rate subsidies on loans to the shipbuilding industry for approved mergers, an interest rate subsidy to shipping companies in Japan to buy Japanese ships and a series of favourable tax measures. The Japan Development Bank was instrumental in providing loans to the industry, and a number of the quasi-public and private banks were also encouraged to participate. In the early stages about 70 per cent of all industry financing was from the JDB. In some cases, the interest rate subsidy went as far as a deferral of repayment up to 15 years.

The government provided significant tax benefits to the industry. It allowed reserves for price fluctuations to be tax free, a large special depreciation account, establishment of export and investment losses reserve to avoid taxes, as well as tax and other financial incentives for investment in overseas market development. In one company studied, about 5 billion yen per year — one-third of its tax burden — was subsidised through these tax measures alone during the mid-1960s.

While low interest and deferred loans for consolidation, price subsidies through the sugar license, and tax subsidies, aided the industry's development, perhaps the most significant assistance to shipbuilding came from customer financing provided at very favourable terms through the Japanese Export-Import Bank. During the 1960s, about 70-80 per cent of all loans made by the Bank were in the shipbuilding industry, and the terms of some of these loans provided a considerable subsidy to the manufacturers. Both the easy availability of financing and the competitive rates were of great assistance as Japan expanded its world market share.

By the late 1960s, Japan was the world's lowest cost producer of ships. The provision of low cost steel from Japan's efficient steel industry, the relatively cheap price of Japanese labour (pre-yen revaluations), and the large scale of Japanese shipyards allowed by the rapid growth of the industry during its development phases, all contributed to Japan's dominance in world shipbuilding. In the early and mid-1970s, Japan launched over 50 per cent of all the world's ships and shipbuilding companies were highly profitable.

During the maturity phase (late 1960s, early 1970s), government assistance to the industry all but disappeared. The government reduced tax subsidies, eliminated export price subsidies, virtually ended the JDB loans, refusing to allow deferrals on payments, and reduced export-import financing considerably. During the early 1970s, for example, the company previously referred to received only a 9 per cent reduction in taxes (entirely from depreciation) instead of the 32 per cent it had received during the growth phase; it did not receive any JDB loans.

The Japanese industry entered its declining phase after the 1973-1974 tanker boom. In 1975, Japan launched 17 million gross tons of ships. In 1978, Japan's launchings had fallen to 6.3 million tons.

The collapse of the tanker market was the major cause of this decline, but Japan's market share also dropped from 49.7 per cent in 1975 to 34.7 in 1978 as lower wage countries like Korea, Spain, Brazil and Taiwan increased their share. There has been a rise in Japan's share of the market in 1979 but it is still significantly below mid 1970s levels. Currently, about 150,000 people are employed in shipbuilding in Japan, of which about half are considered redundant. As a result of the market collapse, between March 1977 and March 1978, 28 small and medium-sized shipbuilders went into bankruptcy. Most of the large companies have withstood the serious situation so far, because they are associated with major Zaibatsu or steel companies and can absorb losses.

The Ministry of Transport, (MOT), which has jurisdiction over the shipbuilding industry, established an advisory commission which, in 1976, recommended significant cutbacks in the industry's capacity to achieve a supply-demand balance by 1985. The Ministry has proposed that the major seven companies reduce capacity by about 40 per cent. The government wants small companies to close down. A package to boost demand by retiring government ships ahead of schedule and expanding Japanese exports of ships to developing countries as a form of economic assistance has also been put forward. Finally, the government wants to refocus some industry capacity on liquid natural gas tankers, floating factories and other more sophisticated types of ships.

The Depressed Industries Law has given the MOT tools to realize these objectives. However, the firms in the industry cannot agree among themselves nor with the government on a plan to bring about this rationalisation. Large and small firms have disagreed about who should bear the burden of capacity reductions, with small firms claiming that the large firms can afford to bear a greater weight, and large firms believing all should suffer equally. In addition, the large firms are disagreeing among themselves as to the appropriate mix of capacity reductions. Finally, the industry does not want to scrap capacity permanently and is calling for greater temporary financial assistance from the government. In January, interest rate subsidies to the shipping companies were again restored and there are some signs that the government will provide some temporary subsidies even without the completion of a rationalisation plan, as the employment and bankruptcy developments in shipbuilding have increased political pressures to rescue the industry.

The Sasebo case illustrates this pressure.[1] Sasebo Heavy Industries (SHI) is the eighth largest shipbuilder in Japan. Its major stockholders are Nippon Steel and Nippon Kokan, Japan's two largest steel companies, and its major bank is Dai Ichi Kanqyo. It is a major employer in the city of Sasebo so its announcement in early 1978 of financial difficulty and its intention to seek voluntary early retirement by 1,000 employees produced concern. Concern became crisis later when the major stockholders decided not to guarantee future loans, and the banks refused additional funds without guarantees. Confidence in the company's management was low and could not be restored. The major Ministries involved — Finance and Transport — and the Bank of Japan chose not to arrange a rescue and were prepared to see the company declare bankruptcy. The consensus of the regular policy making apparatus was that the company should be allowed to fail.

This became politically unacceptable, however, when the workforce and the Sasebo community petitioned members of the Diet including the Prime Minister to intervene. The Prime Minister requested the two Ministries to find a solution. This was not forthcoming. Finally, the Prime Minister ordered that a solution be found. Eventually, the banks, major stockholders, and Ministries put together a package which the banks grudgingly accepted. It included some government financial relief, a hastily arranged American ship repair business, to bolster demand, a syndicated bank loan from 18 different banks, and a modest new capital infusion from the major shareholders. All of this was premised on a carefully negotiated change of management.

The Sasebo case is interesting primarily in its demonstration that politics can and occasionally will thwart the regular policy consensus process. The policy making community had reached a clear consensus — Sasebo should be permitted to fail — but the nation's highest elected officials (members of the

[1]This discussion draws heavily on an unpublished paper by Kent E. Caldér of Harvard University entitled *The Emerging Politics of Aid for the Uncompetitive: the Case of Sasebo Heavy Industries.*

70

Diet) could not resist expedient measures and they over-rode standard procedures. The Ministries were aggrieved at this outcome, for it has clearly complicated the solution of the broader shipbuilding problem. Shipbuilder's ⌐ resistance to the 'rational' schemes of the public policy community has grown.

The resolution of the shipbuilding crisis is still unclear. Some of the major companies have been able to shift their capacity to other businesses such as heavy industrial machinery and plant exports. The underlying obstacle to consensus is less whether the problem will go away and more how should the cutbacks be distributed among the producers. The producers are a heterogeneous lot — small versus large, diversified versus specialised and they simply have very different reactions to any proposed solution. Recently, a company was formed to purchase excess stocks. Loans totalling 90 billion yen have been obtained, 90 per cent from private financial institutions, five per cent from shipbuilding companies and five per cent from government. The government has played the role of catalyst in this venture.

Summary

The plight of the aluminium and shipbuilding industries in the late 1970s in Japan is instructive. Traditionally, Japan has demonstrated an ability to face major issues of industrial policy squarely. The Structurally Depressed Industries Law, by attempting to cushion the social problems at the same time as accelerating the restructuring of the industry, is in this tradition.

So far, the Law has not been successfully implemented owing to disagreements among the parties which must reach consensus. Further, political concerns have also intervened. The challenge to a long term sound public policy is great.

VI Industrial Machinery and Information Electronics Industries

The last two case studies focus on sectors which are growing rapidly and are of increasing importance to Japan's future international competitive position: industrial machinery and information electronics. These studies show how industrial policy in Japan is applied to businesses where there is significant technology change and where Western companies are still competitively formidable. Both these industries are undergoing changes in their competitive structure and the challenge to industrial policy has been to anticipate and to lead events in the market place.

In industrial machinery, the areas of intense competition and high growth have shifted away from single machine manufacture toward developing computer controlled production systems and supplying whole plants, particularly for the rapid growth export market. Accordingly, government policy has focused less on industrial concentration and more on systems research and development and export financing.

In the information electronics sector, which includes data processing, telecommunications and other applications of semi-conductor technology, competition among the major international companies and economies is intensive, and the Japanese government has made an enormous commitment to advancing the Japanese position. A complex pattern of government-sponsored co-operation in both research and development and equipment leasing has for at least a decade accompanied the intense competition among Japanese companies in designing, manufacturing, and marketing their own systems. Government has sought the advantages of both large, central research efforts at a national level and unrestrained competition for market share of a large and growing domestic market among the companies. While the government and the industry often disagree and the results of some programmes have been disappointing, it is clear that Japan's global position has advanced materially and that the government financing and co-ordination have been crucial to this progress.

Industrial Machinery

The Japanese have long regarded the machinery industry as critically important to the country's development. A knowledge intensive industry employing highly skilled labour, it has a high growth potential and is shielded from competition from developing countries. Japan currently accounts for less than eleven per cent of all OECD industrial machinery exports, behind Germany, the USA and the UK and only slightly ahead of France. This industry is destined for aggressive development in the future. Industrial policy for this industry has evolved in response to changes in the competitive position of machinery businesses throughout the world; the aim of industrial policy is for Japan to progress towards leadership in the industry.

The changing competitive position

In the 1950s and 1960s, the machinery industry consisted of two basic types of businesses. The first was the production of mechanical components such as gears, bearings, valves, heat exchangers, springs, etc. Production of mechanical components usually consists of pressing, machining, and some type of finishing operation. Competitive success depends primarily on large scale production and long runs of standard products together with a sufficient volume of production to be able to dedicate production lines for special products. Marketing and engineering, while important, tend to be less significant, and large volume production enables an easier amortisation of costs.

The second type of business was machine assembly, in which mechanical components and structural metals and castings are assembled into paper machines, steel rolling mills, or metalworking machine tools, etc. Since machine redesigns have an enormous effect on sales, research and development is crucial in this type of business. It has traditionally required coupling prime mover technology and metallurgical engineering to produce faster, more accurate, more powerful machines. The scale of production is less important to competitive success, although in some cases, large scale may enable a producer to gain advantage by manufacturing components within his own organisation.

Two broad industry trends have had a significant impact on industrial machinery businesses in the 1970s. The first is the development of so-called 'systems businesses' or the sale of whole plants. Here, various machines are assembled with construction materials into whole plants and are sold and installed as a package by one producer (though he may subcontract parts of it).

One reason for the growth of systems businesses has been the increasing importance of developing countries as markets for machines. As industrialisation proceeds in OPEC and COMECON and advanced developing countries, non-OECD countries have come to account for roughly one half of all OECD machinery purchases. These countries are less able to design their own plants, whether for ethylene production or food processing, and prefer to buy them ready made. The ability to sell, for example, a dairy separator, may, therefore, hinge on the ability to offer the whole plant in which it will operate.

The growth of systems businesses has also been accelerated by progress in process control. Co-ordinated systems now allow the computer centralised (or microprocessor distributed) control of a whole factory, increasing the effectiveness of industrial machines. Maximum efficiency in the overall process is achieved by designing an entire plant for a given application, rather than by assembling well designed individual machines.

The development of the whole plant sale businesses has increased the significance of applications engineering in the overall cost structure of the industry. Because purchases are bigger, the importance of long-term buyer financing and insurance of seller's risk has also increased.

The other major development in the machinery industry in the 1970s has been the introduction of new technologies to be integrated into machinery design, particularly miniature electronics, lasers, and ultrasonics. Intelligent control in machines, the use of laser cutting and printing, and ultrasonic testing, etc., are examples. As a result, machinery makers have had to undertake massive research and development in unfamiliar fields in order to remain competitive in the industry.

Japan's place in the world industry

Japan was far behind major European and US companies in production and design capability in the 1950s and early 1960s partly because of war damage, but by the mid-1970s had virtually closed the gap. As its producers have become more successful, the Japanese government has shifted its policy from massive aid and very close direction to a looser form of assistance and co-operation. The types of aid offered have also changed along with the needs of the industry, as it evolved from one which imported technology to one on the cutting edge of new developments.

Japanese government policy has recognised the complexity of the machinery industry, which is made up of both small and large companies with very different cost structures. Because of this heterogeneity, Japanese policy toward industrial machinery has consisted of almost 100 programmes over the past twenty-five years. We will mention only a few important ones.

Active policy in the industry began in 1956 with the Extraordinary Measures Law for the Rehabilitation of the Machinery Industry, aimed at rationalising the industry's production and creating initial demand for its products.[1] The law focused on basic components and some simple machinery. Twenty-one industry areas were eventually designated under the Law, including bearings, springs, gears, simple presses, castings, and machine tools.

Between 1956 and 1960, the Japan Development Bank provided funds for modernisation of equipment; MITI authorised rationalisation cartels for purchasing parts and importing materials; standards were set for the industry and guidelines were established for production technology improvement. During this period, the government provided almost 400 loans totalling about 10 billion yen. Roughly 25 per cent went to the machine tools industry, 13 per cent to car parts, and the rest to various component makers of tools and gears. The main goal at this stage was to impose basic standards on an industry made up of thousands of small producers. To the extent that these standards could

---

[1]Before 1956, the Reconversion Finance Bank and the Japan Development Bank had helped to rebuild some of the large machinery manufacturers from before the war in order to supply the needs of UN forces in the Korean conflict. This aid, however, was not part of any industrial plan.

74

not be met by weaker companies and they left the industry, the industry as a whole was rationalised. In general, however, rationalisation measures were carried out primarily within individual firms.

In 1961, the Extraordinary Measures Law was extended and aimed at further rationalisation, this time through merger and joint investment rather than within one company. The government made available Japan Development Bank loans and preferential tax rates to encourage joint investments and mergers, and the Small Business Finance Corporation (established in the late 1950s) began to make loans to firms in the industry to assist rationalisation.

Between 1961 and 1965, the JDB made loans totalling over 34 billion yen on more than 644 projects, primarily in the car parts, machine tools, and bearings industries.

Throughout this period, there was a twofold policy approach appropriate to the machinery industry. In areas like car parts and bearings where large scale production and long runs are essential to achieve low cost, mergers were encouraged. In other areas, like the making of special springs, gears, or castings, or certain parts of the machine tool industry, where scale of production is less important, modernisation was encouraged within the small companies. Industry associations were formed to facilitate the flow of information and rationalisation cartels were authorised, but the emphasis was on financing, through the Small Business Finance Corporation, to modernise equipment.

By the mid-1960s, these measures had succeeded in rationalising the simple machine industry. When the Law was extended again, emphasis shifted to making the companies internationally competitive. Major overseas enterprises were carefully examined as to size, capacity, and level of technology. In order to improve the structure of the Japanese industry, a cartel was formed to allocate product categories among companies, group enterprises, and to establish joint ventures. In some businesses like chemical machinery, individual producers were encouraged to co-operate in the development of new products; in other businesses, like machine tools, certain enterprises were encouraged to drop certain products. In other cases such as printing machinery, joint ventures and mergers were sponsored. The Japan Development Bank provided over 30 billion yen during the period 1965-1969 for this purpose.

In general, the industrial policy of the late 1950s was aimed at improving individual company efficiency; in the early 1960s, basic mergers to consolidate the industry were encouraged; and in the late 1960s, emphasis shifted to the encouragement of greater specialisation.

Protection and stimulation of the home market

Throughout the 1950s and early 1960s, only machinery which could not be made in Japan was allowed to be imported. This guaranteed a market for Japanese producers and encouraged foreign producers to license their technology or to form joint ventures in Japan, since outright exports to Japan were impossible.

In addition, a series of loan programmes helped domestic machinery suppliers become more competitive in the home market (Table VI.1). In addition to these loan programmes, a series of special depreciation laws were enacted both to promote mechanisation and to encourage the purchase of Japanese made machinery. A recent survey by the Japanese taxation agency reports that between 1963 and 1976, the government forfeited over 174 billion yen of tax revenue in these special depreciation programmes. Finally, in 1961, the government instituted a credit insurance system designed to protect the suppliers of machinery against defaults by customers, particularly small enterprises.

Table VI.1   Loan programme examples

Between 1964 and 1969, a programme existed to allow Japanese producers to compete against foreign companies with instalment low interest sales*. The Industrial Bank of Japan (IBJ) and the Long Term Credit Bank provided funds to enable the domestic industry to offer similar credit conditions to domestic users of machinery. The funds came from the Treasury. Loans were provided in the area of machine tools, plastic moulding machinery, printing machinery, etc. Loans of more than 25 billion yen were made during this period.

In 1974, the Japan Development Bank (JDB) lent roughly three billion yen to manufacturers of packaging machinery allowing them to establish a joint venture leasing company specialising in packaging machinery.

A series of measures during the 1960s and 1970s to assist leasing of labour-saving, safe new machinery (including packaging machinery, metalworking machine tools, conveying equipment, etc.) was provided by the Long Term Credit Bank, Industrial Bank of Japan, and Nippon Credit from Treasury financing.

The JDB made loans in the 1960s to enable manufacturing companies to introduce new machinery in a comprehensive way so that the whole production process could be modernised.

*This is a method of selling which provides long term low interest credit to the buyer. The ownership of the equipment is transferred at the time of sale to leasing companies.

These programmes served two purposes — they encouraged the modernisation of all Japanese industry and at the same time aided the Japanese machinery industry.

Export promotion

The Japanese developed a variety of highly inventive means to encourage exports of machinery, including the formation of associations, export price subsidies of various sorts, both short and long term export financing, and tax incentives.

The Japan Machinery Exporters Association was established in 1953 with a subsidy from the government to provide advice on technology together with information and promotional services to assist Japanese exports. The Association is exempt from the anti-monopoly laws and can help the industry to implement orderly marketing agreements, to put price floors under exports, and to negotiate with MITI on export matters. With 600 members, it can co-ordinate the formation of groups of companies to handle large overseas plant export orders as well as being in a position to co-ordinate financing arrangements and to provide government contacts in foreign countries.

In the early 1950s, a 'linking' system enabled Japanese exporters of machinery to price competitively on international markets. The government controlled the import of raw sugar, but in order to provide a subsidy to machinery exporters, the control of raw sugar imports was handed over to the Machinery Exporters Association. The Association sold the sugar at the international price and the profit they obtained was meant to compensate machinery exporters for losses incurred in building export sales. By awarding this right to machinery exporters who priced at international or even lower levels, it compensated them for losses incurred in building export sales. This 'linking' system was extremely important in shipbuilding as well.

Partly in order to improve its position in international trade negotiations, Japan has since reduced direct export grants to a minimal level. The only major grant programme still operative is the assistance given to the export associations by the bicycle racing fund (p. 42), which totals about three to four billion yen per year.

Loans, on the other hand, remain a major factor in export promotion. The Japan Export-Import Bank is much like those in other countries in its operations; an ever increasing proportion of its funds has gone to the machinery industry. Both supplier and buyer credits are extended according to the rules laid down by the OECD.

In all of these loan programmes, MITI has review rights which give them influence over individual companies. Any transaction by the Export-Import Bank not settled within six months must be submitted to MITI for approval. Thus while MITI does not actively screen each transaction, it has a means of review whenever it is necessary. In Japan, the controls on foreign transactions have not been dismantled, just relaxed.

Similarly, reviews are made of the credit worthiness of all manufacturers and exporters. This evaluation was especially important in the 1950s and 1960s when capital was short and the export advance bills given by the bank were crucial to overall company financing. This made exports very popular, especially with smaller machinery companies.

Tax incentives have also played an important role in export promotion. The government has used a variety of different measures over the years, as shown in Table VI.2.

These measures played a very significant role in the 1960s, but have become less significant in the 1970s. Although several are still technically in effect, only the technology export income deduction is significant today. In 1976,

Table VI.2 Export promoting tax measures

Dates when measure was in operation	Measure
1953-1964	*Export income deduction.* This measure directly shielded export income from taxation.
1953-1959	*Export loss reserve system.* A reserve against the possibility of cancelled export contracts was non-taxable.
1953-1959	*Special depreciation for overseas offices of trading companies.* All depreciable assets in a new office overseas were subject to a 50 per cent write-off the first year.
1959 to present	*Technology export income deduction.* Companies are allowed to deduct a portion of royalties paid from abroad from their taxable income. The objective is to stimulate saleable technology development.
1964-1972	*Overseas market development reserve.* A small portion of the revenue from current exports can be put into reserves from taxable income. Like all Japanese reserves, this must later be returned to the income stream. This provision still applies for small businesses.
1964 to present	*Overseas investment loss reserve.* A small percentage of current foreign investment expenditure each year can be put into reserve to insure against investment losses. This reserve fund is non taxable.
1964-1972	*Export accelerated depreciation.* Accelerated depreciation was allowed on capital investment where the output was to be exported. The degree of acceleration depended on the proportion of plant and equipment devoted to export.
1968-1978	*Export special depreciation.* This is an overlay acceleration on the previous provision.
Early 1950s to present	*Free trade zone investment loss reserve.* This measure is a variation on the overseas investment loss reserve extended for free trade zones.

these measures in total added about 32 billion yen to the cash flow of companies of which almost 20 billion came from the technology provision in the machinery industry. This accounted for about five per cent of taxes actually paid in the industry.

In addition to these measures, the government has two export insurance programmes, one covering all industries and another compensating for losses caused by inadequate consultation on overseas machinery projects.

Policy in the 1970s and 1980s

By 1970, the process of industry rationalisation had essentially been completed. World scale component producers co-existed in Japan with a number of efficient producers of machines. The Japanese industry enjoyed a predominance in its home market and had made inroads into world markets for some products, particularly simple machine tools and textile machinery.

In the early 1970s, government policy turned away from rationalisation, home market protection and stimulation, and export assistance measures, and towards research and development assistance to companies for whole plant sales abroad. The goals are to move Japan into the forefront of machinery technology, to build world market share by attacking the new growth markets in developing countries, and to build upon strong Japanese process industries to emphasise whole plant sales.

These efforts to guide industry development have achieved considerable success. Japan has only a small export share in ordinary machine tools, compared to Germany and the USA, but a high share in numerically controlled machine tools. Over 50 per cent of Japan's machinery exports went to non-OECD countries in 1974-76, compared to 40 per cent for the USA and 30 per cent for Germany. Finally, Japan's most rapid export growth has been in steel mills, chemical plants, and other 'whole plant' sales.

Research and development

The primary thrust of Japanese industrial policy in machinery is currently in research and development. The policy includes grants, loans, and tax subsidies.

A number of grant programmes currently operate to benefit industrial machinery businesses. MITI's Agency for Industrial Science and Technology (AIST) administers the government's conventional research and development grants. This programme gives matching grants to specific research and development projects proposed by individual companies. On average, about four billion yen was provided annually to the industrial machinery sector during 1973-76 and three billion during 1977 and 1978. These appropriations have been primarily directed to the area of machine and whole plant integration.

A second source of research and development grants is the national Large Scale Research project, referred to in Chapter III which combines resources from the government and companies to fund development in areas of nationally critical technologies. In the industrial machinery area, a seven-year programme to develop an ultra-high performance laser applied complex control system (a highly automated machine tool system) will receive 12 billion yen in government assistance plus individual contributions from companies.

A third source of research and development funding is the Bicycle Rehabilitation Association (JBRA). In 1976, the JBRA awarded almost five billion yen for research and development in the machinery area. An additional

150 million yen is awarded from a minicar racing fund. MITI undoubtedly influences, although it does not officially control, these allocations.

Another minor source of government funding is the subsidy for research and development by small businesses. This is administered in matching funds programmes primarily through the Subsidies for Important Technologies budget. About 450 million yen was allocated to industrial machinery through this channel in 1976.

Finally, the AIST maintains permanent research laboratories whose work principally benefits the industrial machinery area. The institutes include the Mechancial Engineering Laboratory in Tokyo and the Industrial Research Institutes in Osaka (materials) and Nagoya (forming processes). About six billion yen in financing for these labs was provided by AIST in 1976.

In total, between eight and ten billion yen per year is spent in direct grants for research and development in the industrial machinery industries in Japan. In addition, there is a complex series of loan programmes to stimulate research and development. Over the years, this lending, primarily carried on by the Japan Development Bank, has grown steadily and is now well over 30 billion yen per year, of which about eight to nine billion on average goes to industrial machinery companies.

These project-related loans are essentially a means of providing low cost funds to manufacturers and buyers in areas such as the development of heavy machinery, commercialisation of new technologies in industry, development of prototypes for commercial production, and commercialisation of new technology for small enterprises. For example, the JDB will finance users' purchase of prototype machinery, manufacturers' purchases of equipment to be used in making new types of machines, and the actual development of new types of machines.

The final series of measures the government uses to aid technology development involves tax incentives for research and development. Twenty-five per cent of all new spending on research and development can be taken by a company as a direct credit; these credits were worth about 12 billion yen to the machinery industry in 1976. In addition, the government allows special depreciation on equipment. Although the impact of this provision is hard to measure, we estimate its annual value at roughly 5 billion yen.

From 1968 until 1975, a special depreciation programme existed for machinery embodying commercial application of new technologies. Regional property taxes as well as corporate income taxes were shielded by this programme, which assisted both users of new machinery and manufacturers. Overall, about 78 billion yen of equipment was covered in this programme during its existence.

Finally, tax credits are allowed on the dues for establishing co-operative research associations among companies. Over 25 of these associations have been created and the funds paid into them can be subtracted from the individual company's income as depreciation.

Over the past few years, grants and loans have accounted for 10 to 15 per cent of all research and development spending in the machinery industry. Tax credits related to research and development have averaged about three per cent of the industry's total tax paid.

Whole plant sales

A second major thrust of current industrial policy in machinery is to aid whole plant sales. Many of Japan's institutions work effectively together to promote whole plant sales. MITI has published a 400-page book on whole plant selling and has informally assisted the formation of groups of companies to study particular market opportunities. The industry association and trading companies also play an important role in co-ordination. The informal connections among MITI, the banks, the industry associations, and the companies, along with the legislation which enables cartels to be formed, allow a flexible mode of interaction very helpful in making the complex arrangements needed for whole plant sales.

Financing is crucial to the purchase of large plant, particularly in developing countries, which now account for about half of the market for machinery. Fully 60 per cent of Export-Import Bank loans are now directed to plant export; these loans are often supplemented by financing arranged through large banks (to which the government has close ties). The most significant form of financing assistance, however, is government-to-government credit (in yen), often indirectly tied to machinery sales.

Large national projects sold to the governments of other countries can be financed by mechanisms which fall under the broad heading of economic aid, and thus (in contrast to ExIm Bank loans) are not regulated by the OECD. In Japan, the agency responsible is the Overseas Economic Co-operation Fund, a public policy company funded via the FILP and under the direction of the Ministry of Finance, the Ministry of Foreign Affairs, and the Economic Planning Agency. Yen credits are a highly desirable form of financing from the borrower's point of view — very low interest is charged (three per cent and less); amounts can exceed the value of the narrowly defined project; and longer repayment terms than those of ExIm or private financing can be provided.

It is often difficult to discover an explicit link between a government-to-government or even a central bank-to-central bank financing package and a particular large machinery or plant order. Yet clearly such connections are there. Though the Japanese feel that the French are the masters at this type of activity, they themselves have devised a number of inventive financing measures, helped by the strength of the yen and Japan's large dollar balances.

Apart from sales arranged between governments, the trading companies play the most significant role in arranging financing, making three-cornered deals, and putting together packages for a sale as well as doing promotion and research, etc. The government may review prices or give guidance on selection of a particular subcontractor, but most of the work is done by the manufacturers and trading companies involved.

Summary

Although Japan is currently behind some other OECD Countries in the

81

export of industrial machinery, the priority placed on this industry will clearly make Japan an increasingly formidable competitor.

The groundwork being laid by government research and development, whole plant export co-ordination, and financing programmes will no doubt assist the industry greatly over the coming decade. Though these programmes have existed for a number of years, their results will be most pronounced in the near future. These measures reinforce the extremely good co-operation among Japanese companies which allows a prompt and well co-ordinated response to market opportunities. Western companies in this industry would be well advised to keep a close watch on current and potential Japanese competitors.

Information Electronics

Computers and semiconductors are the heart of information electronics. The Japanese government is committed to developing an internationally strong position in computers, and has given the industry significant support. The task of overcoming American leadership is a large one. US companies have over one-third of the Japanese market, dominate their own large domestic market, and are keenly fighting the Japanese challenge. Japan's overall trade balance in computers, including peripherals and attachments, is distinctly negative. In 1977, the value of imports were three times as great as the value of exports although exports were growing considerably faster. The two leading Japanese producers — Fujitsu and Hitachi — together have had a smaller share of the Japanese market over the last five years than IBM in the value of computers sold or leased. Japanese producers have advanced quickly but so, too, have manufacturers in other countries.

Most of the Japanese industry is concentrated in six companies — Fujitsu, Hitachi, Nippon Electric, Toshiba, Mitsubishi Electric, and Oki. They all produce computers, peripherals and semiconductors, and most of them produce telecommunications equipment as well. Jurisdiction over this sector lies primarily with MITI although the Ministry of Post and Telecommunications has some responsibility for the development of the telecommunications industry.

Computers

The government's assistance to computers can be reviewed under three categories — technology development, leasing and financing, and market protection.

Technology development

The government provides funds for approximately one quarter of all computer related research and development in Japan, while three-quarters is funded by the manufacturers of computers and private laboratories. Total computer research and development in Japan in 1976 was 116.5 billion yen. Government grants to companies and associations were 18.9 billion yen. (Major undertakings like the Very Large Scale Integration (VLSI) circuit

82

development project typically involve matching funds from business and government to ensure a worthwhile effort.) Another 5.8 billion yen of public funds was spent in university and government laboratories. In addition to direct government spending, two tax mechanisms — the research and development tax credit and accelerated depreciation of research and development facilities — offer significant assistance to the industry. One estimate puts tax saved by the computer manufacturers at 3.4 billion yen per year, roughly 5 per cent of total expenditure on research and development in the industry.

The government has also offered special help to the software sector. In 1967, the Japan Information Processing Development Center was established as a joint venture of government, the major manufacturers and the software houses to develop general purpose end user application software. The government invested one billion yen in equity and between 1970 and 1977 contributed eight billion yen in research and development funds. Not surprisingly, Japan Development Bank is the largest lender. Special tax benefits have been made available to the software industry as well.

The principal rationale for government research and development assistance is the small scale of Japanese producers relative to the American leaders — despite the concentration of all major computer and semiconductor activity within a few Japanese firms. Up to the mid-1970s research and development funded by Fujitsu, Hitachi, and Nippon Electric combined was less than half of IBM's total expenditure on research and development, the combined semiconductor research and development expenditure of these Japanese companies is less than Texas Instruments' total.

As with other Japanese industries, MITI has tried to use government funds to rationalise the industry's research and development effort. MITI has also tried unsuccessfully to rationalise the industry itself through mergers. The companies have preferred to remain independent and a system has emerged in which there is co-operation in the funding of new technology projects, rationalisation and concurrent specialisation in peripherals, but continued fierce competition in existing products and in the production and marketing of new products.

The first co-operative research and development project was in 1962, when MITI formed an association of Fujitsu, NEC and Oki to develop a new computer. After IBM introduced the 360 model in 1964, MITI conceived a more ambitious large scale computer project and budgeted for 10 billion yen of government funding. In designing this project MITI matched the five participating companies and tasks very carefully. Fujitsu, Hitachi and NEC were asked to build the memory and central processing unit and to develop operating system software. Toshiba and Oki were asked to build timesharing peripheral equipment. (Mitsubishi, the sixth competitor, did not join the project.) Later, MITI organised a peripheral equipment production cartel which enabled the six producers (each of whom had low production scale because of substantial product line overlap) to pool and specialise some equipment. The products handled through the cartel included standard peripherals whose design had stabilised and where further innovation was remote. Seven types of punched card and paper tape equipment were cartelised in 1969. Line printers and magnetic drums were added a year later.

In the early 1970s, MITI tried to organise the industry into three groups (Fujitsu/Hitachi, NEC/Toshiba, and Mitsubishi/Oki), again to force a specialisation of development efforts and, it was hoped, a long-term competitive segmentation of the business. Then the target was the IBM 370 series and a government sponsored joint development programme was conceived. By 1975, however, the targets of this programme were obsolete, and an extraordinary joint effort — the Very Large Scale Integration (VLSI) semiconductor project — was substituted. The four year project involves all major Japanese producers and two government electronics research laboratories in diverse roles; it is budgeted at 72 billion yen. Roughly 40 per cent is government funded. The technical targets are highly ambitious, aimed at developing the 'state-of-the-art' technology in both logic and memory circuits. Completion is scheduled for 1980-86. The project's key members are shown in Figure VI.1

Figure VI.1   Very large scale integration project

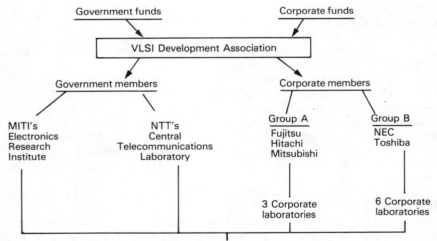

Central Laboratory at MITI's Institute (in close co-operation with respective supporting laboratories)

While Japanese producers have co-operated in these development efforts and benefited enormously, they continue to compete independently on existing products and new systems. MITI has tried to consolidate their computer operations but has failed, and must now rely on the market mechanism to re-structure the industry. The business moves extremely fast, and it is not clear whether MITI's policy initiatives of the 1970s to reduce the number of competitors were appropriate or not. On the one hand, computers will turn out to have been an expensive adventure for some Japanese producers, as for some large American and European companies. On the other hand, it is difficult to predict which company will succeed and in what sector in this rapidly changing business.

Leasing and financing

Apart from support for research and development, the government's major contribution to the industry has been in giving financial assistance to purchasers of computers, a crucial element in computer marketing.

In the early 1960s, it became clear that by leasing rather than selling computers, IBM was using its financial position to take advantage of its Japanese competitors who could not compete in the leasing arrangements, though MITI proposed a joint venture of government and computer manufacturers; this joint company would lease only Japanese made computers. Neither the manufacturers nor the Ministry of Finance would accept government equity participation, and the compromise reached in 1961 was a joint venture, with the equity shared among the seven manufacturers then active, financed heavily by the Japan Development Bank. This venture was called the Japan Electronic Computer Corporation (JECC).

JECC purchases computers from the manufacturers and then leases them to customers. At the end of 1978, the gross value of JECC's rented assets was over 400 billion yen. Over one third is financed by the Development Bank at interest rates roughly one per cent below the market rate, while city banks finance most of the rest. JECC has been generally successful, particularly in financing the explosive market growth which took place in the 1960s. In recent years, the two major manufacturers — Hitachi and Fujitsu — have increasingly leased directly to customers as far as their cash flow permitted. The reason for this is the competitive nature of the market. Large users want a better price than is permitted by JECC's fixed price policy. If the large manufacturers do not try to accommodate these large users by dealing with them direct, the transaction would in all probability go to a foreign supplier.

When a new computer model appears, customers trade in the existing leased equipment, and the manufacturer must repurchase at JECC book value. As technology moved swiftly in the 1960s, the resale value of the equipment sank well below book value, this created a new financial problem for the manufacturers. MITI and the Ministry of Finance developed a tax reserve in which initially 10 per cent, then 20 per cent of the original selling price to JECC could be reserved from taxable income against future estimated trade-in losses. After five years, the reserve had to be put back into the company's income stream. The cash flow effect of this provision reached a peak in 1972, when 10.3 billion yen in taxation was saved by the industry. Since then, budget pressure has forced a cutback in the provision. In 1977, three billion was saved.

To help clear the market of obsolete machines and make way for the new models, and to promote the use of computers among small businesses, the government has encouraged the Chambers of Commerce to repurchase traded-in leased machines from JECC. Resale price is set at 60 per cent of the original book value; half is paid by government and one quarter each by the user and by the original manufacturer, who then charges it against his trade-in tax reserve. Total government subsidy in 1976 was 40 million yen.

Other devices to preserve the manufacturers' cash flow and develop the market have also been used. Special accelerated depreciation is extended to some computer production facilities. Special depreciation was also established in 1970 for the purchase of larger computers, which enabled buyers to write off 20 per cent of initial book value in the first year in addition to normal depreciation. This provision aims to make the ownership of a computer more attractive than the leasing of foreign computers in Japan. Computers were also afforded preferential treatment in property taxation. Industry pays a standard local tax of 1.4 per cent of taxable real assets every year; the taxable value of the computer can be reduced by 20 per cent. There are miscellaneous other tax benefits, including a tax credit for training expenses for data processing engineers. The sums involved are far smaller than those committed to technology development and JECC.

Market protection

The government has used both direct and indirect forms of market protection. Tariffs assessed against computers and semiconductors have always been high relative to Japan's other products. Quantitative restrictions on both components and computer systems were the last to be lifted in the mid-1970s. Until recently, MITI actively discouraged Japanese companies from buying foreign computers as long as a domestic offering met the specification. At present, however, the private sector computer market in Japan is essentially open. Western companies can import or manufacture what product they wish. Informal protection continues in the public sector market, which includes all of civilian government and military expenditure as well as a large portion of the university and research institute market. Consequently, while domestic producers have between 50 and 60 per cent of the total Japanese market in value, they have over 90 per cent of the public sector portion. The only exceptions to this informal rule arise when the Japanese supplier cannot meet the specifications or when a Japanese supplier subcontracts a key part of the system to a superior foreign supplier in order to outperform other domestic bidders. MITI does not like this practice, but it does occasionally happen.

In the semiconductor area, government purchases are confined to domestic producers and, for different reasons, much of the private market is closed to foreign suppliers. Japanese computer and telecommunications equipment producers are both the major users and major suppliers of integrated circuits. Consequently, only where Western technology is unique or the cost is dramatically less are chips imported. The lengthy period of market protection posed a dilemma for MITI. The prohibition of any foreign investment into Japan, in either new ventures or existing domestic producers, preserved the industry's domestic character. As a consequence of this protection, producers were to some extent more dependent on MITI because of its influence on the market and the financial incentives it could provide. On the other hand, protection delayed any shakeout among the six producers, and there was not enough competitive pressure to make producers bend to MITI's consolidation schemes.

Telecommunications

There are four major telecommunications equipment suppliers in Japan — Nippon Electric, Fujitsu, Oki, and Hitachi (the Big Four). MITI and the Ministry of Post and Telecommunications delegate most policy authority to Nippon Telephone and Telegraph Corporation (NTT), a public corporation charged with maintaining a domestic telecommunications network. The Ministry of Post and Telecommunications controls NTT and authorises its budget; the directors of NTT are appointed by the Prime Minister with Diet approval. In addition to controlling the telephone and telegraph systems, NTT monopolises all common carrier network transmission in Japan, including data, and offers data processing time-sharing services in competition with private companies. NTT also licenses all communications, including private micro-wave and citizenband radios.

Japanese industrial policy in telecommunications has concentrated on supporting research and development and helping the industry to build an export capability by allowing high prices to be charged on domestic sales. Telecommunications research and development and system engineering is generally performed by NTT laboratories, much as Bell laboratories serves American Telephone and Telegraph Company in the USA. NTT makes all decisions on technical specifications, and engineers of the Big Four manufacturers are invited to develop new equipment jointly after basic research is completed by NTT's own engineers. Therefore, all research and development expenses incurred by manufacturers are mostly application and production related. Since new equipment is jointly developed by NTT and its designated manufacturers, NTT assigns actual production and supply to each manufacturer, depending upon availability of technical capacity and actual performance of the company on past assignments.

NTT's research and development programme has evolved as competitive needs have changed. In the 1960s, development of each component was assigned to a manufacturer (e.g. the switch frame to NEC and high speed transmissions to Hitachi). In order to develop overall telecommunication/computer technology, however, all four manufacturers are now involved in jointly developing future technical specifications with NTT. Opportunities are given equally to manufacturers to learn everything, from the switching system components to materials technology.

In addition to assistance for research and development, NTT also helps its suppliers in financing exports. The relationship between NTT and its major suppliers — Fujitsu, Hitachi, NEC and Oki — has helped these manufacturers to finance the growth of their businesses. First, prices are not bid but negotiated on a generous cost plus basis (somewhat less generous in recent years because of NTT's operating losses). Profit margins are widely alleged to be higher on NTT business than on export sales, though figures are not publicly available. Second, the exclusion of foreign equipment stabilises prices and production volumes. Third, NTT advances a portion of the purchase price to the manufacturer, in effect providing interest free funds.

As a result of these factors combined with NTT's financing of the research and development, the manufacturers can be very flexible in pricing exports. In this respect, Japanese producers enjoy an advantage over some major international competitors such as ITT and Ericsson.

Japanese companies got off to a late start in telecommunications exports, in large part because of their undistinguished technology. However, the boom in the OPEC and developing Asian markets in the middle and late 1970s, combined with lower growth at home, brought them into export markets. Exports, only eight per cent of sales in the early 1970s, are now 18-20 per cent. Because of the higher investment required in the new generation of digital equipment, NTT is encouraging firms to export more in order to spread the revenue base. The indirect forms of assistance which have been indicated, combined with liberal financing from Japanese banks, have contributed significantly to this goal.

Telecommunications policy is closely related to that of computers, which brings the MOPT into close contact with MITI. Co-ordination of policy between them is difficult. MITI has pressed for a faster and more meaningful liberalisation of imports in telecommunications equipment than MOPT has conceded. Disagreements arise over research directions and over data communications policy. The two ministries are being brought into more contact by the convergence of data processing and data communications technologies; policy co-ordination will continue to be difficult.

Summary

As with the nuclear reactor and aircraft industries, the computer and telecommunications industries have been the subject of government interest throughout the world. The US Defence Department research and development funding and purchases were essential to the development of the miniature electronics industry in the USA, and governments have played a key role in the development of the computer and telecommunications industries in a number of European countries.

Japan continues to make a large commitment to information electronics. It is too early to tell whether these policies will be successful. The Japanese still have not achieved technological parity and the strong, agressive US leaders are unlikely to follow the mistakes of their counterparts in steel and consumer electronics.

Postcript

In this booklet we have focussed on two distinguishing facets of Japanese industrial policy: the economic and competitive principles that underlie it and the broad based, interactive process through which policy is generated. Together they help to produce good, workable policy and provide a clear framework within which businesses can develop their strategies.

It is important to keep these two strengths in mind as we look to the future. Commentators who attribute Japan's success to date principally to a labour price advantage, unfair trade practices, and government protection of domestic markets typically argue that Japan's trade performance will level off now that Japan is no longer trying to catch-up the West. Japanese industrial wages are now equal to the European average, competitor countries are strictly enforcing their laws against unfair export practices and Japan's markets have essentially been opened.

Since we do not credit these factors as essential to Japan's success historically, we do not believe their absence will be critical in the future. Instead we look to the transition that Japan is making in its industrial structure and policies. Japan no longer tries to compete seriously in businesses where wage rates are central to a competitive cost position. Japan's modern manufacturing companies remain profitable, continue to invest and are probably more confident than at any time before. Government policy toward industry remains very active, though its targets have changed. It has shifted focus from protecting markets and bringing Japan's production scale up to Western standards, toward selectively placing major research and development funds, financing important plant export deals, and restructuring declining industries. In short, Japan's momentum and the thoughtfulness and determination behind its new directions should not be underestimated.

This is not to say, however, that Japan will continue to succeed competitively. Rather it is to say that if Japan's impact on world markets withers, the cause will not be changes that have taken place internally within Japan, but changes in the behaviour of its competitors — both companies and countries. Serious Western executives and industrial policymakers are increasingly coming to understand the corporate and national policies and behaviour patterns which have attended the surrender in certain areas of their international business and economic leadership. The more alert of them are responding with longer and more realistic planning time horizons, greater investment in the critical competitive areas, and more broad based policy discussions among the constituencies affected by industrial policy including governments, management, labour, and banks, to promote consensus.

For many government and business organisations where the traditional culture resists this view, this change may be difficult. But it is becoming increasingly clear that in a sophisticated international competitive world, traditional government policy focussing on macroeconomic variables alone is no longer adequate. Similarly, corporations cannot continue to rely on those strategies which brought them leadership in the domestic market. Finally, government, business, labour and finance can no longer establish policy separately. As Western companies and governments learn these lessons, the competitive environment faced by the Japanese will toughen.

There is of course a great danger in transposing the experiences of one society on another. We have been generally positive about Japanese industrial performance by both government and industry, though we have pointed out many mistakes and failures. While the basic economic and competitive principles of Japan's approach should be instructive, neither its manner of making and carrying out policy nor the specific themes and programmes of Japanese industrial policy need be appropriate to any other nation. The lessons for Western economies are more subtle than direct. They have more to do with the discipline of analysis and the importance of consensus than with the elaborateness of specific plans or the spending of large sums of money.

THE ART OF MENDING

Elizabeth Berg

THE ART
OF MENDING

A Novel

DOUBLEDAY LARGE PRINT HOME LIBRARY EDITION

RANDOM HOUSE ✳ NEW YORK

This Large Print Edition, prepared especially for Doubleday Large Print Home Library, contains the complete, unabridged text of the original Publisher's Edition.

This is a work of fiction. Names, characters, places, and incidents are the products of the author's imagination or are used fictitiously. Any resemblance to actual events, locales, or persons, living or dead, is entirely coincidental.

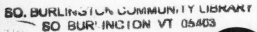
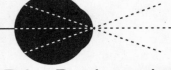

This Large Print Book carries the Seal of Approval of N.A.V.H.

For those who find forgiveness

by way of the truth

and for those who find the truth

by way of forgiveness

*Out beyond ideas of wrongdoing and rightdoing
There is a field. I'll meet you there.*

—RUMI

*Anyone's childhood can be an act of disablement
if rehearsed and replayed and squinted at in a
certain light.*

—CAROL SHIELDS, FROM *UNLESS*

*The foxes were having their pups. . . . If a stranger
appeared near the pens, if anything too startling
or disruptive occurred, they might decide to kill
them. Nobody knew whether they did this out of
blind irritation, or out of roused and terrified
maternal feeling.*

—ALICE MUNRO, FROM *LIVES OF GIRLS AND WOMEN*

ACKNOWLEDGMENTS

Kate Medina has believed in me unequivocally since she first read me, and she makes no secret of it. I make no secret of this: I love her, and my gratitude to her is boundless. And I think that this time, she just needs to have the whole page to herself.

THE ART OF MENDING

It is a photograph of a staircase that I took with my Brownie camera over forty years ago. On the newel post hang three jackets. At the bottom is mine, a turquoise corduroy, with deep pockets in which I used to hide Kraft caramels—I ate them every morning on my walk to school. Over my jacket is my brother Steve's: denim, with a fleece lining. And over that, my mother's stylish brown tweed car coat, an apricot-colored scarf spilling out of the pocket. Late-afternoon sun is streaming in through the window beside the stairs, illuminating the coats as well as three paper bags of groceries resting on the floor. I remember we'd been to Red Owl with our mother, and Steve and I had been given our own carts to select items from our own lists. That's why I took the picture: I was proud of the grown-up work we'd done. Nearly out of frame are the rounded tips of shoes. Someone sitting on the staircase, waiting for us to see her.

1

This is the Minnesota State Fair I remember most:

It was 1960, a Saturday morning when I was eleven years old, and I was the first one up. I had brought my mayonnaise jar stuffed with dollar bills and coins into the living room, spilled the money out onto the carpet, and then stepped over it to turn the television on to a low volume. I was going to watch *The Three Stooges* while I sorted my fortune.

I had just finished counting when my father came into the room. He was wearing a pair of trousers and a T-shirt and his battered old leather slippers speckled with paint the color of my bedroom walls. His blond crew cut was damp; you could see the glistening of water in it, making him look anointed, and he smelled of a citrusy aftershave. He was headed for the kitchen, where he would make coffee and bacon. This was his Saturday routine: He'd take a cup of coffee up to my mother in bed, prepared the way she liked it, with an eighth of a cup of cream and three level teaspoons of sugar. Then she would come down in one of her silk robes and make pancakes to go with the bacon.

I always hoped she would wear her peach-colored robe. It was my favorite, for its generous yardage and elaborate ruffled trim. Seeing what my mother wore was always interesting to me, whether it was the three-quarter-sleeve blouses she wore with the collars up, or the full skirts, tightly belted, or the pastel-colored cashmere sweater sets, or one of her many bathing suits, works of art designed to showcase her spectacular figure. Those suits came complete with cunning little skirts and jackets to wear over them, and broad-brimmed sun hats trimmed with fabric bands in coordinating colors. Before she was married, my mother worked for several years for an up-scale department store, parading beautiful clothes before rich men's wives. She inspired more sales than any other model before or after her; everyone wanted to look like her, though of course no one did. Think Grace Kelly with red hair and green eyes— that was my mother. But it wasn't just her model's training that made it so interesting to see what she wore, it was a quality inside herself. Charisma, my father said, but it seemed to me to be more than that. Other people had charisma. No one had what my mother did.

She had a large collection of jewelry, too; sometimes she allowed me to take one necklace at a time over to her bed, where I would lay it out and turn it this way and that, making it shine hard in the sunlight. "Are these real diamonds?" I once asked, and she said, "Why have them if they're not?"

That Saturday morning, my father saw me sitting on the floor and came over to survey my neat stack of dollar bills, my coins piled high. "How much have you got there?" he asked.

"Forty-seven dollars and eighty-three cents." I kept my smile tight to hold back my pride and stuck all my fingers between all my toes for the low pull of pleasure.

My father whistled between his teeth in a falling-bomb way I greatly admired and could not emulate despite hours of practice. He took his glasses off to polish them on the bottom of his T-shirt, then held them up for inspection: still dirty—he never managed to get them completely clear. "How'd you get that much?" He resettled his glasses on his face, pushing them up snug against his nose, a gesture I associated so strongly with him that I reflexively took issue with others doing it.

I said I'd been saving for a long time. I told him about the groceries I'd carried in for Mrs. Riley, "Mrs. Five Operations," my mother called her, for her incessant replaying of the laminectomies she'd endured. I'd pulled weeds for Muriel and Helen Lockerby, the two wild-haired old-lady sisters who lived around the corner. I'd babysat for little Rachel Thompson every Thursday after school while her mother went to run errands, and I'd occasionally walked their dog, an arthritic old German shepherd named Heintz, who seemed to me to grimace every time he lifted his leg. I'd made pot holders and sold them around the neighborhood—once, a man who answered the door in his bathrobe had bought my entire week's inventory, which made him in my eyes equally wonderful and weird. Also, though I did not tell my father this, I'd recently found a ten-dollar bill on the street, and I'd made no effort whatsoever to find the owner.

My father told me to wait for just a minute and disappeared. I sat immobile, my high spirits on hold, because I thought he was going to consult with my mother about how much I'd have to share with my eight-year-old sister, Caroline, who had saved little, and my seven-year-old brother, Steve, who had saved nothing at all. But that's not what happened. Instead, my father reappeared, holding his wallet. He took out a twenty-dollar bill and handed it to me. Mutely, I put it on the bottom of my pile, so no one would see. But I found out later that each of us kids had received the same gift.

I still remember what I brought home from the fair that day: a lantern that glowed Gatsby green in the dark, which I intended to take under the covers with me to read by; a bag of Tom Thumb doughnuts so redolent with the scent of cinnamon sugar it nearly levitated me; a poster of a brown mare and her foal, lying in a field full of daisies. The rest of the money I'd spent on rides and on chances to win something big on the midway. Over and over I tried, and over and over the carnies at the tacky wooden booths smiled and said, "Sorry. Want to try again?" They knew what I'd say. From the time I was quite small, I had about me a certain air of heedless determination.

When my funds were gone, I went to the blanket my parents had spread out near the edge of the fairgrounds. This was our meeting place, our refueling station—our family went to the fair once a year and stayed there all day. We kept a cooler filled with drinks and sandwiches and fruit, deli containers of various salads, Oreos and Chips Ahoy!—all this though we knew we would be gorging on fair food. There were also pillows and Band-Aids, suntan lotion and insect repellent, aspirin and a couple of Ace bandages. My parents took turns manning the station, sitting in a lawn chair and amusing themselves in their own way—my mother flipping through fashion magazines or crocheting, my father doing crossword puzzles or reading one of the historical tomes he so enjoyed. He tried often to interest us kids in history, saying it was invaluable for putting things into perspective. "You think something's really great?" he'd say. "A long time ago, there was something just as good or better. You think something's really bad? Look in the past—you'll find something worse. Think something can never happen again? Wrong! History repeats itself—*that's* what you can be sure of." But we, like most children, did not resonate much to things beyond the day at hand. History had nothing to do with us.

My father also liked people-watching—he could sit for hours and stare at all the fair-goers who passed by him and feel perfectly entertained. He just got a charge out of people, their frailties and foolishness as much as their more admirable characteristics. I remember once lying in bed and over-hearing an argument between my parents. This was a rare thing; they almost never crossed each other. But that night my mother was yelling: "Is *everything just fine* with you, then?" After a moment, I heard him say simply, Yes, everything was. An accusatory silence followed. I rose up on one arm and leaned toward my parents' bedroom wall. I heard the ticking of my bedside clock; the movement of night air in the trees outside my window; then, finally, the even, comical sounds of my father snoring. I lay back down and fingered the buttons on my nightgown, and contemplated the disturbing possibility that my parents were not perfect.

On that day at the fair when I came back to the blanket, my mother was off with my brother and my sister was with a new neighbor her own age whom we'd brought along in the desperate hope that Caroline and she would become friends. My father was alone. I sat on the blanket beside his chair, and he gave my shoulder a little squeeze. Then he moved out of the chair to sit beside me. He looked at me for a long moment, then asked, "How are you doing, Laura?"

I held my hands out, palms up. "I spent it all."

"Yes," he said. "But I meant, how are you doing in general? Is there . . . well, how's life treating you?"

I smiled. I thought he might be kidding. Sometimes he would ask me about politics in the same false and jocular way. "How about that Eisenhower?" he would say. And I would shrug and say, "*I* don't know." But his expression now was serious; he asked me again how I was, so I said, "Good, I guess." Then, feeling this was not enough, I described my excitement at finding out I'd be getting the teacher I wanted that year at school: Mrs. Lindemeyer, who was old as the hills, and an easy grader.

My father nodded. "So you're okay, then, are you? You're happy?" The question was odd to me—I didn't ever really think about whether or not I was happy—but I said yes. It seemed he was looking for something he couldn't name and I couldn't decipher, and the closest I could come to satisfying us both was for me to say I was fine; I was "happy." He returned to his chair, and we sat in uneasy silence until the others returned.

My brother, his mouth rimmed with red from a candy apple he'd just eaten, had spent all his money too. My sister had spent none. I remember being astounded at this; angry, too, that Caroline would be left with so much when I now had nothing. "How can you have fun if you don't even spend any money?" I asked her.

A pleated caramel-apple wrapper skittered by, and she captured it beneath her shoe. "I had fun."

I snorted. "How?"

She looked up at me, an irritating calmness in her eyes. "I watched." The new neighbor, Linda Carmichael, confirmed this: While Linda rose high up in the sky on the Ferris wheel, Caroline stood watching and waving from below.

"That's retarded," I said. I could tell Linda agreed with me, and I remember thinking that she and Caroline would never be friends; here was yet another opportunity Caroline had lost.

"You mind your own business, Laura," my mother said quietly. That's what she said when I told Caroline she was stupid not to eat the treats that were handed out at various classroom celebrations, too. Every time there was a party at school, Caroline ate nothing. No candy corn at Halloween, no message hearts on Valentine's Day, no red- and green-sprinkled spritz cookies at Christmas, no garishly decorated cupcakes brought in because someone in class was having a birthday. Instead, anything she ever got she tented with paper towels and then carefully carried home on the school bus. As soon as she walked in the door, she presented it to my mother and my mother ate it.

I never understood this about Caroline. Now I do. It's all clear now: the times Caroline, as a small child, lay in the hall outside the bathroom door while my mother bathed. The presents she later bought for her with babysitting money: barrettes, scarves, lipsticks. Paperback books and velvet roses. "Brownnoser!" I once whispered after she'd given my mother a bottle of dime-store perfume. Caroline ignored me; she sat at the kitchen table where I was doing homework and began pulling books and papers out of her schoolbag. She was in sixth grade then, and I in eighth. "Brownnoser!" I said again, out loud.

"Laura," my mother said, and I returned to my homework. There was a tiny smile on Caroline's face, and I kicked her under the table. She did not kick me back; rather, she moved away to another chair and straightened with pinched-nose efficiency a stack of notebook paper that did not need straightening. She cocked her head slightly to the left and the right as she did it. I hated it. I glared at her between narrowed lids; I believed I could feel heat coming from my eyeballs. All this was to no avail; Caroline looked at her schoolwork only.

Then came a gift I remember particularly well, something given to my mother by Caroline the Christmas she was sixteen. It was the last gift opened that year, and it was a framed photograph, an 8-by-10. My mother stared at it briefly, murmured a low thanks, and started to put the picture back in the box.

"What is it?" I said. "Let me see!" I snatched it away. The picture was of Caroline wearing one of my mother's slinky evening gowns, her hand on her hip. Caroline's auburn hair, the same color as my mother's, was styled in a twist like the one my mother always wore. Her makeup was heavily applied in a style exactly my mother's own, and she stared unsmilingly into the camera. It was chilling, the look on Caroline's face: the flat eyes, the hard line of mouth, the *remove.* I had never seen

such a look. "What is this supposed to be?"
I asked.

My brother took the photo from me and
looked at it. He burst into laughter, the
goofy adolescent-boy kind, and Caroline
grabbed the picture from him and threw it
onto the floor. "It isn't for you," she said.
She turned to stare at my mother, who did
not look back at her, and then left the room.

"Caroline!" my father called after her.
"Come back here!" But she did not return.
My father rose, as though to go after her.
Then he saw the picture, and he sat back
down.

This I understand now, too—as well as
what my father meant that long-ago day at
the fair, when what he was really asking was
if I knew.

2

I was the one who was supposed to get married first. I was the oldest, I was the one who was boy crazy, and I was the one with overly strong domestic leanings. I preferred putting a tray of Snickerdoodles in the oven to things like playing Capture the Flag or roller-skating or going swimming. I did like making joke phone calls, and lying in the grass staring up at the sky held a certain dreamy appeal. Occasionally I would play a board game, or jacks, or venture alone into the out-of-doors, where I would often be pleasantly surprised by what I found. But my mind was mainly on the world of homemaking and fake flesh; the biggest reward of a nature walk was that I could come back with a bouquet for the cardboard kitchen cupboard of my "house," a generous corner of the basement I had appropriated at age five and had no intention of ever giving up. I had a rug remnant for my living room, and two folding chairs placed side by side and covered by a chenille bedspread served as a sofa. I had a photo of a television from the Sears catalog taped to the wall. The photo was absurdly small, of course, but my imagination was not. I had a good-sized cardboard box lying on its side to serve as a coffee table, and my mother's discarded magazines were fanned out there in imitation of the way she arranged her own. Nearby, dolls lay sleeping in cribs or sitting in perpetual alertness in the rickety high chair.

Years later, I told all this to a therapist, a Dr. Madeline Marrone, who asked me to "start our work" by telling her about my favorite place as a child. I saw that therapist on a dare by my chronically unhappy college roommate, who insisted she saw signs of a deep unacknowledged depression in me, but who actually, I came to believe, merely wanted a companion in her own dark trench. The therapist suggested that a serious disorder in my family made me seek such specific comfort in my own small "home." But I didn't think so. I thought I just liked caregiving and eating cookies warm from the oven. I declined to make another appointment, and I changed roommates.

My relatives still make fun of me for my love of things domestic, especially my Aunt Fran, who, whenever we visit, always tells me she's saved her ironing and mending for me. Actually, I wouldn't mind doing it. I like ironing. It's the physical equivalent of staring into middle space. I think it waters the mind, if you know what I mean. As for mending, I think it's good to take the time to fix something rather than throw it away. It's an antidote to wastefulness and to the need for immediate gratification. You get to see a whole process through, beginning to end, nothing abstract about it. You'll always notice the fabric scar, of course, but there's an art to mending: If you're careful, the repair can actually add to the beauty of the thing, because it is testimony to its worth.

My sister, Caroline, got married early, at barely twenty years old. She'd stayed the weird one, the one we all thought would never find anyone. But she married another architecture student she met when she was a freshman at the University of Minnesota. She's been married for thirty-one years now and lives in a house an hour away from my parents. Her daughter, Eva, is grown and gone, a public relations consultant living in Los Angeles.

My brother, Steve, got married before me, too. He's gotten married a lot. He's on number four, a sweet woman called Tessa—I hope this one will last. No kids for him. His children are his boat and his airplane, the new car he buys every year, and the bar that he owns, called Pud's. It's located on Rush Street in Chicago, and according to him it's the hippest place in the city.

But I waited a long time to get married. I was forty when I finally fell in love with a man who was a widower. He'd been married exactly one week when his wife died. Car accident—she'd gone out for butterscotch topping for the sundaes they were going to have after they finished wallpapering their bathroom. He didn't date for five years after her death, and he didn't think about marrying again until fifteen years after that, when he met me. Her name was Kate. She was a lovely black-haired woman who taught nursery school and wrote exquisite poetry. I know Pete is devoted to me, but I also know that a corner of his soul is reserved for her. I don't mind. She deserves it. And so does he.

Pete comes from a big Italian family. His parents, Rosa and Subby (for Sabastiano) Bartone, visit us at least twice a year, making the voyage by RV from their retirement village in Arizona to our ramshackle house in North Dakota. I can honestly say I'm always sorry when they leave. I put flowers in their room before they come; they leave homemade pasta sauces in my freezer before they go.

Pete and I have a daily routine, which started when we were dating. Every night, sometime after dinner, we tell each other about an incident that occurred that day, and then we share a memory from the past. It began as a corny but extremely effective way for us to get to know each other. Now it's part of the way we stayed grounded and entwined. My neighbor and best friend, Maggie, says you have to have a lot of sex

in your marriage because it works like glue.
So does this.

Many of the memories Pete has shared
have had to do with his parents. He's told
me about vacations to Alaska and about
smaller moments spent sitting at the
kitchen table. One of my favorite memories
has to do with a time he sat with his three
sisters and his little brother, eating biscotti
dipped in cocoa for an afternoon snack
while they watched his mother make dinner.
She spoke softly in Italian to the red sauce
she simmered in the Dutch oven, to the gigantic meatballs she rolled, to the gold-
colored rosemary-scented focaccia she put
on a TV tray out on the front porch to cool.
She went out to the garden and made a
bowl of her apron, and Pete filled it with let-
tuce and peppers and white-freckled tomatoes.

He's told me about his father sitting on
the edge of the bathtub, playing his banjo
and singing songs from the old country for
his wife, who soaked in her milk bath. And
about the time his father was instructed by
Rosa to harshly discipline Pete and his
brother, Danny, for the crime of stealing a
pair of their neighbor's gargantuan under-

pants off her clothesline and using it to wax their bicycles. Subby took the boys into his bedroom, shut the door, and whispered to them to howl while he struck the mattress repeatedly with his belt. They were a little too convincing; when they all filed back into the kitchen, Rosa planted her fists on her hips and said, "You think you make a fool of me?"

My memories don't often focus on my parents, and if they do the stories are not like my husband's. Much of our food, for example, came from cans, and our dinners were mostly silent. Eating was not something to be celebrated. It was done because it had to be, rather like cleaning out your ears. You ate, you bused your dishes, and then, as quickly as possible, you went back to the more interesting and rewarding parts of your life. It took many years for me to understand what people meant when they described the joy of a good olive oil, the perfect balance that comes with mixing goat cheese with fig compote and black-olive tapenade.

My family did not go on vacations together. Our summers were lazy and unstructured; we kids were left to come up with our own entertainment, and I loved it. There'd been one summer when we were sent to camp, each of us to a different one, but that must have been seen as a failure, at least in my parents' eyes—we never went again. I'd been glad about that. My camp had a predictable dearth of domestics and what was, in my opinion, an overabundance of physical challenges. In addition, I'd been afraid of Cynthia Mayfield, a hugely overweight girl who constantly threatened to beat me up for no reason I could discern; and I'd been equally afraid, though for another reason, of the raven-haired Jinxie Benson, who sat cross-legged on her bunk every Sunday night making lists of who was cool and who was not—and why. These lists were circulated among the campers and were eagerly—if anxiously—read and taken to heart, even by the counselors, who confiscated and denounced them but also had been known to sit at their table in the back corner of the cafeteria poring over their own personality reviews. I'd been suspicious of the Chapel Under the Pines, thinking it fostered idolatry. And what was one to *do* with Eyes of God?

So the stories I told Pete focused less on

my parents and more on me and my siblings. There was the time I'd told Caroline I
had the ability to turn myself into another
person, someone called Kathy, who looked
like me but was in fact someone entirely different, and she believed me. "What do you
think of Laura?" I'd asked, and then, later,
when I'd "turned back" into Laura, I'd punished Caroline for the negative things she'd
said about me. "How did you know?" Caroline had asked, massaging her punched
arm, and I'd said, "Kathy told me."

I told Pete about the time I made my little
brother sit in the corner of my basement
house for a couple of hours in order to be
my husband. "What do I *do,* though?" he'd
asked, and I'd said, "Nothing. You're at
work." While he sat idly scratching his
ankle, humming tunelessly, practicing
belches, and then, finally, lightly dozing, I
busied myself. I rocked babies, vacuumed
(using a discarded canister model I'd found
by someone's garbage, a five-star discov-
ery), and made tissue paper carnations for
a window box I planned on making out of
the next shoe box that came along. I chatted on my plastic telephone. Finally, I made
a chocolate cake in my Easy-Bake oven

and awakened my husband to share it with me. "It's *raw,*" he complained, which earned him immediate expulsion from the basement. Not that he'd minded.

It often came to me, telling these stories to Pete, that there'd been a terrible cruelty in me as a child, but then I suppose all children have such moments. A friend of mine told me about the matter-of-fact notation she used to put at the top of her diary page almost every evening: J.C. This was not a religious ritual but acknowledgment of the fact that once again her brother, Jason, had cried that day. She'd never tried to find out why; she hated crybabies. Once when she and her brother were in their forties and having a drink somewhere, laughing and talking about their growing-up times, she apologized in an offhand way for never having made inquiries as to the nature of his despair. She expected him to wonder what she was talking about; instead, he stopped smiling and said, "Well. It's about time."

Pete and I had children right away, and though I feared the results of the amnios, and then of the births, both our boy, Anthony, and our girl, Hannah, couldn't be healthier. They're fourteen and twelve now, respectively, and Pete and I are beginning to realize we've gotten our freedom back. We haven't had a babysitter in two years; and I'm finally able to do my work in a way that allows me to focus for long hours at a time.

I make my living as a quilt artist, and for the most part the work I do is commissioned. I charge a hundred and fifty dollars a square foot, not without guilt. But I have whole days when I stand at my design board moving pieces of fabric around, and I don't sew a stitch. Then something clicks, and I hit the machine. The money I charge pays for the thinking time too; I explain this to my clients. And people do pay it, willingly—I have more clients than I can handle. The wait for a finished quilt is four to six months, but people don't seem to mind that, either. I think there is a longing for things that reflect a certain kind of slowness; perhaps the pendulum is beginning its inevitable swing back. I'll be glad if it does—I'm computer phobic and one of the few people left in America who don't have e-mail. A friend once told me she didn't want e-mail because she doesn't understand how it works. Well, I said, you don't know how a mixer works, either, but you use that. True, she said, and added that it was pretty depressing to realize the only equipment she *did* understand was what she used for hanging out the wash, and even then she didn't get the spring-type clothespins, only the little people ones.

I don't even have a cell phone, though I am just about ready to get one of those, mostly due to Anthony's constant re-minders that soon he'll be driving and really has to have one in case of roadway emer-gencies. I can envision these "emergen-cies": *Dude! I've got the car; want me to come and pick you up?*

Pete keeps saying that if I continue to do this well with my quilting, he's going to quit his job and live off me. I tell him, Go ahead, but I don't think he ever will. He owns the hardware store in the center of town, and he loves being there. It's how I met him. I'd come to town for a quilting convention, and I needed some wooden dowels. For me, it was love at first sight—I asked him out to dinner that night, and by the time we had dessert I was fantasizing our fiftieth-anniversary celebration. Pete's the kind of guy who doesn't mind spending fifteen minutes helping old ladies pick out just the right plate hanger from his carefully organized bank of plastic drawers. Oftentimes those ladies come back the next day with a basket of muffins for him and his staff. He'll give them a kiss on the cheek and they'll make embarrassed little Aunt Bee clucking sounds and smile, all but waving the hankies they store up their sleeves, in a mix of pleasure and distress. I met Pete at a time when I was ready for a truly nice guy, out from under the wildly erroneous assumptions that dangerous men are fun and inconsistent men are interesting. You can have your pouty-mouthed bad boys; I'll take the guy most people would fault with being overly sentimental. "That's because you're *old,*" Hannah said, when I told her recently about the qualities I prize most in a man, and she was probably right. That, and I'm pretty sentimental myself.

Today I needed to go to the fabric store to select the yardage I wanted to use for the border of a quilt I was making with Japanese overtones. It was for a woman who believed she'd lived many times before and that one of those past lives was as a geisha. It's funny how people reveal themselves in the quilts they commission. One client had a bitter divorce but she wanted me to use her wedding dress to make a quilt that honored marriage. A truck driver commissioned a wildly feminine floral design to sleep under when he was on the road. A woman alienated from both her children had saved every item of clothing they'd ever worn as babies and toddlers, and she had me use them along with items of her own clothing to create a pattern of interlocking circles. She wept when I delivered the quilt to her and then hid it away in a box she'd bought especially for it.

After I came home from the store, I needed to pack for our annual drive to Minnesota the next day. It was state fair time again. Everyone in my family went, every end of August. Our annual family get-togethers, like most people's, were a mix of great fun and misery. They were what I did precisely one year after I'd said I'd never do them again. And each time, I could hardly wait to get there.

3

It was unusually quiet at Fabric World. I lingered at the shelves of blues for longer than I might have ordinarily, knowing I wouldn't have to wait a long time to get my selection cut. Two store employees, Joanne and Ellen, stood leaning against the cutting table chatting and laughing quietly, their arms crossed. I'd been coming to Fabric World for years—Hannah actually took her first steps here—and until recently you never saw the employees relaxed like this. They'd always been told that if there were no customers, they should straighten bolts of fabric, cut up remnants for quilt packs, even dust shelves. Now there was a new manager, a flamboyantly gay man named Gregory, who had made everyone's life better. He designed wedding dresses in addition to working at the store, and he gossiped viciously about all his clients, much to the guilty enjoyment of everyone around. He answered the store phone saying, "Fabric World, what *now*?" I still didn't quite understand how he was hired, never mind made manager; the owners of the store were rumored to be quite conservative. I thought it was because Gregory couldn't help being charming, even when he was insulting you. And people trusted his taste—they bought anything he told them to.

"This is beautiful," Joanne said, when I brought the cobalt-blue fabric I finally settled on over to the table to be measured and cut. There were black cranes printed on it, some standing on one leg, some flying, their wings thrillingly outstretched.

"It's for a border," I told her. "I need a yard and a half."

She began cutting and we stopped talking, both of us listening, I think, to the sound of the scissors. For those of us enamored of the world of textiles, this sound is a little symphony. It conjures an image of a head bent over a machine, the feel of fabric slipping through fingers, a small light focused on a field of intimate labor.

I saw Gregory on the other side of the store, stopping to straighten some of the colorful bolts in the juvenile section. When he noticed me, he came over to the cutting table. "Help," he said. "I've dreamed about seed pearls for the last three nights."

Seed pearls! I thought. Maybe a few scattered across this quilt I was making. And binding made of a fabric that suggested water—some wavy, indistinct lines of blue on white.

"What are you working on?" he asked.

"Something sort of Japanese, this time. A lot of circles mixed with squares."

"Sounds divine. *Anything* but a wedding dress sounds divine. I want to make my niece some very cool pants, but instead I have to labor on a dress for a whale. I mean, why doesn't she just wrap up in a lace-patterned shower curtain and call it a day?"

"Great attitude."

"The truth hurts. Hey, have you got time for a cup of coffee? Come in the back with me and I'll show you some samples of things I just ordered."

I looked at my watch. "Can't. I've got to go home and pack—we're going on vacation tomorrow. I'll take you up on it when I get back, though."

"Ta-ta," he said, walking away and waving over his shoulder. And then, to Joanne and Ellen, "Which one of you wants to give me a full body massage? No fighting, *please.*"

After I got in the car, I took the fabric I'd bought out of the bag and stretched it across my lap so I could sneak looks at it on the way home. Before I'd taken the first cut, I'd already transformed it a thousand times.

We ate pasta for dinner, with some puttanesca sauce that Pete's mother, Rosa, had made and I'd defrosted in the microwave. I was amazed at how the flavor held; no one could cook like Rosa did. "Have you packed yet?" I asked Anthony.

He nodded, his mouth full.

"Yes?"

He nodded again, less emphatically, then shrugged. "Almost."

"What does that mean?" Pete asked.

"It means I know everything I want to bring. I just have to put it in the suitcase."

"Right after dinner," I said. "We're leaving early."

"I *know.*" He rolled his eyes. Beneath the table, I suspected, his knee was bobbing up and down.

"How about you, Hannah?" I asked. "Did you lay out what you want to take?"

"Yes, and I can pack by myself now. I don't need you to do it."

"Well," I said. Meaning, *Yes, you do.* If I let Hannah pack by herself, she'd put in books, her Swiss Army knife, art materials—everything but what she needed most.

"Why are you such a control freak?" she asked.

I looked quickly at Pete, surprised, although he accused me of the same thing often enough. "Why must you oversee *everything*?" he once asked. We were in the family room, watching a movie we'd rented that neither of us much liked, but neither of us had the energy or inclination to turn it off. Instead, we talked over it. "I don't oversee everything!" I'd said. He'd stared at me, a half grin on his face. Then he'd said, "Okay.

I just said, 'I think I'll get a snack.' You said, "There's frozen yogurt or beer pretzels.' Am I not capable of choosing my own snack?"

"I'm only suggesting," I'd said. "I know what's around because I buy the groceries. I know what's fresh—I'm actually protecting you. I'm trying to prevent a bad snack experience."

He didn't respond to my attempt at levity. "Stop trying so hard to prevent things from happening," he'd said. "What are you so afraid of?"

"Nothing," I'd said. "Choose your own snacks from now on. Get salmonella." But the very next time he said something about wanting a snack—in the same situation, actually; we were in the family room watching a movie—I said, "There's licorice in the cupboard." And then I'd stared intently at the screen so he couldn't say, *See?*

But this was a different situation. "Hannah," I said. "I'm not trying to control anything. You just need a little help packing, that's all."

Hannah readjusted her headband, then patted the top of her head. She spent hours grooming now; in the kids' bathroom were at least seven products for her hair alone.

"I'm done," she said, pushing back from the table. "I'm going to call Gracie, and then you can *help* me, 'cause I'm too *lame* to pack by *myself.*" She flounced out of the kitchen, a defiant gesture that merely served to entertain the rest of us.

"Why don't you help *me*, Mom?" Anthony said. "In fact, you can pack everything for me."

"You can do it yourself."

"No fair," he said, grinning. He tipped his chair back on two legs. "Hey, Dad. I saw this car for sale? Two blocks over?"

"No."

"Just to work on. It's only fifty bucks! We could keep it—"

"No," Pete said. And then, though I knew it would only make matters worse, I said, "Anthony."

"What?"

"Chair."

He sat forward, righting the chair, muttered, "Jesus."

"What was that?" Pete asked.

"I said *Jeez.* Okay, Mr. Cleaver?"

"I heard what you said."

Anthony looked at me, shook his head. Neither of us was sympathetic to Pete's in-

ability to tolerate any word that is or ap-
proximates a "swear," as Hannah called it.
But I usually let it go—I did, after all, have
my own proclivities toward extreme old-
fashionedness.

"Hey, Dad."

"What."

"Would you buy me a concert ticket for
the fair?"

"I suppose."

"Would you buy me two?"

"Who's the other one for?"

"I don't know. I might get lucky."

Pete started clearing the table. "Yeah, I'll
buy you two concert tickets."

"All right!" Anthony stood, stretched. "I'm
going to pack now. Then I think I'll stay up
all night so I don't have to get up early." He
pulled my apron string as he walked past,
then told me, as he always did, "Hey, Mom.
Your apron's untied."

I started rinsing the dishes while Pete finished clearing. "So today," he said, "this old
lady comes into the store and asks me
where I keep the pliers. I tell her, and she
goes back there for a really long time. Then
she comes past the checkout counter with
a pair of pliers sticking out of her purse.

'Excuse me,' I said. 'You going to pay for those?' And you know what she says? She says, 'Well, I wasn't planning on it.' "

I looked at him, laughed.

"I swear!"

"So who was it?"

He shrugged. "Beats me. Jeannie said she thought it might be Theresa Haggerty's mom, who's visiting her from Florida. I guess she's not quite all there."

"I guess *not.* So, did she pay?"

"Yeah, she paid. And then she tried to give me a tip."

I shook my head, smiling, and rinsed the last of the silverware, loaded the dishwasher, and set it to start a few hours later.

"So what happened to you today?" Pete asked, sitting down again at the kitchen table.

I sat opposite him. "Let's see. I got a call from a woman who wants a quilt made for each of her seven grandchildren. *And* I saw three ducklings cross the street by Save Mart. All the traffic just stopped, waiting for them to cross, and them taking their sweet, waddly time. I love it when that happens— kind of puts things in perspective."

Pete smiled. "Yeah, it does."

"And here's a memory for you," I said, "Once, at the fair, I went into the tunnel of love by myself. I was Hannah's age. Ahead of me was this couple, kissing away. And I just couldn't stand it, I wanted so much to have a boyfriend. I took my gum out my mouth and threw it at them. I wanted it to get in the girl's hair."

"Nice."

"I know."

"So what did she do?"

"I missed. It landed on the back of the guy's neck. He got really mad. He turned around with this killer look, and I yelled, 'I didn't do that! I don't know where it came from; I just saw it fly past. I didn't do it!' I'm sure he knew I was lying, but he went back to his girlfriend."

"You want me to take you in the tunnel of love this year?"

"Yes. And on the Ferris wheel. And to the pig barn. And to see the butterheads. And to the cheese curd stand, and for roasted corn and caramel apples. And pie. And Swedish coffee. And to see the tractors and the home improvement stuff. And I'll go to the technology building with you if you'll come to creative arts with me. I want to see the dog shows. And the horse shows—I don't want to miss the Lipizzaners again."

"Go help Hannah pack," Pete said. "I'm exhausted already."

Just before I fell asleep, the phone rang. Pete answered, then said, "Oh, hi, Caroline; here's Laura," and handed the receiver to me. He's never been one to chat on what he calls a modest instrument of torture, but you would think he might have learned to be a bit less abrupt. My sister was used to it by now, of course, but I was always having to explain to new friends that my husband was really a very nice guy, he just had no telephone etiquette.

"Were you sleeping?" Caroline asked.

"Not yet."

"You weren't . . ."

"No."

"Okay. Listen, I'm sorry to call this late, but I wanted to catch you before you got to Mom and Dad's. I've been . . . there's something I have to do."

"Yeah? What is it?"

"Well, I want to have us kids get together, just by ourselves—you, me, and Steve. A restaurant, maybe; we could go out for dinner or something."

"Why?" To plan Mom and Dad's anniversary? I wondered. It would be fifty-five years this September: admirable, but not something you usually make a big deal out of.

"I want to talk about some things."

"What things?" I began to get alarmed. "Is it something about your health?" Pete turned on the bedside lamp, mouthed *What's up?* I lifted my shoulders: *I don't know.*

"No, it's . . . I've just been thinking a lot, lately, about the way we were brought up, and I—well, there are some things I want to ask you and Steve, with no one else around. This will be a good time to do it. Bill's not coming this year; he's going to finish putting in our new bathroom. And Tessa won't be there either; Steve said she's got to be in Atlanta. Pete won't mind if the three of us take off for a couple of hours, will he?"

I didn't know whether to be worried or annoyed. "But . . . Caroline, just tell me, what do you want to talk about?"

"I don't want to get into it now. But I'd

really like to have us all get together. Would you just help me arrange it?"

"Well, *yeah.* We'll pick a day when we're there and just do it. It's not that hard."

"I'd hoped we could pick a day now. And then maybe you could call Steve and let him know. It'll be harder for him to say no if you and I have already agreed to it. Would you please do that?"

"Fine. How about the second night we're there? The first night we'll have to hang around. But the next night we'll go out somewhere. How about Snuffy's; you want to go to Snuffy's?"

"Anywhere. Thank you, Laura. So you'll call Steve tonight?"

"It's better with Steve if you don't plan ahead. I'll just tell him. He'll come."

"Okay. I'll see you tomorrow."

I leaned over Pete to hang up the phone and lay down again. "Caroline wants to talk to me and Steve alone. I don't know what about."

"Is she upset about something?"

"No, I wouldn't say upset, exactly, but she sounds kind of . . . intense."

"Well. What else is new?"

"This felt different. She says she wants to

talk about some things that happened when we were growing up. I hope she doesn't mention the time I told her about Jesus on the cross. I hope she forgot about that."

"Why, what did you say?"

"Oh, just . . . you know, I told her the story of the crucifixion. And made her cry."

Pete turned out the bedside light, settled down under the sheets, yawned. "That's not so bad."

"No, you don't understand. Religious education wasn't the goal. Making her cry was. Not that it was hard. Caroline was always oversensitive. She cried if you looked at her wrong. Literally." I moved closer to Pete, closed my eyes.

"I'm waiting," he said.

"Why do you have to be such a good listener?"

"What did you say?"

"Well, I overdramatized a bit, okay? I talked about how it hurts when you stick a pin in your hand. And then I said, 'And just imagine. They put NAILS in. They *pounded* NAILS in.' Stuff like that."

"You said that? That *is* pretty bad."

"Yeah, I know. But you did some terrible things to your brother and sisters."

"I can assure you I stayed out of the God area."

"Yeah, but when Stella was only four, you told her you turned into a werewolf at night."

"How do you know that?"

"She told me. And she also told me that you lined shoes up along the top of your door and then yelled for Danny to come quick, and when he pushed the door open all the shoes fell on him. And gave him a black eye."

Silence.

"You robbed Tina's piggy bank twice."

"All right. Good night."

"Oh. Oh! And you—"

He leaned over, kissed me. "Good *night.* We have an early morning." He turned on his side, closed his eyes, and fell asleep. It's amazing. Head on pillow, and he's out.

I lay awake, wondering what was up with Caroline. I thought of the drive ahead of us, how the kids would ignore each other for the most part but how there would also be a few fights to contend with. It was only a five-hour drive, though, and then we'd be there. The garden would be perfectly tended, the bird feeders would all be full.

There would probably be sheets and up-side-down shirts and pants on the clothes-line; my mother was a big believer in line drying. One summer I'd tried it myself, but the romance had drowned in the inconvenience.

The food would not be memorable, of course, but the setting would be nice. We'd eat out on the back porch on a green painted table with an embroidered table-cloth, nice old flowered china, a huge vase of flowers, and the cut-glass salt-and-pepper shakers that had belonged to my grandparents—whenever I saw them, I remembered those shakers being on their Formica kitchen table. I remembered, too, my grandfather using his tongue to pop his lower dentures out of his mouth, then gulping them back in, one of the many things he did to thrill us grandchildren. For a long time, I hadn't known they were dentures, and I'd thought my grandfather was an extremely talented man. I had spent long periods of time lying on my bed trying to loosen my own bottom teeth so I too could perform this interesting feat. My mother had come into my room one day with a laundry basket and had seen me yanking away at my back molars. "What are you doing?" she'd asked. And when I'd told her I was trying to do Grandpa's trick, she'd laughed and told me his teeth were false.

"But where are his real teeth?" I'd asked.

"Gone."

"But gone where?"

"I don't know," she'd said. "Just gone."

"But—"

"Laura." She'd touched my shoulder. "Don't ask so many questions. You always ask so many questions. Don't do that. Just . . . accept things." She'd moved to my dresser to put away neatly folded stacks of underpants, talking with her back to me. "Don't ask questions and don't look back. Believe me, you'll be much more content."

I'd grown silent, trying to figure out what *that* meant. Then I'd gone back to thoughts of my grandfather's teeth.

It was strange how my memory was changing. More and more, someone would refer to something that had happened fairly recently, and I would have forgotten all about it. I misplaced my glasses, the cinnamon, the name of an actor I'd always known. An abiding comfort was that it was happening to Pete too. "Guess who was in the store today?" he'd say. And then he'd get this panicked look on his face. "It was . . . oh, you know. You know who I mean." We would stand in the kitchen, blankly staring at each other. "Oh, man," he'd say. "Hold on a minute." He'd concentrate for a while, eyebrows knit together, arms crossed, one foot tapping the floor, and then he'd throw his hands up in the air and give up. Hours later, he'd remember. Or not.

Other things, especially from times long ago, I remembered clearly. I recall, for example, every detail about a time I lay on my belly next to the stream that used to be half a block away from our house. It was a hot morning in July; I had just turned ten, and I'd wanted to go somewhere to be alone and consider my oldness—two digits! I remember the algae swaying seductively in the greenish water, the quick thrill of a school of minnows swimming past, the grit of dirt against the exposed strip of skin at the top of my yellow pedal pushers. I remember the onion-scented smell of the long grass there, and the way it imprinted a pattern of itself against your skin after you lay in it.

That same summer I buried Necco wafers in the dirt and then dug them up again and ate them, to show I was not afraid of germs. The sun had been setting gloriously when I popped the candy into my mouth; I remember the sky looked as though it were on fire. There'd been a ring of admiring neighborhood kids around me, including a six-year-old girl picking her nose rapturously with one hand and holding a Tiny Tears doll wrapped in a pink-checked blanket with the other. I wanted very much to hold that doll, but for obvious reasons I feared touching it. A twelve-year-old boy, the senior member of the impromptu gathering, had tossed a baseball from hand to hand, weighing insult versus compliment, I knew. In the end, he'd split the difference and had said, "Huh!" before he walked away.

And this memory has persisted too: my mother holding a laundry basket against her hip that day she came into my room, telling me what she believed was necessary for living a happy life.

It is my grandfather, sitting in a nubby green oversized armchair in his living room. The flash of the camera is captured in his eyeglasses. He is wearing his gray cardigan sweater, a plaid shirt, and some loose-fitting pants. On one side of his lap, I sit holding a lollipop and leaning back against him, smiling. On the other side is Caroline. Though my grandfather has his arms securely around both of us, she is trying to pull his arm closer still. Her fingers appear to be digging into him. She looks tense and unhappy, trying so desperately to delay his letting go that she hastens it. I remember the exact moment after that photo was taken: a sudden gust of wind lifting maroon draperies printed with exotic lime-green fronds; the smell of frying chicken in the air; my grandfather standing up to go into the kitchen "to help Grandma make the gravy"; and me pinching Caroline because I knew it was she who made him leave. I cautioned her not to tell or I would pinch her again, harder.

4

My father had sent us an article from the *Pioneer Press* about some things that would be at the fair this year, and Anthony was slumped in the backseat of the car, reading aloud from it. We'd been driving for three hours, and an edgy monotony had set in.

"There'll be two hundred and fourteen port-a-johns," Anthony read. "And they'll use twenty-two thousand rolls of toilet paper."

"Gross," Hannah mumbled.

"What's gross about toilet paper?" Anthony asked. "What would be gross is if there *weren't* any."

"*Eeeeuuuuwwww!*" She returned to her paperback, a story of three teenage girls who explore the Arctic by themselves.

"They'll have elk ragout," he said. "And walleye on a stick."

"That walleye's actually very good," Pete said. "I've had that. I might get it again."

"Listen to this breakfast," Anthony said. "Smoked pork chop, scrambled eggs, fried dumplings, and a kolach. I'm getting that."

"I'm eating *only* fried food," Hannah said.

"Well, you're in luck. Listen to this: They have fried ravioli, French fries, cheese curds, onion blossoms, and fried dough. And look at this: deep-fried *pickles*! Hot damn!"

I saw the color rise in Pete's face at Anthony's mild epithet, and he started to turn around but opted instead for paying attention to the road. But his eyes sought out Anthony's in the rearview mirror.

"Sorry," Anthony said quietly.

"You know, Anthony, you just don't seem to get some things," Pete said.

"I *said*, Sorry!"

"He's smiling," Hannah said. "He's not sorry."

"Hannah!" I said, at the same time that Pete said, "I can see him, Hannah."

It was thickly quiet for a moment, and then Pete said, "I guess if you can't remember to respect my rules, I can't remember to give you money for concert tickets."

"Dad, I'm sorry, okay? It just slipped out. It's not—I don't know why you get so bent out of shape about this! It's just an expression everybody uses. I don't get it, why you're always so—" He stopped, exasperated. Stared out the window. "It's *weird*," he said, under his breath.

Pete put the blinker on and moved to the right lane to pull off into a rest stop.

"Uh-oh," Hannah said. "You're gonna get it."

"Pete," I said, "don't be so—"

But he stopped the car, cut the engine, stared at me in a direct bid for support, and turned around to look at his children. "There are certain things in your life that will become very important to you," he said. "You might not be able to explain to anyone else why they're important. But you will expect the people who love you, the people who are your family, to respect those things. If any of you need to swear, do it somewhere else. It *bothers* me."

"But—don't get mad, Dad, okay?" Anthony said. "I just wish you'd tell me *why* you think it's so bad."

Pete faced forward and rubbed the back of his neck. "Just . . . don't. Okay? I tell you again, don't do it around me. *Period.*" He started the engine.

"Do you want me to drive for a while?" I asked.

"I'm fine."

"I'll drive," Hannah said, and I was relieved to see Pete's small smile. I too once asked Pete why it was so terribly offensive to him when people swore. It had been many years ago; we'd only been dating a few months. We were out walking in a park, and I'd asked more or less the same question, and Pete had stopped to examine a leaf on a tree. He'd been turned away from me when he'd said, "It's just . . . it's a need I have. It doesn't matter why."

"Okay," I'd said. And I thought maybe I'd have to stop seeing him—his answer had made me really uncomfortable, and I had a habit of swearing a lot. But there'd been nothing else so tightly wound about him.

Anyway, by then it was too late: I loved the planes of his face, his black hair and blue eyes, his elegant table manners, his deep voice, his love of animals and children, his otherwise easygoing manner. I loved *him.* I would forgive him this and hope he would forgive my own irritating mannerisms.

"They have sixty-five rides," Anthony said, reading again from the newspaper.

Silence.

"In 1965," he said, "Princess Kay of the Milky Way wore a formal gown made of butter wrappers."

"All *right,*" Hannah said. "Just be quiet, now, I'm trying to read."

"Okay, but just one more thing. You know what else?"

She sighed. "What?"

"You know how they make those sculptures out of butter? The head of Princess Kay of the Milky Way?"

"Yeah. And her court."

"Right. Well, most of them freeze their heads. But this one princess? She melted hers down for a corn feed."

"Let me see," Hannah said.

I leaned my head against the window and tried to doze while peace reigned, but I couldn't. First I imagined that practical Princess Kay dressed in jeans and a plaid shirt and loafers, hair in a ponytail, standing over a Dutch oven in some farm kitchen, watching her likeness melt down into nothing. Then I thought of my parents, waiting for us. My mother would be wearing some new outfit she'd purchased for the occasion, and she'd meet us at the door, chatting a mile a minute. My father would be puttering in the basement, and when we arrived he would solemnly come into the kitchen to offer his muted greeting. Standing in that familiar place, I believed I would feel the usual odd mix of sensations. Some of it would have to do with the inescapable nostalgia and apprehension—even preemptive irritation—that accompanies any visit home once you've moved out. The rest would be because of something I'd always felt but could never name. My mother, smiling brightly, looking directly into your eyes before she embraced you tightly, would feel a million miles away. My father, averting his gaze before he took you into his arms, would be the one who felt close.

5

My mother was out cutting flowers when we arrived, bent over roses such a deep red color they looked black. She turned when she heard our car doors slam and shaded her eyes. She was wearing a white linen blouse, black linen pants cut to just above the ankle, and red strappy sandals. Cute. "Look who's here!" she cried, and, removing her gardening gloves, headed toward us, arms open wide. "You're the first ones. I'm so excited!" She hugged Pete and me, then the kids. "You've grown!" she told Hannah.

"You always say that," Hannah said, smiling.

"I know. But it's always true. You've become a *lovely* young lady." She turned to Anthony. "And you! You're gorgeous!"

Anthony laughed, embarrassed, then took his bags and headed for the back door. "Grandpa inside?"

"Down at his workbench," my mother said. She started to take one of the suitcases, but Pete took it from her. "Save your strength, Barbara," he told her.

As we headed indoors, we heard a car honk. It was Steve, pulling up to the curb, and then we saw Caroline's car pulling up right behind him.

"Well!" my mother said.

"Good timing," Pete said, but my mother seemed more unsettled than pleased. She smoothed down the collar of her blouse. Raised her chin. It seemed to me that there was, in these movements, a strange sense of preparation for battle. But then I decided my perspective was skewed by what Caroline had told me the night before. I waved at her and Steve and headed inside.

It was almost midnight. Pete and I were lying in bed in the basement guest room, a room my parents used mainly for storage of out-of-season clothes. Beside us, in the dim light of the moon coming through the tiny, high windows, I could see our makeshift nightstand: a TV tray holding an alarm clock, a tiny lamp, a box of Kleenex, and a small porcelain dish, put there, I knew, for holding Pete's change. There was a cozy completeness to this utilitarian still life. It occurred to me that one of the values of going away was that you saw that something far less complex than what you were used to would do just fine. More and more, I looked at my house, at my life, and thought, *Why do I need all this stuff?* Maggie and I had been talking about this need to simplify, about what it might mean; she'd been feeling it, too. "It's the first step in getting ready to die," Maggie had said, in her usual no-nonsense way. "It is not!" I'd said, but I thought she was probably right.

Upstairs, I could hear the muted conversation of my parents, still up and sitting in the TV room. Soon they'd go to bed and then continue talking quietly, I knew, until they fell asleep.

I lay there, Pete beside me, and the sound of my parents' voices seemed to erase him; seemed to erase me too, at least as the middle-aged person I was. I became instead a young child, fresh from the bathtub and smelling of Ivory soap, the doll I'd chosen for the night mummy-wrapped in a receiving blanket and held in the crook of my arm. I was not responsible for anything but my own daily meanderings. The purpose of reading the newspaper was to check up on Nancy and Sluggo. Monetary decisions had to do with what kind of candy to buy with the change I had left over from going to the corner store to buy milk for my mother. My parents were my clock and my calendar; they told me where to go and when. My parents were also the arbiters of judgment, of taste, and of politics; I stepped into their values like an outfit they'd laid out for me on my bed. Later, of course, I forged my own beliefs and rebelled against nearly everything they'd taught me. But every time I came home, some large part of me surrendered itself to the past and relished the sense of being the one who was cared for, if only by a TV tray serving as a bedside table. I was in my midfifties, but in my parents' house I was forever made to feel uniquely safe by the late-night murmurings of the people who were in charge, leaving me free not to be. No matter what anyone said, it seemed to me that not only *can* you go home again, you are helpless not to.

I dozed lightly, then woke up again. I'd been dreaming of Caroline, or at least thinking of her in the kind of nether land that precedes sleep. She'd been remarkably quiet at dinner and seemed to be trying to catch my eye at odd times. Something was really bothering her.

I looked at the clock: 1 A.M. I leaned over Pete, gently touched the top of his head, whispered his name. "Are you sleeping?" No response except deep breathing. I got out of bed quietly and headed upstairs to the kitchen. I turned on the stove light and went over to inspect the contents of the refrigerator. Here were the things I rarely bought anymore but always wanted to eat: butter, salami, heavy cream, cheese, mayonnaise. In the cupboards were great varieties of cookies and chips. And in the bread drawer, white bread and a box of cinnamon rolls covered by thick frosting. My father had high blood pressure and cholesterol problems, but my mother disbelieved certain tenets of modern medicine. She had a particular disdain for mental health workers. When I once told her about a friend of mine who was in therapy, she'd said, "Psychiatrists. They're crazier than anyone." There'd been no humor in this remark. There'd been venom in it.

I was sitting at the kitchen table having a salami sandwich when Caroline appeared, ghostlike in this dim light. "Hi," she whispered. I waved at her, my mouth full. She opened the bread drawer, took out the package of cinnamon rolls, brought it over to the table. "I can't believe I'm eating again," she said. "It's like coming home late at night when we were in high school. Remember how hungry we always were?"

I nodded, smiling. "Yeah. Remember the time you and Steve and I were eating and he dropped that bowlful of spaghetti all over the place?"

Caroline took a huge bite of her roll, talked around it. "And he really wanted it, so he ate a bunch of it off the floor."

"Right." I finished my sandwich and went over to the cupboard to take a look around. "Want some Oreos? Oh, boy, they're double-stuffed."

She didn't answer, and when I looked over at her, I saw her face pressed into her hands. "What's wrong?" I closed the cupboard and came back to the table. "Caroline? What is it?"

She smiled sadly. "I'm sorry. I don't want to talk about it now. Not here. It was just . . . a moment."

"They're asleep," I said. Amazing how quickly we could lapse into the shorthand of sides: us versus them; kids versus parents.

"We'll talk when we go out. When Steve's here too."

I leaned back in my chair, picked up a cinnamon roll, and started unwinding it. "I was dreaming about you just before I came up here."

"Were you?"

"Yeah. You were upset."

"Well, I *am* upset."

"Well, I *know.*"

She stood, tightened the belt on her robe, and put the box of cinnamon rolls back in the drawer. "Anyway . . . I'm glad you're here. I'm glad we all are."

"Yeah. Me too."

"So . . . I'll see you in the morning." She

sighed. "I'm sorry I'm such a wreck. But we'll talk, okay?"

She turned to go and I grabbed her hand. "Hey, do you want to go out now? Take a car ride?"

"I want Steve to be here too."

"Want me to wake him up?"

"No. I know you'd love to, though."

"He used to like it when I woke him up late at night."

"He's older now."

From upstairs, we heard the sound of a toilet flushing. "I'm going back to bed," Caroline said quickly. The hall light turned on, and she disappeared into the living room, where she was bedded down on the sofa.

Then the overhead kitchen light turned on and my mother was standing there, squinting against the brightness. "Is everything all right?"

"Yes, I was just hungry. I had a little snack."

"Are you the only one up? I thought I heard talking."

"Caroline was up. But she went back to sleep."

"Oh?" She looked back toward the living room, then expectantly at me.

"She was just up for a minute. You didn't miss a thing. Go back to bed."

I started for the basement steps and she said, "Are you comfortable down there? Cool enough?"

"We're fine."

"Because I've got another fan if you need it."

"We're all right."

"Maybe that little revolving one. You could put it on the night table."

"Mom!"

She raised her hands in surrender. Then she turned to exit the room, that old runway spin.

"Mom?"

She turned back.

"Thanks, though."

"You're welcome."

Pete awakened as I climbed back into bed. "Hi," he said sleepily, pulling me close to him. He kissed my neck, started caressing my breast.

"Don't," I whispered.

"Why?"

"It's my *parents'* house."

"And?"

"Come on. I can't do it in my parents' house."

"I can," Pete said. I kissed him quickly, then turned away from him, saying, "Go to sleep." But then, after a moment, I reached back and put my hand on his thigh, and we both stayed up awhile longer. Sometimes it embarrassed me, how happy we were. Sometimes it seemed like I was making it up.

6

I was up early, starting coffee in the kitchen, when my mother appeared. "I don't think I slept more than three hours last night," she said.

I turned, coffee measure in my hand, midair. "Why?"

She sat heavily at the table. "Your father. He said he felt dizzy last night, and then early this morning he said his arm felt numb."

"Oh, my God, it's his heart!"

"No, no, it's not. It's nothing like that. He just had a checkup. I think he slept on it wrong."

"Let me take a look at him," I said. As if I'd know anything. But I was the oldest, so I acted like I did.

"He's asleep again. I'm sure it's no emergency. Let him be."

"You're sure?" I looked toward their bedroom.

"Yes. Believe me, this is not the first time he's kept me up half the night with one complaint or another that turns out to be absolutely nothing. He's beginning to become a bit of a hypochondriac. It's hard not to, at our age, when so many of our friends . . ." She stood, took the coffee measure from me. "Anyway. I'll do this. And then let me make your breakfast. What would you like, French toast? Pancakes?"

I sat back down at the kitchen table. "Just coffee. The kids will be up soon, and then we're going right over to the fair."

"Are you all going together?" She flipped the switch for the coffee and sat down with me. Almost instantly, the satisfying aroma of brewing coffee filled the air. "Are Steve and Caroline going with you too?"

"Yes. And you and Dad are coming too, right?"

"Maybe you should go on ahead of us—he was awake so much last night. Call me in a couple of hours. I'm sure he'll be up by then, and we'll figure out a place to meet."

"Are you're really sure he's all right?"

"I'm sure. When he wakes up, he'll be in better shape than *I* am."

Caroline came into the kitchen, yawning. "Is the coffee done?"

"In a minute," my mother said.

"Yeah, but I need a cup right now. Don't you have one of those coffee interruptus things?"

"It'll be done in a minute, Caroline."

Caroline sat at the table with us. "I suppose you'll be wanting to go on the roller coaster again," she told me.

"Don't I always?"

"Aren't we too old now? It'll kill our backs."

"It didn't hurt last year," I said.

"Yeah, it did."

"Did it hurt just *you* or both of us?"

She smiled and fastened her long hair up into a twist that she anchored with a barrette she pulled from her robe pocket. "Actually, you complained for hours after we got off."

"Really?"

"Yes."

"Oh."

My mother got up to put coffee mugs on

the table. "I haven't been on one of those things for thirty years. Your father used to make me go with him, but I always hated it. I kept my eyes shut and gritted my teeth the whole time."

"Wasn't your first date with Dad at the fair?" I asked. We grew up hearing stories about my parents' romance. The most interesting one had to do with the time my father was in the navy and got a letter from my mother, who at that point was his fiancée. He opened the envelope on deck on a windy day, and the letter blew out of his hand. He actually jumped into the ocean after it.

"But that's crazy!" I'd said, when I head the story. And he'd said, "Yeah, I guess it was. A lot of my shipmates said the same thing. They thought it was wrong for a man to be so much in love with a woman." He chuckled. "But I was." Then, leaning closer to me, he'd said, "I still am, too."

I'd said, "Well, that's great, Dad," but I wasn't sure I really meant it. I appreciated the outlandish sentimentality of his diving into the drink, but I thought his friends were right: To love someone that much was a dangerous thing.

The coffeemaker beeped and I got up to pour for all of us. My mother took a sip, then said, "Well, you remember that we met at the movies. And we sat together that night. But, yes, our first official date was going to the fair. We were nineteen years old, can you imagine? Your father had never paid to get into the state fair in his life. It was a matter of honor with him. So he gave me money to get in and told me where to meet him. Then he went and snuck in under the fence."

"What fence?" I asked. "I'll send the kids, save a few bucks."

"It's not there anymore," my mother said. "And shame on you."

"Shame on her?" Caroline said loudly. "*Shame* on her?"

My mother and I both looked over at her. "It's a joke," I said finally.

"No," Caroline said, "it isn't."

"Caroline," I said, sighing.

"Is it, Mom?"

My mother, flustered, started to answer when the basement door off the kitchen opened and Pete appeared. "Morning!" he said. And then, "What's wrong?"

"Nothing," we answered, all three of us

together. And then, while my mother poured coffee for Pete, Caroline headed for the bathroom and I went upstairs to tell the kids to get ready.

7

Pete, Steve, and the kids were on the roller coaster for the second time. Caroline and I were sitting on a bench waiting for them. Caroline was right—we were too old to go on that ride. My rib cage hurt from where I'd slammed into the side of the car and Caroline's knee was bruised from the safety bar. "Tell you what," Caroline said, "let's make a deal. Let's support each other in vowing never to go on that damn ride again. If anyone asks, we stand together in our absolute refusal."

"Fine with me," I said. My back hurt too.

Caroline leaned against the bench and smiled at the sight of a mother pulling a wagon by us, two sleeping children in it. She looked at her watch. "Eleven o'clock. They conked out early, huh?"

"They've probably been here since six," I said. Seeing a pattern I liked in the leaves of the tree across the way from us, I pulled a small sketch pad out of my purse and did a rough drawing. It was the overlapping quality I liked, an edge next to an edge next to an edge.

Caroline looked over my shoulder. "What's that for?"

"I don't know. Something."

She sighed. "Always working."

I looked up at her, surprised. "I'm not always working!"

"Yeah, you are. You've always got your nose to the grindstone about something. Always."

"No, I don't!"

"Oh, don't get so upset. It's not a criticism. It's just an observation. You've always been that way. Busy, busy, busy." She tossed back her hair, now hanging in loose curls, and pushed her sunglasses up on top of her head. "It's getting cloudy. Do you smell rain?"

"No." I did, actually, but my anger made me want to disagree with her. I was thinking about what she'd said: *Busy, busy busy.* Was I? I stretched out my legs. "So what are you going to talk to me and Steve about, Caroline?"

"Not now."

"Just tell me what it's *about.*"

"I did tell you. I want to compare notes. I have a lot of bad memories, and I need to know, finally, whether . . ." She crossed her arms over herself, then crossed her legs. If she were a turtle, I thought, she'd pull her head in. But then she looked directly into my eyes. "This is what it is," she said. "I just feel like I can't get past some things until I talk this out with someone who was there when I was growing up."

I started to say something but didn't. Instead, I nodded. Sort of.

"I know," Caroline said.

"What?"

"I know you think I'm a pain in the ass."

"Oh, it's not that," I said. "I just . . . well, frankly, Caroline, I worry about you. I mean, when does it ever just get easy for you? I wonder if you need to just stop thinking so much. Feeling so much."

"I don't decide to feel what I do. It just comes. I wouldn't mind not feeling so much, believe me."

I turned toward her, attempting a tone of compassionate reason. "But . . . can't you decide what to do *with* it? Can't you—?"

"Laura, I've come to a point where I just have to know some things. That's all. I can't even work anymore. I've become obsessed with finding out what happened to me that made me so . . . well, I just feel like if I can find out some things, if I can validate them, I can finally head in a different direction. I won't feel this terrible sense of . . ." She teared up. Then, tightfisted, she stared straight ahead. When she spoke again, her voice was angry. "I don't know why I'm telling you this. I don't think you can understand what I'm talking about at all."

"Oh, come on, I—"

"No. It's not the same for you, Laura. We're so different. We always have been. I love you, but we're just . . . different." She looked down at her hands. "I've been seeing a therapist. I started a few months ago; I'm going twice a week. At first I was getting nowhere. I'd walk out of there feeling guilty that I was spending a hundred and twenty-five dollars an hour for nothing. Well, not for nothing. For trying to entertain a woman who was supposed to be helping me. But what finally happened is that I stopped goofing around and started doing some real work. It helps. Before I went, things had gotten really bad. I hadn't even been able to get out of bed on some days, I just . . ." She looked over at me. "I couldn't get out of bed."

"Why didn't you tell me?"

"I don't tell you things like that. I don't tell anybody in the family things like that! Do you? I mean, for one thing, I know when you feel bad, you don't exactly get immobilized and lie in bed all day. You'd never do that. You'd leap up and make a cobbler." She reached out to touch my hand. "I mean that in a complimentary way, okay? I really do."

She was right. I was more like Maggie, who, the last time she was sad, painted her garage and then, in a fit of good neighborliness, painted ours as well.

"I couldn't tell anybody I knew, really. So I started seeing this therapist and we got into some childhood stuff, and I remembered some things that were . . . I remembered some things that were pretty awful. And then all of a sudden I started to doubt myself. I started to think maybe I was making it up, maybe this was some sort of therapy-induced fantasy. And I need to talk to you and Steve to see if you remember any of it as well."

"But you mean . . . abuse of you?"

"Well, yes, basically. But of a very specific kind."

"Like . . . sexual?" An image of my father came to me: Best Loved Teacher, year after year, standing before a class of high school freshmen, their faces raised to him.

"No. No." She looked over at the roller coaster. "Look, we can't get into it now. We need time. And also I want to talk to you about . . . I think Bill and I are getting divorced."

"What?"

"Yeah." She raised her eyebrows, smiled an ironic smile. "Eeeeyup."

"Well, Caroline, you . . . I mean, you sort of add this *on*! This is a big deal! They're both big deals!"

She stood and pulled her purse higher on her shoulder. "Here come the kids."

I stood up beside her. "I hate it when you do this," I said quietly. I smiled and waved at the little group coming toward us. "I hate it when you start something and then just—"

"You're the one who pushed to talk about it. I wanted to wait until later." She smiled widely at Hannah, now beside her. "How was it?"

"Awesome! We're all going *again*! Just one more time!"

"Hey, Mom!" Anthony said. "Come with us! Please?"

I started to say no, but then agreed to go. It wasn't often that my kids asked me to do things with them anymore. I handed my purse to Caroline without asking if she'd mind holding it.

It took awhile to get through the line, but finally we all climbed on board. Once, when the front car I was riding in with Hannah hesitated at the crest of an incline, when it took that agonizing pause before starting its mad descent, I looked over and spotted Caroline sitting alone on the bench, our purses in her lap. She looked so small. I

suddenly remembered our promise to each
other never to go on this ride again. And
then it occurred to me that I didn't forget it
at all.

Caroline is sitting on her heels in the dirt, wearing her blue dress with white rickrack trim. She is about seven years old. I am standing above her taking the picture: you can see my elongated shadow on the ground beside her, my short braids bowing out from the sides of my head like broken handles. I have caught Caroline burying something, and she will not tell me what it is. I say I am taking her picture because she looks so pretty, but that is not the reason. I am taking it so I will know where to look, later, when I sneak out and dig up what she is trying to hide. She smiles shyly, her hands folded in her lap, squinting in the bright light. I never do return to the site. I am not interested enough to go back and look for anything of hers.

8

We were finally getting close to the end of the long line for cheese curds when a tall and massively overweight man wearing dirty jeans, a black T-shirt, and a black leather vest cut in front of us. He was entirely nonchalant, sliding in as though we were holding a place for him. He was balding but had a long stringy ponytail hanging halfway down his back and many gold hoops on one ear. He reeked of beer. I looked at the kids and started laughing. But Caroline tapped him on the shoulder. "Excuse me," she said. "You just cut in front of us."

The man turned around.

"Caroline . . ." I said.

"No! He cut in front of us!"

The man sneered, then turned away.

"Excuse me!" Caroline said again, louder, and this time Steve said quietly, "Caroline. Let it go."

She looked at Steve for a long moment, and I saw the tension in her jaw from clenching her teeth. Then: "Fine," she said. "I'll wait for you outside." She walked away and Hannah shouted after her, "Aunt Caroline! Do you want us to get you some?"

She turned back, shook her head no, and disappeared into the crowd.

"Whoa!" Anthony muttered.

"She's just a little nervous today," I said.

"She's always like that! Seems like any little thing—"

"Enough," Pete said. "She was offended by this guy's bad manners. She's right—he shouldn't have cut in front of us."

The man turned around, belched in Pete's face, and put his back to us again. I saw Pete waver for a moment, as did I, and then we all exploded into laughter.

When we reached the counter, I ordered

cheese curds for Caroline anyway. She'd eat them. I knew her.

When we came outside, we saw her sitting at a picnic table piled high with other people's litter. She was on her cell phone, frowning. She held up a hand to indicate that we should be quiet. *Busy, busy, busy,* I wanted to say to her. But when she snapped the phone shut, she said, "That was Mom. Dad's at St. Joseph's Hospital."

The image of my mother appeared, dressed in the robe she'd had on that morning, waving away my concerns about my father.

"Do we have to leave?" Hannah asked.

"Yes." I took her hand and started walking quickly. Ten minutes to get to the exit, at least. Another fifteen to walk home—that would be faster than trying to get a cab through this traffic. I'd told her it was his heart and she'd said to leave him alone. I'd known it wasn't right. I'd known it and I'd listened to her anyway.

"Is it okay to eat my cheese curds?" Hannah whispered, and I nodded a tight yes. It would take fifteen minutes to get to the hospital, if there was no traffic.

During the quick and silent walk home, I

did not think of my father. Instead, I thought of Caroline, of all the times she'd come home from school, crying. Or come in from outside, crying. The way she would moon over a book where some horse died. The way she would go to sad movies over and over. I was so tired of her theatrics, her fragility, her deliberate forays into melancholy, her complicated secrecy—not just now but always. I worked myself into a pretty nice state of anger at her, which kept me from having to think about what my father might look like right now. I had lived this long and had only seen a dead man once. He was lying on the floor of a shopping mall, right outside the entrance to Penney's. His face had been gray-blue, his mouth slightly open. There'd been a woman kneeling beside him who was attempting CPR, in vain. Her purse and shopping bags lay scattered about her; and one of her shoes had come loose off her heel. "He's gone," she'd kept saying, but then she would give him another breath and pump on his chest, counting aloud in a high voice that shook a little.

I'd thought, *This morning, he picked that shirt to put on.* I'd thought, *I wonder why he came to the mall today.* And then I'd walked away. I'd told myself that it was because it was indecent for people to make a ring around the man, gawking at him. But the truth was, I'd left because I couldn't stand looking at him and realizing people die. As soon as I turned away, I'd told myself to forget about him. And I had. I'd gone into a store three doors down and looked at bath oil, and then I'd bought some. All the way home, I'd imagined not the sudden loss of another soul on earth but rather how nice it would feel to be submerged in warm water, breathing in the scent of white gardenia. It had been so easy to erect my barricade against fear, against pain, against knowing. Now it seemed that my house had blown down. I was about to meet the wolf.

Aunt Fran was sitting in the waiting room of the ICU when we arrived. She was wearing light-colored pants with circles of dirt stains at the knee—clearly, she'd been working in her garden when she was called. She shared a love of gardening with my mother, but there the similarities ended. Where my mother was stunning, Aunt Fran looked . . . friendly. The same could have been said of Steve and me; it was only Caroline who inherited my mother's great beauty. I was "pleasant looking"—I'd heard that all my life—with widely spaced brown eyes and even features. I used to have a good body, but now I suffered the usual humiliations of getting older. Steve looked like an All-American boy, even at his age.

There was another and more important difference between my mother and my aunt. Where my mother was uptight, Aunt Fran was unfailingly relaxed and open. I had loved visiting her as a child. I used to ask her why she couldn't be my mother. I'd concocted a fantasy whereby she in fact *was* my real mother; she just gave me to her sister because she had too many other children. But I preferred being around Aunt Fran. She let you crawl onto her lap, she read to you with clear enthusiasm, she told jokes, she let you eat cookies between meals, she sang loudly along with the radio, she helped you build sheet tents and cardboard forts, she asked you about your life because she really wanted to know the answers.

Once, she'd been lying out in her lawn chair on a hot summer night, and her four-

teen-year-old son and I were sitting in the
grass on either side of her. We were drinking lemonade from aluminum tumblers with
little terry-cloth wraps that kept your hand
from getting too cold. We'd just finished
brownies that Aunt Fran had whipped up on
the spur of the moment: just like that, no
problem, made from scratch, no recipe.
"Tell me about the stars, Eric," Aunt Fran
had said. And he had, and she'd listened to
him in wonder, her eyes wide and staring
upward into the darkness above her.

He had begun by saying, "Well, our sun is
a star," and Aunt Fran had gotten all excited
and said, "Really? Really?" I'd listened to
the rest of what Eric said, and the whole
time I'd had a thought flitting around my
brain like a moth repeatedly bumping into
the light: This is what a family really is. This.
This. This.

Mostly, when you were around Aunt Fran,
you enjoyed a buoyancy of spirit: There was
nothing *wrong*. There had been a thickness
in the atmosphere at our house, a vague
and ongoing sense of something amiss. It
was the kind of thing you didn't particularly
notice until you were away from it. But
once, when I'd asked Aunt Fran yet again if

I could live with her, she sat me down for a serious talk. I was seven, but she treated me as though I were an adult. She told me my mother loved me very much, even if it did not seem obvious to me. She told me my mother had had a difficult time with *their* mother. "It was like Mom was jealous of Barbara," Aunt Fran had said. "And as far as she was concerned, Barbara couldn't do anything right, not one thing. My mother was all right to me, but it was very bad, the way she treated Barbara. It broke her spirit. Your mother does the best she can. You have to realize that people have reasons for the way they behave. All I can say is it's lucky your mother met your father. I don't know what she would have done without him. I love her with all my heart, but I couldn't save her like your father did."

It had been easy to believe my grandmother had been cruel to my mother; my memories of that grandmother were not good ones either. There had been about her a sense of constant disapproval. You could not touch her white porcelain poodle with the little puppies chained to it. You had to take your shoes off before you came into the house. If you drank from anything but a glass, you were a heathen. Once, in her bathroom, I'd seen a douche bag hanging from the shower rod. When I'd asked my grandmother what it was, she'd whisked it away angrily, saying, "What is the matter with you? What kind of person would ask about such things?"

When I was around five, I'd been alone with her one day; I don't remember why. But I'd come upon her when she was staring at herself in the mirror, and I was startled by the look of relaxed pleasure on her face. When she'd seen me, she turned around and regarded me with her usual expression, a half smile that was not really a smile. It was the forced pleasantry of the overburdened saleswoman who asks how she can help when what she really wants is just to go home. "What is it, Laura?" she'd asked. "It" wasn't anything; I'd just been wandering around the house. I'd simply wanted to be by her. But with my grandmother, there had to be an agenda. If you were doing nothing, you were up to no good.

The only time she touched us kids was when we were leaving—then we got a quick hug, her face directed away from us. It was like being pressed to a wall. I'd known she was warmer to Aunt Fran's children, and for a while it had bothered me. But soon enough I gave up on her altogether; we all did, and Steve and I always made vicious fun of her in the backseat every time we drove home from her house. Caroline laughed at what we said, but she wouldn't join in. Neither of our parents ever reprimanded us for our behavior at those times; rather, their relaxed posture seemed to suggest they condoned it.

My grandmother died when I was twelve, just nine months after her husband, who was really nothing more than a shadowy presence. At her funeral, I'd played hangman with Steve. As far as I was concerned, my only grandparents were my father's parents. My mother had wept for days after her mother's death, and when I'd asked her why she'd said, "Now there's no chance of anything changing. Do you understand? I'm not sorry to lose her, as she was. I'm grieving for what can never be. I'm grieving for *me.*"

Now, before anyone could ask how my father was, Aunt Fran put down her magazine and said, "He's absolutely fine. The tests don't show a thing. They're going to keep him overnight just as a precaution. He can go home tomorrow."

I slumped onto an orange plastic sofa. "Oh, good. Good." Again, the image of my mother in her robe. *I told you.*

"I'm going to go talk to the nurses," Caroline said, and Steve told her to wait, he'd go with her.

"I was sure something really terrible had happened," I told Aunt Fran. "I was really sure."

"Not at all. Your mother said he ate some hot peppers last night. He can't really do that anymore, but he just won't quit."

"Mom shouldn't buy them then."

"She didn't. He did!"

I smiled and moved over a bit so Pete could fit beside me.

"I think I'm going to run home for a while," Aunt Fran said. "Want me to take the kids back to your mom's house?"

I looked over at Anthony, who hated hospitals and had ventured no farther than the entryway to the lounge, and at Hannah, sitting nervously at the edge of a chair, her empty cheese curd container still in her hand. "What do you think, guys?" I said. "You want to go back to Grandma's?"

"We'll stay if you want us to," Anthony said, and I could hear the plea in the back of his brain: *Say no.*

"I guess they don't really need to be here," I told Pete. "Why don't you go too? You might as well take them back to the fair."

"Can we?" Hannah asked.

"I think maybe we should stay for just a while," Pete said.

"Well, go in and see him if you want," Aunt Fran said. "But really, he's fine. He's mostly embarrassed. Sitting there in that silly gown."

"I'll be here," I told Pete. "Caroline and Steve will, too. You go ahead. There's no point in all of us hanging around."

He stood, his hands in his pockets, deliberating. Then, "All right." He kissed the top of my head. "I'll see you later. I'm going to go back to the fair and eat some more of the stuff that will put *me* in here next."

As soon as they left, Caroline and Steve came back into the waiting room. "Only one visitor at a time," Caroline said. "Mom's in there with him, but she said she'd be out in a minute."

"I'll go in next," I said.

"How come you get to go first?" Steve asked.

"Because I'm the oldest."

He flopped down onto a chair. "Right. I knew you were going to say that."

"Then why did you ask?"

"I just wanted to hear you say it again. Warms my heart. Brings back a lot of happy memories."

My mother came into the room and nodded to us. She looked exhausted: face wan, lines pronounced. Her hair had not been combed; it was in the same messy twist that it was this morning. I stared at her in some removed kind of fascination: I was trying to remember if I'd ever seen her go outside the house this way. As though she was aware of my thoughts, she reached up to push back the sides of her hair, to tighten her pearl studs. "I must look a fright. I left the house without doing anything."

"I doubt they'll take points off for your appearance, Mom," Caroline said.

"My appearance matters to me."

"Well, I guess we all know that."

"Stop, Caroline!" I exploded.

"Never mind," my mother said. "We're all a little edgy, that's all."

"I'm going in to see him." I walked down the short hall to the intensive care unit. Inside, the lights were low. Two nurses sat at the desk, working at computers. One looked up and smiled at me, and I said I was there to see my father.

"His name?"

"Oh," I said. "Right. Stan Meyer."

"Mr. Meyer is right here," the nurse said, and opened the door to one of the small rooms. My father was dozing, snoring lightly. I sat quietly in the chair beside his bed and looked around at all the equipment, most of which I'd only seen on television. Three moving lines of glowing green ran across a small monitor screen. There was an IV dripping into my father's arm, a bruised area around the place where the needle was inserted. I could see one of the electrodes on his chest; they'd shaved the hair off around it. On his thick wrist was a plastic name band, and for some reason the sight of this really bothered me. He could be anyone in a hospital. Therefore, anything could happen to him. I thought of a friend who'd lost her father recently, how she sat in the chair beside his unconscious form and told him she forgave him everything and that she hoped he forgave her too. How, moments after that, she'd watched him die.

I changed my position in my chair, cleared my throat. Then, "Dad?" I whispered.

His eyelids fluttered, then opened. He stared at me, blinked. "Oh, hi, Laura. I was dreaming. I was home, outside, painting the fence." He smiled. "Isn't this is a kicker? That's the last time I'll have those jalepeños."

"What happened, Dad?"

"Well, it's the damnedest thing. I ate a few last night, and then a few hours later I woke up and I was so dizzy. Then this morning, my arm went numb—your mother says I was lying on it. But I got all dizzy again too, and kind of scared, I must admit, so I called nine-one-one and they sent an ambulance. Anyway, the doc told me the good news, which is that it doesn't look like it's my heart. Might be what they call a TIA, a ministroke, but I can come back next week and get checked out for that."

His speech was a bit slurred, his mouth dry. I felt sorry for him, lying there with a half-full urinal hanging off the bedside rail—he was normally a very fastidious man. Then it came to me how lucky I was, to be feeling sorry for him because he was in a hospital bed and not walking the fairgrounds with us. He was fine; he'd go home tomorrow. So many others had been faced with so much tragedy—our family had been remarkably lucky.

"You know," I said, "you're messing up our amazing track record."

"What do you mean?"

"Nobody's ever been hospitalized in our family except for childbirth."

He nodded slowly, then said, "Well, that's not exactly true."

"Really?"

"It was . . . something happened a long time ago that I never told you kids about. I wasn't sure I should. But I was lying here after I first came in, and I thought, My God, this could be it. I could never make it out of here. And all of a sudden . . . well, I just wanted to say so much to all of you. I wanted to apologize to you kids for keeping some things from you. I wish I hadn't done that. It took coming in here for me to realize that. And yet now there's nothing wrong, I don't know if it's a good idea to tell you after all, to dig up such old bones." He smiled. "You know what I mean? Maybe it's better just to let things be."

"What are you talking about, Dad?" *Medication?* I thought. *Is he confused? Should I tell the nurse?*

But then he smiled, his old self, and reached out to touch my hand. "I don't know. I just don't know if it's right. And yet if something comes to you so strongly when you think you might be dying, shouldn't you go ahead and take care of it when you're alive?"

"Take care of what?"

"Of . . . apologizing, I guess."

"But for what?"

He hesitated for a moment, then smiled. "You know what, honey? It was a long time ago. I don't know. Forget it." He sat up straighter in his bed. "Is your mother still out there?"

For a moment I thought about pressing him to tell me what he was going to say, then decided against it. I'd talk to him about it later, when he came home. It couldn't be that important, if he'd never mentioned it before now.

"Yeah, Mom's out there. Aunt Fran left, and I sent Pete and the kids back to the fair."

"Good. I'm coming home tomorrow, I'll go with you then. But maybe I'll lay off the fried food."

"Okay." I stood up to move beside him, kissed his forehead. "I love you," I said, and he answered, "You're my girl," which was what he always said when I told him I loved him.

"Want me to send Mom in?"

He nodded, closed his eyes. "Tell her not to be offended if I'm sleeping. I'm so sleepy."

When I got back to the lounge, Caroline and Steve were sitting together on one of the sofas.

"Where's Mom?" I asked, and Steve said, "Gone out with Aunt Fran. She'll be back in an hour or so."

"Well, he looks fine," I said. "He's sleeping now."

Caroline closed the magazine she'd been reading. "Let's go to the cafeteria. I need coffee."

Steve said, "I'm too full."

Caroline said, "Just come, okay?"

He looked quickly at me, shoved his hands in his pockets, and we all headed for the elevator as though it were a gangplank.

9

"You know I want to talk to you both," Caroline said. "It might as well be now." She was nervous; her hands were clenched tightly before her.

We were sitting at a small round table, off by itself. The cafeteria was all but empty. But Caroline's voice was so low I could hardly hear her.

"*Now?*" Steve asked.

"Do you mind? I mean, we're here."

Steve and I looked at each other and then sat quietly, waiting for her to begin.

Finally, she said, "All right. I was at

a friend's house, not long ago. She had some new perfume, and she was telling me about how she always let her husband pick out her perfume, because her mother told her that that and good cooking were ways to keep your man happy. And then she started telling me all these other things her mother told her, most of them funny but some of them really wise, and I started trying to think about what Mom had told *me.* And I realized she'd never told me anything."

She looked up from her coffee at me, then at Steve. He was staring straight ahead, probably trying very hard not to drum his fingers on the table.

"I don't know what you mean," I said.

"I mean she never told me *anything.* Like . . . about how to iron, or sew, or cook." I rolled my eyes at this last—who would want to learn to cook like our mother?—but Caroline saw me and said, "*Or* about fashion. Or how to talk to boys. Or girls! And when I started thinking of that, I realized—"

"Caroline," Steve said.

"What?"

"Is this going to be . . . I mean, are you

going to tell us about all the injustices you suffered at the hands of our terrible, terrible mother?"

"Steve," I said.

"What?"

"Let her talk."

"She can talk. I'm just asking what this is *about.*"

Caroline leaned forward, spoke earnestly. "I want to know something, Steve. I wonder if you can tell me about one time when you saw some tenderness in her. Let's just start there."

"In Mom?"

"Yeah."

"Well . . . lots of times."

"Such as?"

He slumped back in his chair and looked around the room, impatient. "I don't know, like when I got hurt and stuff. Or sick."

"What did she do then?"

"Look, Caroline. I know you've got problems with Mom. You always did. But I don't want to sit around and talk about my relationship with her. I don't have any problem, okay? So if you want to talk about it, you need to talk about you. But just say it, and don't make such a big fucking stageplay out of it!"

"You know what, Steve?" She smiled bitterly, started to speak, then stopped. "Never mind. What a dumb idea, to think I could talk to you. You're not here. You've never been here. You avoid thinking about anything; you just buy big-boy toys and—"

Steve stood and pushed his chair hard under the table. "I figured when you said you wanted to talk to me and Laura, it'd be some crap like this. You know what I think, Caroline? I think you should grow up. You're fifty years old, for Christ's sake."

"Fifty-one, thank you. And excuse me, I should grow up?"

"I'm going back upstairs," he said. "Dad's in the hospital. That's why we're here, remember? Believe it or not, we're involved in something here that has nothing to do with you."

"Steve," I said, but it was too late. He walked away.

Caroline watched him disappear out the swinging door. "I don't know what I was thinking. He's never cared anything about me."

"That's not true," I said.

"It is. I shouldn't mind, really. I should be used to it."

"He does care about you. He doesn't like to talk about things, that's all. I mean, you ask him about tenderness . . . he's not like that. He's a guy, only worse. And—well, Dad *is* in the hospital."

"I know he is, but he's fine! And I just figured, since we were all here together, now was as good a time as any. I needed something. I really needed something from him, and I thought I'd ask."

"Well, ask then. You've got to be direct with him."

She looked down. "It's hard."

I wanted so much to say, tiredly, Everything is hard for you, Caroline. But I didn't. I looked out the window, at the birds flying free, and said, "Well, ask me, then. I'm here. Ask me."

She nodded, took a deep breath in, blew it out. "One thing I want to know is what I was asking Steve. Really. I want to know if you can remember anything . . . tender that Mom ever did."

"Okay, so you mean being hugged and kissed, stuff like that?"

"No. I know she did that sometimes, but

it was always . . . it felt like it was for show.
It was always in front of someone else. No, I
mean other things. Things she did just for
you, without an audience. Like . . . did she
ever just sit on your bed and talk to you?"

I thought back and tried to remember.
Truthfully, I couldn't recall anything like that.
And so I said, "No. I don't think she did.
But, see, I don't think I minded."

She pushed her cup aside, leaned in
toward me. "All right. Let me ask you this,
then. Do you remember her ever being
overtly cruel to you?"

"Oh, Caroline. Weren't you, as a mother?
Weren't you ever cruel to Eva?"

"Yes. Yes, I was, I'm sure. But not . . . it
wasn't intentional. It wasn't dispassionate
or calculated."

"What does that mean? You think Mom
was intentionally cruel to you?" I was beginning to wish I'd walked out with Steve.
Given my mother's background, it was un-
derstandable that she wasn't particularly
cuddly, that there was about her a certain
dark mystery. But she had never raised a
hand to us, had rarely even raised her
voice.

"She was. And she crippled me in ways I

can't even . . ." She closed her eyes, rubbed her forehead. Then she looked at me, her green eyes hard. "This is part of the deal I made with the therapist, okay? I promised I'd talk to you and Steve. If I can just get some sort of acknowledgment—"

"Caroline. I'm sorry for what you've been feeling. I am. I know your life growing up was difficult; you were a very sensitive kid. And . . . highly imaginative in ways that I think hurt you. I think you hurt yourself because of the way you seemed to dwell on sad things. I thought you'd have to be hospitalized after we saw *Bambi.*" I smiled at her, but she didn't smile back.

I leaned in closer, chose my words carefully. I didn't want her to know what I was thinking, which was that she was a liar. I had to find a gentler way to say that—and to think it. Deluding herself; that might be a better way of saying it. I'd think of something.

For the time being, I just said, "Look. I understand you're going through a lot of pain now. I wish I could help—I'm worried about you. But you're talking in circles. I think we should go back upstairs. We can talk more about this later, I promise." I stood, picked up my purse. Caroline stayed seated.

"Are you coming?"

She didn't look at me. But she said, "One time, when I was about seven, she came into my room and I was lying on the bed, naked—I wanted to see how it felt to have all my skin against that silky coverlet I used to have. And she yanked me off the bed and shoved me up against the wall and said, 'Shame on you! Shame on you!' and shook me so hard I thought my neck would snap." She swallowed. "Then she put her hands around my throat and wouldn't let go. She didn't squeeze, but she wouldn't let go. Finally, I bit her. Then she let go."

I sat back down at the table.

"That's not the only thing she did like that. She told me it was my fault, that I made her do these things to me. I believed her." She laughs. "And you know what? Telling you all this now, I can feel some part of me still believing it."

"Caroline, is this really true?" She looked up quickly at me, and I said, "I'm sorry. I'm sorry, but is it? Tell me honestly, now."

Caroline laughed, a short, bitter sound. "Right." She slid out of her chair and walked quickly away, and I cast about for the right thing to do. Call her back? Call her names? The truth was, I didn't believe her. I couldn't imagine my mother doing such things. Then it came to me that maybe what I couldn't imagine was my not knowing. And by extension, of course, my not doing anything about it.

I remembered a winter night when Caroline and I were perhaps eight and ten. We were lying together in my bed, the blankets pulled up high over us. We'd had a flashlight that we were using as a microphone, and we'd been playing some sort of game where I was the host and Caroline was a glamorous movie star who was being interviewed about her glamorous life. "And how many Christmas presents did you get this year?" I'd asked, and Caroline had said, in a pleasingly affected voice, "Oh, my heavens, so many; too many to count. I got a horse, a Tennessee Walker. And I got a jewelry box full of diamond necklaces. And I got toilet paper made of satin and silk." We'd giggled, I remember, and then, all of a sudden, she'd turned to me and said, "I wish I could die." At first, I was confused, thinking the "star" was talking. But then I had understood it was Caroline, speaking for herself. "Don't you?"

"Don't I what?" I was beginning to be afraid of her. I could feel a coldness rising up my spine. I hated how her bangs were cut crookedly, how pale she was, the bruise-colored circles beneath her eyes.

"Don't you wish you could die now?" she whispered. "Just like this?"

"*No!*" I'd said, and she stopped smiling. I think she was genuinely surprised at my response. "Why would you wish a thing like that?"

"Because. We'd go to heaven if we died right now. If we live much longer, we probably won't. Our sins will get bigger and bigger." She had turned on her side, facing me. "Anyway, I don't like it here. I don't really like it."

I'd lain still for a moment. Then I'd said, "Go back to your own bed. You're creepy. You're so creepy. I'm telling what you said."

"No, you won't," she'd said. And she'd been right. I'd always let her bear her peculiar burdens alone.

*   *   *

In the ICU waiting room, Steve was hunched over a magazine, one leg draped over the arm of his chair. "Where's Caroline?" I asked.

"Don't know. Don't care." He looked up at me, shrugged.

"She just told me something really incredible." I repeated for him the story Caroline had told me about our mother. When I finished, he straightened in his seat, put down the magazine. "Jesus."

"I know." I supposed he was thinking the same things I had: How did I miss this? How could the mother I had be the mother who did such things?

The door to the lounge opened and a somber-faced woman entered and sat on the chair closest to the door. She was wearing blue-jean shorts and a sleeveless white blouse, a pair of sneakers with no socks. She carried a large straw purse, and lying across the top of it was a battered teddy bear. She nodded at us, her eyes shining with tears.

"Hi," I said softly.

"Hi." She picked up a magazine, stared determinedly at it, shivered slightly in the air-conditioning. The room was rich with a unique kind of silence that was full of things that needed to be expressed but couldn't be. I looked at Steve, pointed to the door, and he followed me out.

"She must have a child being admitted," I said. "My God. Can you imagine your child being in the ICU? I'd go crazy if one of my children had to be in there."

"Where do you think Caroline went? Speaking of children."

"Beats me."

He leaned against the wall, crossed his arms. "Well, now I feel like a real jerk. But do you think . . . don't get mad, okay? But do you believe her?"

"Oh. . . . No. Probably not. That's why she left, because I made her feel like I don't believe her. I'm sure it's not literally true; Caroline always exaggerates everything so much. But if she—"

The elevator dinged, the doors parted, and we saw my mother coming down the hall. I watched her, trying to see if there was something about her that would confirm or deny what Caroline had just told me. But she was only my mother, the woman signing my report cards, applauding my first ride on my bike without training wheels,

chopping onions with a match held between her teeth to keep from crying, carpet-
sweeping the living room, standing at the
foot of my bed to hold Anthony as a newborn, her hand protectively cradling his
head with great skill and care. I had to talk
to Caroline's husband. If not her therapist.

My mother had changed clothes,
combed her hair, regained her regal bearing. But as she came closer, I saw a look on
her face I couldn't quite decipher. "I just
saw Caroline on the way out," she said.
Neither Steve nor I said anything back.
"She's going home, she said. She's not
coming back."

"Ah," I said, as though it made perfect
sense. As though it were what I'd been
waiting for.

"I do not understand that child," my
mother said. "I never have and I never will."

"She's going home to her house?" I
asked.

My mother nodded. "I'm going in to see
your father. I'm going to tell him something
came up for Caroline at work that she's got
to go home and take care of. He doesn't
need to know she didn't care enough to see
him come out of the hospital tomorrow."

"Well, she'll be over, I'm sure," I said.

My mother looked at me, angry. "You know what I mean."

"I'll tell you what," I said. "I'll go over there. I'll go to her house and talk to her."

"You want me to come?" Steve asked, and I shook my head no. I pressed the button for the elevator. "Tell Pete where I went. I'll see you later."

10

Anthony was right: I had to get a cell phone. I was standing at a bank of phones in a hall adjacent to a road-stop restaurant. I was squeezed between two callers: one a young dark-haired woman hunched over the receiver who apparently was attempting to have a secretive conversation, the other a wiry trucker sucking hard on a cigarette and yelling that he couldn't possibly arrive on time, no, he could not possibly arrive on time; where was Phyllis, put Phyllis on the line, she was the only one in the whole place that knew what was really going on, where was goddamn Phyllis?

On the way to Caroline's, I had suddenly wanted to talk to my friend Maggie, to hear a voice from home saying that everything there is fine, everything there is still the same. I thought if I could hear her voice, I would be better able to visualize my house: the late-afternoon sunshine that makes an ellipse of light against the living room wall, the folded piles of fabric on my sewing table, the wooden spoons standing at attention in my kitchen, the doors to the kids' rooms open halfway. I'd be able to see the hydrangea blossoms heavy on their bushes in the backyard, the treehouse that Hannah reads in. In addition to comforting myself with such images, I wanted to tell Maggie what had gone on, to ask her what she thought I should do. She was very good in situations like this.

But she wasn't there.

If there is one thing I can't stand, it's being in dire need of talking to a girlfriend and having her husband answer the phone and say she's not there. Then you have two problems: the person you so much need to connect with is not available, *and* you have to rearrange your emotions to converse with a man. There is not a thing in the world wrong with Maggie's husband. Doug is affable and generous and a good cook to boot. But he is of the Y-chromosome school of emotional receptivity. So instead of trying to tell him what was going on, I took in a deep breath, turned down the anxiety flame, and said, "Okay! Well, I'll just try later." And then, in as friendly and even a tone of voice as I could muster, I said, "So what are you doing home in the middle of the day?"

"It's Saturday," he said.

And I said, "Oh. Right."

When I hung up, I stood for a moment in front of the phone, my arms crossed. It occurred to me to call Caroline and leave her a message letting her know I was on my way, that I'd be there soon after she arrived. But I didn't.

I got back in the car, started the engine, then turned it off. I rolled down the window, rested my forehead against the steering wheel, and closed my eyes. I'd only wanted to come home and go to the fair, just like always. Instead, I felt like I'd walked into a room where the door had slammed shut behind me, then disappeared altogether.

*   *   *

A few blocks away from Caroline's house, I pulled into a 7-Eleven. I'd decided I did want to call before I showed up; it seemed only fair. But when I tried her number, I got her voice mail. It was possible that she hadn't arrived yet, but that seemed unlikely. It seemed more appropriate to imagine her lying in bed, fully clothed down to her shoes but under the covers, the way she sometimes was found after a bad day in high school.

I bought a package of Twinkies, always our favorite as kids, and a *National Enquirer.* *A little joke, ha-ha; here you go, Caroline, now let's finish talking and get this over with.*

I pulled into her driveway and parked behind her car. Caroline lived in a beautiful old Victorian that she'd bought when it was a wreck—raccoons had been living there. But she'd loved the bones of the house and saw its potential immediately. Now it was the nicest place on the block.

I went up to the front door and knocked quickly, then tried opening it. Locked. I called her name once, twice. Nothing. I rang the doorbell; then, shading my eyes, I looked in the uncurtained windows of the living room. And there she was, sitting in a chair with her purse at her feet, staring right back at me.

"Open the door," I said.

She didn't move.

Louder, I said, "Caroline! Open the door!"

She got up slowly, came to the door, and opened it. Then she went back to her chair.

I came in, closed the door, and moved to the sofa near her. The mantel clock ticked loudly in the silence. Ticked questioningly, I felt, speaking for Caroline: *What–do–you–want?* I leaned forward, touched her hand lightly. "Hey."

Nothing.

"I brought you something." I pulled the Twinkies out of the bag, the *National Enquirer.*

She wouldn't look.

"Want a Twinkie?" I asked, and then realized the stupidity of it. The unkindness, really. "Caroline," I said gently. "What's going on?"

"I tried to tell you. You called me a liar."

"I did not call you a liar."

She looked over at me, smiled bitterly.

"I didn't call you a liar! I simply asked you if you were *sure*. Come on, you told me this incredible thing, and I just was having trouble . . . I mean, you seem to think you can just—"

The phone rang and I stopped talking, grateful for the interruption. But Caroline made no move to answer it.

"Aren't you going to get that?"

"No."

The phone rang twice more, stopped, then immediately started again.

"Maybe it's important," I said.

"I don't care. I'm not going to answer the phone."

"Well, then, I will."

I started to get up and she said, "Don't! This is not your house. You are not allowed to use the phone."

"Caroline. Dad's in the hospital. It could be about him."

"Dad is fine." The phone stopped ringing again.

"I'm calling home, goddammit." I went into the kitchen, dialed my parents' number. My mother answered immediately. "It's me," I said.

"Yes?"

"I'm here at Caroline's and the phone

rang and we didn't . . . we missed it. It wasn't you, was it?"

"No, it wasn't. What's going on there? Is everything all right?"

I looked toward the living room. "Yes. It's fine. We're just talking."

Caroline came into the kitchen, took the phone from me and hung it up. She turned the ringer off. Then, facing me, she said, "I told you not to answer the phone. I don't want to talk to anyone. Including you." She headed upstairs, and I heard a door slam. I stood still for a minute, then angrily followed her up. I opened the door to her bedroom and found her sitting on the edge of the unmade bed, her hands folded in her lap. Her closet door was open; I could see that Bill's clothes were gone. It was true, then; they were separated.

My anger faded and I sat beside her for some time, saying nothing. Finally, she looked over at me, and I put my arm around her. It occurred to me that this might be the first time I'd ever done this. Her body was stiff, unyielding. Actually, mine was too. Some part of me wanted to stop then, to get up and leave. Drive back to my parents' house and talk to my children about what they did that day, sit in the backyard that night to watch the crayon-colored fireworks that would be shot off from the fairgrounds. I wanted to shrug off all the things Caroline had said in the way I might an unpleasant encounter in a parking lot. But I saw the wrongness in that.

"I'll wait," I said finally. "Okay? I'll wait right here until you're ready. And then I'll listen to you. I promise." She nodded, and she might as well have been transformed into that sad and mysterious little girl who shared a family with me but who didn't belong—not then and not now, either.

It is taken on Easter Sunday. My mother, a study in perfumed agitation, had hustled Caroline and me outside the house before church, saying we had to have our picture taken together in our identical outfits because our paternal grandmother had (sigh) insisted. Nana had sent us dresses made out of a filmy powder-blue-and-white polka-dotted fabric, as well as beribboned hats and white patent leather purses. We have been made to hold hands, and the expression beneath my smile is pained; I am holding only Caroline's thumb, rather in the way you might hold a thumb you found on the ground. Caroline smiles her usual sad smile and holds her other hand up to her eye, her fingers fashioning a grip around her own imaginary camera. She, the one being photographed, is the one recording the truer image. I remember that the moment the photo was taken, I dropped Caroline's hand and ran toward the car. "Wait for me!" she called, but I did not. I claimed a coveted seat by the window and then wiped the hand that had touched Caroline against the skirt of my new dress, first front, then back, over and over again. I think I might have used my purse to try to block anyone from seeing, but I can't be sure that is not just my horrified adult self, editing.

Well, yes. That is what it is. Because now I remember that when Caroline got in the car she was carrying both her own purse and mine, which I'd left behind. She held mine out to me, all hope, saying excitedly, "Here, Laura, you forgot this! You forgot our new purse!" "I don't want it," I said, staring straight ahead. "I don't even like it." It was the possessive pronoun I objected to. From the corner of my eye, I saw her hesitate, then put the purse gently down on the seat between us. I saw her straighten it just the tiniest bit, then struggle to move herself into a comfortable position without disturbing anything.

11

Caroline and I were sitting outside on her back porch steps, eating salad and drinking Diet Pepsi. "What I really want is potato chips and Lipton Onion Soup dip," Caroline said. "It's the fair. It makes you want only junk food."

"We can have that," I said. "Let's go and get some."

"No." She reached down to slap her ankle. "Damn mosquitoes."

I looked at my watch. I'd been here now for almost two hours. "Caroline—"

"I know." She finished her Pepsi and set the can down carefully, as though it were made of crystal. This opposed to my having crushed my own can with one hand, after which I'd burped and said, "See that? Supergirl."

"All right," Caroline said. "I'll try to tell you. I'll try again. Maybe it would help if I give you some background.

"A few months ago, I'd come to the point where I was beginning to feel paralyzed about doing anything for myself. It's always been hard for me to take . . . well, to take. But it became extreme. Bill and I make good money, we own the house and our cars, I pay my credit card bills in full every month, and yet I find myself standing in a store holding up a blouse and wondering why I'm even looking at it, because I know I won't buy it for myself."

"Well, I do that too, Caroline. I think everyone does. You look at something you want to buy and feel guilty that you're getting it for yourself. Especially women; we think it's selfish if—"

"But it was more than that. It was this feeling that . . . it was the feeling that the world is not for me. Life. It's not for me."

I stared out across her backyard, watched two yellow butterflies chasing each other in circles. Look at that, I wanted to say, but didn't. Of course I didn't. Inside, I could hear my child voice saying, "Come *on.* Let's *go.*"

"I kept feeling worse and worse—I couldn't work, I couldn't sleep, I couldn't read—I'd just look at the same sentence over and over. Things were terrible with Bill, and finally he'd just had it. He couldn't help me and he couldn't listen to me anymore, and frankly I don't blame him. He said he wanted to be apart for a while, that then maybe I'd get some help. He'd been asking me to go and see someone for a long time, but I couldn't.

"When he left, though, I finally did call a shrink. One of the things she told me to do was to find something to do with my evenings, to make sure I went out at least once a week. I signed up for a free class, memoir writing—something they were offering at the library. And it was the oddest thing. I found I couldn't write my real life. I could only make things up. I felt afraid of telling a single fact, as though I couldn't be depended on to get it right. Finally, I thought, Well, you know where you *lived,* for God's sake. You know what the *house* where you grew up was like. And I'd start to write about it, but then I'd stop and I'd think, Wait. *Were* there trees along the boulevard in front? *Was* my bedspread blue? I talked to my therapist about this, week after week, and suddenly I realized where it was all coming from, all this self-doubt, all this censorship.

"We'd talked one day about the concept of shame, and I told her that every time I heard that word, I had a visceral reaction to it: I could feel my stomach clench, my heart start to race. She said, 'Well, let's explore that.' And I sat there on her couch and I all of a sudden felt this rush of something *awful* coming, this freight train of emotion. I just came completely apart, started bawling. And then I began remembering things that happened to me. Triggered memories, they call it. They just kept popping up."

I was quiet for a long time, thinking. Then I said, "I wish, for your sake, that I could remember her doing something like that. But I can't think of one time she ever behaved that way. Which is not to say I don't believe you, Caroline. I just don't remember anything."

"She didn't do the worst stuff in front of

you," Caroline said. "I know that. But what I wanted to know from you and Steve is if you remember . . . smaller things. General things. If you can, it will help me to keep going. I just want to know that you saw something too. Do you understand? I don't doubt what happened, but I seem to need something else to help me do something about it."

I leaned back on my elbows and stared up at the sky. It was getting dark out. Clouds were stretched thin as gossamer, and stars were appearing behind them. Whole galaxies above us, whole galaxies within us.

I thought back to our growing-up years, trying to remember a time when Caroline was purposefully slighted by my mother. But I really couldn't. I'd been aware of the fact that, after a certain point, Caroline's attitude toward my mother switched from idolatry to contempt. But that had happened with all of us when we went through adolescence; with Caroline, it had just been more dramatic—no surprise there. Finally, I said, "I guess I didn't pay much attention, Caroline."

Saying that, I suddenly wondered what it

really meant. Why was I so firmly en-
trenched in my own world? What went on in
our house that made me look so determinedly away from everything but my own
fantasies? Was it possible the shrink I saw
in college was at least partially right, that
something wrong in my family made me
seek comfort elsewhere? But couldn't
everyone look back at life as a child and
start blaming their parents for what was
wrong with them? Frankly, I was really,
really tired of that song.

"It's kind of hard, Caroline, trying to remember anything from so long ago. I mean,
stuff from my life alone, to say nothing of
yours. I remember specific moments, but
whole years are just . . . lost."

She nodded. "Yeah."

"But why do you need Steve's and my
corroboration anyway? You said you know
this happened."

"I guess it's that I need to feel I have allies
in my brother and my sister, that I'm not
alone in what I need to do. If I don't con-
front Mom—and Dad too, I guess—I'll never
get past all this. I have to tell them about
what I remember. And that it was wrong."

"Oh, God."

"Laura, you don't know.

"She came into my room one Saturday. I had just started third grade, and I was sitting at the window, looking out at the leaves. It was fall, and they were really beautiful. She asked me why I didn't go outside. I said I wanted to be in. I said, Look at the leaves, they're so pretty and they're dying. She got sort of impatient and started messing around with the stuff in my room, rearranging it. Then she said I had to go out, that I was just mooning around and there was no reason for it, it was a perfectly beautiful day. I said again I didn't want to, and I asked why the leaves had to die, why did things have to die, and she grabbed my arm and started pulling me out of my room. And I remember I yelled *help,* I yelled *help* really loud, and she just went berserk. She started slapping me and kicking me and saying to shut up, just shut *up.* And then she ran into her bedroom and slammed the door and started sobbing—I could hear her all the way in my room. I went and knocked at her door, and then I went in, and she was lying on her side holding a pillow up against her stomach. She said I made her do these things, why did I make her do these things?

I remember I tried to get on the bed beside her, I was so sorry, and she lifted up her head and said in this awful, low voice, '*Get out of here.*' I went back to my room and stayed until dinnertime, and when I came out it was like nothing happened."

"But . . . where was I that day?"

"You were gone somewhere," Caroline said. "Probably over at a friend's house; you were a good girl with a lot of friends. You were forever going over somewhere and baking with someone and then bringing home stuff for the family. Look what I made! Little Miss Martha."

I pictured myself standing in Sally Burke's kitchen, laughing and licking chocolate-chip cookie dough from beaters while Caroline sat at the edge of her bed staring at her hands, afraid to move. "Oh, Caroline. I don't see how you can stand any of us. I can't believe I was oblivious to all this. That we all were. Didn't anybody ever even—why didn't you tell Dad?"

She shook her head. "Well, as I told you, Mom had me convinced that the bad things she did to me were my fault. She truly did. I was so ashamed of the fact that there was something in me that made her behave in this terrible way. I knew she wasn't like that to you or Steve, so it had to be my fault. I did try to tell Dad one day, but it was useless. You know how it is; you can't say anything bad about Mom to Dad. I'm sure he thought I was making it up. He probably thought I'd gotten in trouble for something and had been mildly punished in some way or another, then had exaggerated wildly about what happened. I *was* prone to drama, as you recall."

I refrained from correcting the tense. "But . . . didn't you have marks or something?"

"I had bruises every now and then. But so did you. Only yours came from another place."

"Well, I just . . . I have to say, Caroline, if all that had happened to me, I think I'd just walk away from our parents. Cut off relations."

"Don't be so sure. I have a friend, a guy I met at my group counseling session. And once a month, on the first day of the month, he goes to see his father, who was remarkably abusive—both physically and emotionally. He goes even though he knows that every time it'll be like getting shot in the heart. His father insults him for a while and then basically ignores him. Eddie knows what he's headed for, but he can't stop going. And I understand why. It has to do with himself, what Eddie's giving *himself.*"

"But what *is* he giving himself? He's just sticking his finger into the light socket! There are such things as toxic parents."

"Yes, but . . . let me ask you something. Do you like your feet?"

I pulled my bare feet away self-consciously. I thought she knew that I hated my feet: I have little toes that look like cornichons, according to Pete. And that's a kind analogy. More like slugs, Anthony says. And my fat big toe curves over as though it's trying to commiserate with the little toe. "No."

"Ever had a pedicure?"

"No!"

"Why not? It could help."

"Because then I'd have to show someone my feet close up for a long time."

"Well, why don't you cut them off?"

"My feet?"

"Yeah."

I half smiled. "What are you talking about, Caroline?"

"You've always hated your feet. Why don't you just cut them off?"

Fine. I would play along. "I need them to stand on. To walk."

She nodded. "Exactly."

I sat still for a moment, then said, "All right. I get it."

"I need Mom to admit to what she did, so I can forgive her. Then I can stand. Then I can walk to where I need to go, if I may extend the metaphor."

"Right. I understand." I leaned back on my elbows. "You know one of the things that's really hard about this, Caroline? That you waited for so *long*."

"Yeah. I met a woman who told me about how she finally came to love her mother, who made our mother look like Mother Teresa. She said she was able to love her mother when she began to get more sure of herself. And you know when that was?"

"When?"

"When she was fifty-nine."

I laughed. "Okay. Okay. So what now, then? How do I help?"

"Well, you can start by trying to believe me."

"I do believe you!"

She stood, stretched. "I appreciate your saying that. But here's what I know. Partly you believe me, and partly you don't." I started to protest and she held up her hand to stop me. "That's why you asked me about marks."

I looked away. She was right.

Her voice softened. "It's okay. It's hard, I know. And I know this will all take time. Everything about it will take a long time. I just hope that in the end . . ."

"I hope so too, Caroline."

"We should go in before we get bit up any more."

"Let's go to the grocery store," I said.

"What do you need?"

"I want to help you get something *you* need: chips and dip. I figured we'd start small."

"I don't know if Rainbow is still open."

"I'll see." I went into the house and picked up the phone. "Hey, Caroline, you have messages on here."

"It's just Bill. He calls every night. I'll call him back later."

"He calls every night?"

"Yeah."

"Well, good. That's good, isn't it?"

Nothing.

"Caroline?"

"What."

"That's good, isn't it? That he calls every night?"

"Yeah," she said. "It's good."

I called information, then the grocery store. "They close in twenty minutes," I yelled.

Caroline came into the house, the screen door banging behind her. "Let's go!" It was the first time in so long that I'd seen her look happy. And of course it wasn't the food.

On the way back to my parents' house, I thought of all Caroline had told me. When our family sat down together at dinner on a random Tuesday night, was it possible she was recovering from some sort of horrible event only hours before? What had been held in her silences?

When I was a few blocks away, I turned off the radio. I wanted to think about how much I should tell my parents. I decided on as little as possible: I'd just say Caroline would be over tomorrow afternoon, that there were some things she would like to talk about with the immediate family. I had no idea what I'd do with the kids. As much as they like the fair, they don't like to go two days in a row. I'd have to ask Pete to take them somewhere. There was no reason for him to be around during all of this. I tried not to pay attention to the pinch of resentment I felt; this wasn't how our time here was supposed to go. We were supposed to have fun.

When I pulled into the driveway, I saw the dim figures of people sitting outside. It was Pete and the kids, arranged in an intimate little semicircle, waiting for the fireworks, I supposed. I greeted them, dropped my purse, and sat on the grass before them. I pulled my knees up to my chest, rested my forehead on top of them, and drew in a long breath. I could finally relax. I looked up, smiling.

"Where have you *been*?" Anthony asked.

"Why? Did you miss me?" I rose up to kiss the top of his head multiple times, just to annoy him. His head smelled good, a yeasty smell. "Awww, did you miss me?"

He frowned, looked away.

"Laura," Pete said.

I turned toward him. "Yeah?" Then, my smile disappearing, I said, "What?" And then, as he got out of his chair and started toward me, his face full of sadness, "Oh, my God."

12

When Pete and I had finally gotten around to making our wills, we'd talked about what we wanted done at our funerals. He'd wanted a straight service, something dignified; I wanted something looser. I'd wanted things read by friends and relatives that would entertain and inspire: essays by Annie Dillard, poetry by Mary Oliver. I'd wanted one quilt over me, another one draped over the coffin, and the one called "Water at Night," my pride and joy, the silver and black quilt that won first prize in a national competition—I'd wanted that quilt to be given away by a raffle drawing. When everyone filed out of the church, I'd wanted James Brown to be singing "I Feel Good."

"You don't want James *Brown,*" Pete had said, and I'd said, "Yes I do. I want people to think that's how it is, over yonder. That you feel good."

"Okay," he'd said, in that singsong way that meant *I think you're nuts.*

Of course when you plan your funeral, you do it thinking you won't really die. It's just a good exercise. You plan it in case you die.

You know your parents are going to die, but they are going to die later. They are go-ing to die *sometime.* But that time will not come until you no longer need them. While you still need them, or might need them, they will have the good taste and common courtesy not to leave. This was how I'd al-ways thought of it, I see now.

At my father's funeral I sat frozen, holding Pete's hand tightly and feeling absolutely nothing. The priest was standing at the pul-pit, sharing amusing anecdotes about my father so we could all remember we were here *not to mourn a death but to cele-brate a life.* Amid the sounds of sniffing

and discreet nose-blowing came appreciative chuckles—appreciative or obligatory, I
wasn't sure which.

Steve sat in the row ahead of us, Tessa
leaning into him. On his other side sat my
mother, dabbing at her eyes. At the end of
our row, Caroline sat next to Bill but at a
slight declarative distance from him. I
looked around the church, at the dull sheen
of old gold, the stained-glass windows. I
thought about a quilt I'd once made out of
jewel-colored douppioni silks, designed to
look like stained glass. I remembered a time
I'd sat beside my father when we went to
midnight mass. The decorations were so
beautiful, the music so rich, I'd begun to
quietly weep in awe and appreciation, and
my father, staring straight ahead, had
reached over to take my hand: *I know.* And
now the dam broke and I understood that it
was true; my father had died and I was sitting here at his funeral and he would never
take my hand again.

I remembered him reading to me when I
had the mumps, the same battered Little
Golden Book, over and over again. I remembered him bandaging my knee on a
day I fell off my bike, hugging me before I

left for college, walking me down the aisle on my wedding day, how his eyes filled with tears when he told Pete in as stern a voice as he could muster, "You take good care of her, now." I thought of riding high on his shoulders when I was three, him trying to teach me how to whistle, and how, when I learned, he'd given me a new dollar bill. I remembered the night someone stole my Halloween candy and I came home crying, and he went out for hours looking for some boy dressed as a skeleton. I remembered the first quilt show I had at a gallery, how he had come to the opening and walked up to everyone there, saying quietly, "Hi, how are you, I'm her father; she's my daughter; isn't she something?"

My chest heaved and a whimpering sound escaped that under other circumstances might have embarrassed me. But now, I didn't care about anything except the fact that my father had died and I had not been ready. I had not been done with him. I wanted him to come back for just half an hour, so I could say what I had saved up for another time. For later.

I thought, There was a *tag* tied to his toe.

I thought, His clothes were not folded

and put on the shelf inside the metal locker, they were tossed onto the bottom of it, and his blue shirt was turned inside out.

I thought, His glasses were on the otherwise empty nightstand, and his wallet was in the otherwise empty drawer, only I thought of it this way: His little glasses. His little wallet.

I thought, He didn't know, he had no idea, he was only trying to eat his tasteless hospital dinner thinking that tomorrow night he'd be home to watch television with my mother in the family room, his simple evening pleasure. And then his cup had fallen, and coffee had run from the side of his mouth, and despite everything they tried he was gone.

I squeezed Pete's hand tighter. I thought, *Don't ever leave me, let me go first.* From the corner of my eye I saw the knees of my children. They were so old now, not really children anymore. *Stop that,* I wanted to tell them. *Hold still.*

13

At my parents'—now my mother's—house, the living room was crowded with people who had come over after the funeral. I'd met so many strangers who knew my father, had talked to so many friends and relatives I'd known since I was a child, that I'd actually gotten hoarse. I went into the TV room, needing a break, and found Anthony sitting in my father's leather recliner, his knee bouncing wildly.

"Hi," I said.

"Hi." He didn't look at me. His knee slowed, stopped.

I sat in my mother's blue velvet

club chair. "How are you doing, sweet-heart?"

He shrugged.

"It's hard, huh?" I said. "Hard to realize that one minute he was just—"

"It's not that!"

"Oh." I sat still, waiting.

He looked at me, then quickly wiped a tear away. "It's not that he died. People *die.* It's . . . *this.* I mean, I think it's really gross, what's going on out there. People just . . . chewing their dumb sand-wiches and drinking and laughing. It's not a party! How come nobody's talking about Grandpa?"

"Well, some people are. Here and there. Some people are. But I think I know how you feel. When Great-grandma died, there was a lunch in the church basement after her funeral, and I remember looking around, thinking, This could be anything *but* a funeral."

"Exactly." He looked over at me. "A cele-bration for someone graduating high school or something. A birthday."

"Yes. But I see it differently. I think what this is, is people just needing to do some-thing, to keep going and not be alone. You know? What if these people didn't come back here? Then Grandma would be by herself. And she—"

"She wouldn't be alone! We're here!"

"Well, yes. We're here now. But we aren't going to be staying here. These people all live nearby."

The knee again. And then Anthony reached for the remote. "There's a good baseball game on. Why don't I just watch it?" He looked at me, eyebrows raised. "Okay?"

I didn't know if he was serious or not. "I suppose you could."

"I don't want to watch a game!"

"You could, though, and there would be nothing wrong with it. People . . . they have to find their own ways. Everybody has a different method of coping with grief, and no one way is better than another. You might *need* to watch a baseball game now. It might remind you of your normal life, of what you have to go back to. For Grandma . . . well, she needs to be reminded that people are around to help her. All these people 'eating their dumb sandwiches' will tell her that if she needs anything—"

"Yeah, and most of them won't even mean it!"

"Some of them might not. But others will." I leaned back and felt an edgy restlessness snaking through me. I needed to go outside. Later, I'd ask Pete to take a walk with me. I hadn't had a chance to be alone with him since we'd arrived, and that's what *I* needed. "It's like falling off a cliff, Anthony, when someone dies this suddenly. And these rituals we have, whatever they are—watching sports or having dinner parties, or . . . oh, I don't know, wearing a yellow tie every third Thursday— they provide some sort of support. You know what I mean? So you can watch baseball. Hannah can call her friends— Hannah *is* on the phone with Gracie, right now. And Grandma is in the kitchen peeling Saran Wrap off cold cuts and tossing salads and arranging cookies on platters instead of weeping in her darkened bedroom with the door closed. All of this—I don't know, maybe it forges a new neural pathway, almost. It helps you go on in this new situation. It teaches you how. Don't you think Grandma's heart is breaking? Of course it is. But does she honor Grandpa by collapsing into grief? Believe me, she'll do plenty of that. But for right now, I think it's better if she talks to people and accepts the gifts they can offer. No one is saying Grandpa's life didn't matter. They're just coming together to do what they can. They're providing some structure, some order, to a situation that feels out of control, especially to Grandma."

Anthony listened, biting at his lower lip. Then he stood up. "So what should I do? I'm sorry, I just don't feel like talking to strangers, answering all these dumb questions about how do I like North Dakota, I ought to play basketball, I'm so tall, blah, blah, blah. But I'd like to . . . should I maybe throw away the used paper plates?" He laughed in his harsh teenage way, embarrassed.

"I think that's a perfect thing to do."

He came over to me, put his hand on my shoulder. "And . . . are you okay, Mom? You know, I just realized . . . It was your dad!"

I smiled up at him. "I'm fine. You know what I'm mostly thinking? That I'm so lucky. To have had him, and to have you."

There, a hint of color in his face, his shoulders shifting off some discomfort. I wasn't allowed to show him much affection anymore, no matter how oblique it might be. When he was in second grade, I was allowed to kiss him before he left for school only in the coat closet, door closed. By the time he got to third grade, I got in trouble for even thinking about kissing him. Yet there are still nights when I sit at the side of his bed before he goes to sleep and we talk for a long time—about nothing, really. He lies stretched out under the covers with his hands linked behind his head, smelling of shampoo, his bedside lamp giving him a halo. "O'Conner thinks he's set for a basketball scholarship," he'll say. "Huh!" I'll say. "A scholarship! That's great." And I'll be thinking, *You've become a man, right in front of my eyes. I can't bear the thought that you'll leave soon.*

"You want me to bring you anything?" Anthony asked. "Want a sandwich or something? Cookies?"

"No, thanks. I'm fine."

Just after he left the room, Caroline came in. She sat in my father's chair, looked over at me, and sighed. "Well. That's that."

"Yeah," I said sadly.

"I mean, now nobody will ever believe me."

"Oh, my God. You—" I stared at her.

"What, Laura?"

I shook my head, got up from my chair, and walked out.

In the living room, I caught sight of Hannah sitting alone on the sofa, and I went to sit beside her, took her hand.

"How's Gracie?"

"Fine. She said she misses me."

"Ah. That's nice. It's nice to be missed, huh?"

"I miss Grandpa already. And I feel so sorry. Like for how I didn't do stuff for him."

"He adored you. Do you know that?"

A moment. Then she nodded.

"You did a lot for him by just being you."

"No, I didn't. I should have done way more things. Like every time we were leaving, he used to say, 'Drop me a line, kiddo!' And I hardly ever wrote him. Only about four or five times in my whole life!"

"I guess none of us ever does all that we might have for one another. But I know this: You were a wonderful granddaughter, and you brought great joy to his life. When you were born and he came to see you, I had to practically pry you off him. He sat with you in that big ugly rocking recliner we used to have and talked to you and told you jokes and insisted that you understood every word he said. 'She likes me best,' he kept saying. I think it made Dad a little jealous."

Hannah smiled, looked up at me.

"And when he said, 'Drop me a line,' what he meant was, Keep in touch. Which you certainly did."

"One time when I was six I called him when you weren't even home."

"Did you? What did you talk about?"

"Hamsters. I wanted one, and you wouldn't get me one. He told me"—she covered her mouth, started to giggle—"I still remember, exactly. He said, 'Oh, no, you don't want one of them; they eat their young. You don't want to be watching mama hamster spreading mustard on her baby, do you?' It was *weird*! *Do* they eat their young?"

"I have heard they do, sometimes. See how wise I was not to let you have one?"

Hannah shrugged. "I don't know. But anyway. I guess it's good he died right away, right?"

"Yes, for his sake."

"I wonder if he knew he was dying."

"I don't know, honey." I looked around the crowded room: men talking to men, women talking to women, mostly. "Don't know."

"What will Grandma do now?"

I looked over at my mother, standing next to Elaine Pinkers, the young woman who lives next door. My mother was talking animatedly. She could have been the perfect hostess except that she looked . . . puzzled.

"I don't know what Grandma will do. We'll have to see." Condo, I was thinking. Don't all widows move to condos and make container gardens on their balconies? Go out to lunch with friends and bring home leftovers that they eat for dinner? I'd have to come back and help her move at some point. And I'd tell Steve he had to help—no bowing out of this one.

"Aunt Caroline was crying in the bathroom," Hannah said.

"Was she?"

"Uh-huh. I came in by accident, and she was sitting on the edge of the bathtub crying real hard."

"Well, I suppose we'll all be doing some of that. But it's okay to cry, right?"

"Right. Mom?"

"Yes?"

"Don't take this wrong, okay? But when will we be going home?"

"Don't take *this* wrong. But as soon as we possibly can."

After everyone left and my mother went to bed, Pete and I took our walk. At a school playground a few blocks away, we sat on a bench holding hands, saying nothing. When I started to cry, he pulled me closer, kissed the top of my head. "I'm so sorry."

I nodded, gulped back sobs.

"You want to stay for a while? I can take the kids home, and you could stay and help her figure out what she's going to do."

"I want to go home, though."

"Well, that's what we'll do, then."

"But you're right, I should stay. And not just to help Mom. I need to help Caroline. She's—oh, Pete, she told me the most awful things."

I repeated everything Caroline had said and waited for his reaction. It was not what I had expected. He simply nodded. "Sounds like you do need to be here for a while."

"But . . . don't you find this incredible?"

"Do you believe her?"

"I'm trying to, but I don't know. I can't imagine that these things went on in the house I lived in. That neither Steve nor I knew anything about it. I know my mother's odd about some things. And she's narcissistic—although any woman as beautiful as she was has that problem, it seems to me. But I can't imagine her doing such things."

"Okay."

"What does that mean?"

He looked at me, said nothing.

"What do you mean, 'Okay'?"

"I guess I mean the truth could be either or in between. And that I know this is bad, but it's not as shocking to me as it is to you." He turned toward me. "You know, I never told you this; I never wanted to. But maybe I should."

I waited, then finally said, "What?"

"I just . . . I don't want it to change the way you feel about my family."

"*What,* Pete?"

He leaned back against the bench. "You know why I hate swearing so much?"

"No. Why do you?"

"Because when we were really young, my father used to . . . when my brother and I did something wrong, Subby used to take us out to the garage and yank our pants down and beat the hell out of us. And the whole time he did it, he'd be swearing; it was the only time I ever heard him swear. He did this for a few years, and then he stopped. He just stopped. I don't know why. I don't know if he came to his senses or got in trouble or got some help or what happened. He just stopped."

"Wait. What about that story you told me once? When he pretended to hit you?"

"That's true. That was after."

"So when he hit you those other times, your mother knew?"

"She knew."

"Well, this is just . . . I'm astonished! It doesn't fit with them."

"It doesn't fit with what you know. Knew."

I swallowed hard, said nothing. But then, "You know, Pete, my dad just died. Why did you tell me that? I don't have room for anything else. Why did you tell me that?"

He put his arms around me, spoke softly into my ear. "Because something is not

everything. You know? And because nobody knows what goes on in other families,
because families lie about themselves to
other people. Not only to other people but
to one another. And to themselves."

I pulled away from him. "We don't! Our
family doesn't!"

"Well. Maybe to a lesser degree."

"What do you mean! What do we lie
about in our family?"

"All right. I want to say two things. Three
things. One, we don't any of us always say
what we really feel, do we? Not Hannah, not
Anthony, not you or me. And aren't we lying
to each other in that way?

"Two, we're not finished with one another
as a family, and I hope we never will be. But
things will come up. We will disappoint
each other, we might—things will come up,
that's all. People living with people makes
for conflict. The truth is, we're not such a
peaceful species. But the good part about
conflict is that if you get through it you're
stronger.

"Now. Three. Your dad did just die. And I
want to help you. I want to make things
easier for you. So let's talk about how to do
that. And Laura? Sweetheart? I love you."

I took his hand, stared out at the jungle gym, the boxes-within-boxes pattern of it. Because of the angle. If you looked at it one way, you didn't see them. If you looked another way, you did. "I love you too," I said. The words seemed so small, a cardboard shield.

We sat without talking for a long time, and then I said, "I want to go home tomorrow and get some things. I want my work. Then I'll come back here and sort this all out."

Maggie once told me about a friend of hers who was diagnosed with ovarian cancer. "She only went to the doctor because she was having diarrhea," Maggie said. "She thought it was from a trip she'd taken to Mexico. The doctor told her she had about six months to live, at the outside. She said at first it was like she was lying under a pile of bricks. For about a week, all she did was lie on the sofa and cry. But then she got up and got going again. About a month before she died, she told me that something really good had come of this diagnosis: It had forced a reconciliation between her and a daughter with whom she'd not spoken in years. She said if it hadn't been for the cancer, she might have died without ever saying anything she needed so much to say, without ever saying anything true. I told her, 'But you can't be saying it was worth it, to have gotten this!' And she said yes, that was what she was saying. I said, 'Well, I have to tell you, I find that hard to believe. Surely there's a way other than catastrophe to learn to speak the truth.' And she said, 'Maybe there is. But I would never have found it. In the end, what does it matter how you find the thing you need most? Or even when? Just so long as you find it, and you can die in peace.' " Maggie looked over at me, her eyes full of tears. "But it does matter when," she said, and I said I knew. And then Maggie suddenly reached over to hug me so fiercely it hurt. "We're so lucky," she said, and I nodded into her shoulder. "It's kind of scary to be so lucky," she said, and I nodded again. I knew exactly what she meant. Sometimes being lucky is only waiting for a fall.

14

It was such a different car ride, going back. No fighting in the backseat. Only a respectful silence, occasionally punctuated by a neutral observation or a request to have the radio tuned to another station. I looked out the window and thought about the three of us siblings lined up on my parents' bed that morning, being offered various things of my father's by my mother, she in her bright, brittle way pulling open his drawers, rummaging through his closet. Her eyes shining with tears that she clearly wanted not to acknowledge. I'd taken only his hankies, his initials embroidered in navy blue in one corner. Steve had taken his watch and his cuff links—Steve is the only man I know who still wears cuff links—and his stamp collection. Caroline took a photo of him that was taken just before he married my mother. He stood beside an old jalopy, his foot up on the bumper, smiling broadly. Everything else that my mother had offered—his sweaters, his pipes, a bathrobe he'd never worn—we had refused. I think it was just too early. None of us kids had been ready to put the kind of seal on his death that taking his things would do.

Whereas Steve and Caroline had tiptoed around each other, not speaking, not even looking at each other, she and I had restored an uneasy truce before I left; I told her I would return within the week, and that I'd call her as soon as I arrived back at my mother's house. Now, only a few miles from home, I regretted having made that promise. I felt I needed more time to reclaim my own life.

When we pulled into the driveway, I saw Maggie out in her yard, two houses down. She waved, smiling, then walked over to us. "How was it?" she asked as I got out of the car. Then, her smile disappearing, she said, "Oh. Jeez. Bad trip, huh?"

Pete and the kids greeted Maggie and then headed into the house, leaving us alone. "My dad died," I said.

She stared at me for a moment, trying to understand. "Just . . . now? While you were there?"

I nodded.

"Oh, my God." She hugged me, then stepped back to search my face. "I'm so sorry. Doug said you'd called. But I didn't have your number to call you back."

"I wasn't calling about that. That was before he even . . . I was calling about something else." I looked at our house and saw Pete passing in front of the living room window. He'd be checking everything out, making sure nothing had happened in our absence. The kids were undoubtedly ensconced in their rooms, reconnecting to their real selves as opposed to the hampered individuals they became when they were constantly in the presence of parents and relatives. *Anthony lite,* my son called himself in such situations.

"We can talk later," Maggie said. "You need to go in?"

"Actually, I think I need to go out. Can you?"

"Let me just go and tell Doug, and then I'll meet you back here. I'll pick you up. Where do you want to go?"

"I don't know."

"Well, alcohol or sugar?"

"Salty alcohol."

"Goldie's?" we said together, because of their famous nachos and margaritas. And laughed. It was so good to laugh. I felt as though I too were reentering my legitimate self.

I went into the house to tell Pete I was going out with Maggie, and he told me there was a message on the machine. My mother. Saying that she'd like to come and stay with us for a while. She wanted to fly in the next day.

"No," I said.

"*No?* Well, what are you going to tell her?"

"I'm going to tell her no."

"Laura."

"I said I'd go there!"

"She wants to come here. Do you really—"

"I'm going out with Maggie. I'll call her

when I come back." I looked at the pile of mail and newspapers on the kitchen table. Even this seemed insurmountable. "I just need to go out for a while, Pete."

I went upstairs to tell Hannah I was leaving. She was sitting on her bed, talking on the phone. "Hold on," she said, and looked at me expectantly.

"I'm going out for a bit with Maggie. Okay?"

"Yeah. Can I go out for dinner and shopping for school clothes with Gracie?"

I'd forgotten all about school. It started in three days. "Yes, that would be great, in fact. Dad will give you some money. But remember—"

"I know," she said, rolling her eyes. "Don't spend too much on one thing. And get things that mix and match."

"That's right."

Next I went to Anthony's door, knocked. Nothing. I knocked again, heard him say, "Come in."

He was on his bed, *Sports Illustrated* lying across his belly.

"I just wanted to tell you I'm going out, okay? Dad will take care of dinner."

"Yeah, okay." It was defensive, the way he said this.

"Something wrong, Anthony?"

"No!"

I moved over to his bed, sat beside him. "What's up?"

"Nothing, I just . . . I heard you in the kitchen, with Dad. About Grandma."

I tried to remember exactly what I'd said, how I'd said it. "Yeah?"

"I don't know, I just think it's kind of screwed up that you don't want her to come here. It's probably pretty hard for her to be in that house. Like, everywhere she looks, she sees Grandpa. Maybe she just needs to get away."

"Well, Anthony."

He waited.

"It's just that there are a lot of things . . . I mean, I said I'd go there and help her."

"But maybe she—"

"You know what, sweetheart? Maggie's waiting for me. I'll talk to you about this later. I appreciate that you're concerned for Grandma. I do. But I—"

"Go!" he said. "Who's stopping you?" He returned to his magazine. I stood there for a moment, then headed downstairs. What was in my head were Pete's words: *We don't any of us always say what we really feel, do we?* It occurred to me to go back upstairs and tell Anthony the truth. But I didn't know it yet.

Goldie's was nominally half bar, half restaurant. But you could sit at the bar and have everything on the dinner menu, and you could sit in the restaurant for drinks only. Frank, the owner, was an easygoing guy; everything was okay with him. He had a mixed menu, everything from enchiladas to tandoori chicken to pecan-crusted catfish. Normally, you have to be wary of restaurants like that because, when they don't specialize in anything, nothing is good. But at Goldie's, everything was delicious. Frank once explained to me that his wife, Goldie, who died suddenly at age thirty-three, "never met a cuisine she couldn't conquer." Dinner at their house had always been an adventure; Frank never knew what he'd be coming home to, and he liked that. He'd been a stockbroker before she died; afterward, he decided to open a restaurant in her honor. He knew nothing about the business except that people out to eat were looking for variety and a really good meal, and that was exactly what he provided. He was sixty-one now, a good-looking man with thick gray hair and a stunning physique—he worked out every day to compensate for what he drank every night. I suppose Frank is an alcoholic, but he's an elegant and a sympathetic one. He started drinking seriously only after Goldie died; she'd been everything to him. They never had children, so Frank has fashioned a family out of his customers. He makes it his business to know—at least by name—anyone who comes in more than once.

So it was that when Maggie and I walked in, Frank, seated at the bar, called out, "Hey, Laura! How was the fair?"

"Oh, it was great." I looked over at Maggie, and without saying anything she agreed with me. Now was not the time.

"Bar or restaurant?" Frank asked. Then, reaching into the menu bin, "Late lunch, early dinner, or just drinks?"

"Loaded nachos and margaritas in the restaurant?" I said.

"You got it." Frank threw the menus back

in the bin and led us to the back area that
served as the restaurant. It was five-thirty,
and we were the only ones in the place. "Sit
anywhere you want," Frank told us, "and I'll
put the order in for you."

I sat at a corner table and folded my
hands tightly together on the white table-
cloth. "So."

"Did you bring Kleenex?" Maggie asked.

"For what?"

She reached in her purse, took out a
pack of tissues. "Here."

"I'm not going to cry."

"Okay."

"I'm not!"

She put the Kleenex back in her purse.
Then she leaned forward, smiled a small
smile. "It was awfully sudden, wasn't it?"

"Yeah. Stroke. He was in the hospital for
a little stroke. And then he had a big one."

A young waitress appeared, using both
hands to balance the tray holding our
drinks. "*Here* we go!" she said, her loud
cheerfulness an attempt to compensate for
her insecurity. As far as I was concerned,
her tip had just gone up threefold. She very
carefully set our drinks before us, the pink
tip of her tongue peeking out of the corner

of her mouth. "And!" She looked brightly at us. "Anything else?"

"We ordered nachos," Maggie said. "Loaded."

"Uh-huh, Frank told me. But . . . anything else?"

"We're fine for now," I said. "We'll let you know if we need anything more."

"Okay. Oh! My name's Paula? And I'll be your server?"

"Okay, Paula."

I needed to make a suggestion for Frank's COMMENTS box. *Hey, Frank. Please be the only restaurant left that does not encourage your waitstaff to form intimate relationships with the customer.*

"So he died instantly, huh?" Maggie said. "I guess that's good. That's how my dad died too—a stroke. Only he didn't die right away, he was in a coma for a couple of days. It gave me some time to say some things. Sort of. I mean, I sat by his bed and said some things. And then—well, this is sort of embarrassing to admit—I was trying to be all New Age, and I said, 'It's okay, Daddy. You can go. Just go toward the light.' And my mom leaped out of her chair and rushed over and said, 'Oh, no, Tom, don't go! Don't leave me!' And she grabbed hold of him and started sobbing, and I stood there feeling just terrible."

I held up my glass, clinked it with Maggie's in an ironic toast, and had a long sip. "So what did you tell him?"

"My dad?"

"Yeah."

She looked away, watching Frank put a couple of tables together so he could seat a large group of people who had just come in. "I told him—oh, you know—thank you for helping me sell Girl Scout cookies door to door, for trying to teach me to catch a football, for telling me I was the prettiest girl in the yearbook when we both knew I wasn't. And I told him I loved him, you know, that I'd always . . . that he'd always be—" Our eyes filled with tears, and she dug in her purse to get us each a tissue. "Nothing covers it. No matter what you say. So don't feel bad that you didn't get a chance."

"But I do feel bad. I really do." I wiped at my eyes again.

"This will take some time, sweetheart. There's always going to be an ache. Our dads are—"

"I know." I started crying harder, making

noise now, and looked at Maggie, panicked.

"You want me to quick change the
subject?"

I nodded.

"Okay. Okay." She stood up, turned her
back to me, and said over her shoulder,
"Does my ass look like two watermelons in
these pants?"

I blew my nose. "Yes."

"No, no, don't hold back, just tell me the
truth."

She sat down, laughing, and we accepted the nachos our new friend Paula
had brought over. I ate one, two, and then
looked around the room, trying to steady
myself. "Before my dad died, my sister Caroline told me some things about my
mother."

"Okay, but first: *Does* my ass look like
two watermelons?"

"No. . . . *Hams,* maybe."

"Oh, I see. Thanks a lot. I feel much better now. So. What things?"

I took another drink and began.

* * *

Much later, Maggie and I were sitting in the bleachers of the high school football stadium, where we'd come to talk after Goldie's closed. The stars were so clear; constellations stood out as plainly as star maps. I squinted at my watch. "Whoa, it's two-thirty!"

"Will Pete worry?"

"No. He'll go to bed. How about Doug?"

"He'll worry a little, but that's all right."

I stood, a bit unsteady. I didn't know how much I'd drunk, but it was much more than usual. "We should go."

She took hold of my hand, pulled me down. "In a minute. I want to tell you something first."

"What?"

"Just this story, about . . . well, I used to stay with an aunt and uncle every summer. My family would go to visit them because they lived on a lake—in fact, the whole extended family would come up and find cottages and use their house as headquarters. But I stayed in the house. They had a daughter my age, and I slept on a cot in her room. I loved that family, especially my Uncle Harold. He was handsome, and funny, and so kind. But one summer when I was nine, he spanked me—grabbed me by the arm and swatted me maybe five, six times. He did it in front of other people, I remember; that was one of the worst things, it was so embarrassing. We were in the hallway, but there were a bunch of relatives in the living room who could see us. The front door was open; it was a beautiful day. I remember a breeze that smelled like water, I remember the cotton ball they had bobby-pinned on the screen to keep the flies away, I remember the red shorts I was wearing with this striped shirt with spaghetti straps that tied over my shoulders and the straps hurt that day because I was sunburned. I remember all that. But I don't know why he spanked me, I cannot for the life of me remember why. It was just that one time, but it devastated me. I never wanted to stay with them again. I felt afraid of him; I just saw him as a completely different person."

"Meaning what? That Caroline suffered one little thing and blew it all out of proportion?"

"Well . . . is it possible? Does it make sense to you that that might have happened? Perhaps . . . a few times?"

"I don't know. Maybe."

"I mean, I never changed my mind about that uncle. Even now when I see him I feel a little afraid. And he's just this little stooped-over gray-haired guy. Last year, at a family picnic, I was sitting by him and I all of a sudden said, 'Do you remember the time you spanked me?' And he said, 'No. When did I do that?' And I knew he really didn't remember, and there was no point in bringing it up. I don't know why I *did* bring it up."

"You probably wanted him to apologize."

"I don't think it was that, really. I think I wanted to stop being afraid of him. You know?"

"Oh, Maggie. What should I do? If I let my mother come and stay with me, I betray Caroline. If I tell Mom not to, I betray her at a time when she's really hurting."

"Tell her to come," Maggie said. "Let her be with your family. Then you go and see Caroline. Let her finish."

I sighed deeply.

"Just an idea."

"It's a good idea. I could get together with Caroline and Steve—he's still in town, visiting some of his old high school friends. Maybe if she can just finish saying all she wanted to say, if we can both say we *support* her." I rolled my eyes.

"Would Steve come?"

"Yeah, I think he would. For a few hours or so, anyway. He would if I asked him. I could tell him he needs to come and help Caroline and me do things in the house. Then we could kind of ease into it. I think it's important that Caroline talk to him too."

"I'll cover for you with the kids. Tell them to come over if they need anything. I can work from home better than I can work in the office, anyway. I only go to the office for the doughnuts."

I kissed her forehead. "Oh, Maggie. Thank you. What would I do without you?"

"Let's go home," Maggie said. "You're getting a little sentimental here."

We walked across the field with our arms linked. The only sound was our footsteps, walking over grass grown stiff and strawlike in the absence of rain. I watched the fireflies, their little lights appearing, disappearing, appearing, disappearing.

When I slid into bed beside Pete, I had not exfoliated or washed or toned my face. I had not flossed or brushed my teeth or shoved the proxi-brush between them, or rubber-tipped my gums or scraped my tongue. I had not put on my five-billion-dollar-an-ounce moisturizer that undoubtedly did nothing that Vaseline couldn't. I had not delicately pulled up the flab on my neck and then looked at myself from various angles, sadly considering plastic surgery. I had not taken my gingko biloba in an effort to help my failing memory. A friend of mine recently said about gingko biloba, "I think whatever-that-stuff-is-called works great. I just keep forgetting to take it." Another friend told me about a time she'd answered her cell phone and told her girlfriend, who was the caller, that she was in the parking lot of her doctor's office, getting ready to go in for an appointment, but she was early; she had some time to talk. They chatted for a while and then the woman happened to look down into her purse at the empty carrier for her cell phone. She told her friend, "Dammit, I lost my cell phone." Wait. It gets worse. The friend says, "Well, let's retrace your steps."

So I had not done any of my usual nightly routine and it felt wonderful. I wondered why I cluttered my life so much. I felt so free: I had bothered only to remove my sandals and my pants and to lie down on what was approximately my side of the bed—which felt suddenly like a boat on an angry sea. I put one foot on the floor, and things stopped moving.

"What time is it?" Pete asked.

I looked at the bedside clock and then spoke with great precision—as well as good cheer, I thought; I sounded really very cheerful. "One after three!"

Pete raised himself up on one elbow and looked over at me. "Oh, boy, you're in great shape. Maggie drove, right?"

"Yesh." The roof of my mouth was numb. I touched my lips experimentally. Some feeling there. The face of my dentist, Dr. Paine (I know; he knows; we all know) appeared in my head, his green goggles and paper mask, his curly black hair. *Numb yet, Laura?* No. Not yet.

"Did Maggie drink as much as—"

"No! Jesus—oops! Sorry."

He turned on his bedside lamp.

I shaded my eyes, squinted at him. "What. Are you mad?"

"No. I think you deserved a night out." He turned out the light again.

"Pete?"

"Yeah."

"Tell me a memory."

"I'm tired, Laura. Come on."

"I need to, though. I mean, I need you to." I turned to face him, felt dizzy, and turned back. "I'll tell *you* one."

Nothing. But he hadn't gone back to sleep; I could tell from his breathing.

"Once I got sent to the principal's office for making fun of the math teacher's chin. Which was this huge double chin, like a purse. Mrs. Menafee. Your turn."

Pete groaned. "I don't have one, Laura."

"Yes, you do. Tell me. We've never missed a night, Pete."

He turned on the light again. "Are you all right?"

I shaded my eyes with the pillow. "Yesh."

He gently pulled the pillow away from me. He was wide awake now. "Did you tell Maggie? About Caroline?"

"Uh-huh. We talked about it for a long time. A loooooong time."

"What did she say?"

I took back the pillow, covered my eyes again. "Turn off the light, okay?"

I heard the click of the switch, and then Pete said, again, "What did she say?"

Suddenly, my spirits fell and I was exhausted. I plumped the pillow, arranged it carefully under my head. "She has an idea. I want to talk to you about it. But tomorrow. Tell me a memory and let's go to sleep. A short memory. Not sad."

He lay flat, thought for a moment, and then said, "Okay. Once, I ran away. And the only thing in my suitcase was salami sandwiches."

"How old were you?"

"Eighteen."

I giggled. "Come on."

"I'm serious. I thought I'd figure out the rest later. I was walking to the bus station when Subby found me."

"What did he do?"

"We went to a park and ate some sandwiches and then he took me home."

"What did Rosa do?"

"Smacked me on the back of the head and then hugged me and then made me something to eat."

I thought of Rosa in her apron, weak in

the knees with relief, hitting the head of the son she was so happy to see. I wondered how often it was transmogrified love that made for the worst lashings-out. Something needled at me, making me wake up a little more. "How were the kids tonight?"

"I hardly saw Hannah. She came back with some clothes. And some hair . . . semen."

"What?"

"Well, that's what it looks like. You know, gel, whatever. Hair goop."

"Hmm. She's getting more and more interested in the way she looks. What style clothes did she get?"

"I don't know—she'll show you tomorrow. Anthony and I went and got steaks at Mc-Mannus's."

"How was he?"

"Anthony? Fine. Why?"

"Was he mad at me?"

"No. Why?"

"He thinks my mother should come and stay here."

Silence.

"Pete?"

"Yeah?"

"You do too?"

"Go to sleep, Laura. We'll talk tomorrow."

"Okay, but my today thing? Maggie wants another baby."

"Are you serious?"

"She isn't going to, she just *wants* one."

"Oh. Well, me too. That's my today thing. Okay? Good night."

"You want another baby?" I saw myself in a rocking chair, looking down at my new baby. With my old neck. "You want a *baby*?"

"Sure. But not really."

I lay still for a while, then said, "I'm so glad to be home."

Nothing.

"Pete?"

A deep snore. I closed my eyes and hoped I could sleep late.

It was not to be. At a little before five, I heard Hannah in the bathroom, moaning. I got out of bed and found her sitting doubled over on the edge of the tub. I knelt down beside her. "Hannah? What's wrong?"

She pushed her hair out of her eyes,

looked up at me, and her expression instantly changed. "What happened to you?"

"What do you mean?"

"What *happened* to you?"

"Nothing."

"You look . . . look how you look!"

I went to the mirror, turned quickly away. Then I knelt beside Hannah again. "I'm just . . . I didn't wash my face last night."

She stared at me, considering. Then she said, "I have cramps so bad. Why do we have to get cramps on top of having to have stupid periods?"

"I don't know. Maybe to practice for childbirth."

"And *that* hurts way more than this!"

"You forget all about it, though," I said, perpetuating the lie in the time-honored tradition. I went over to the medicine chest and opened it, surveyed the contents.

"I just did."

"What?"

"I just took something."

"What did you take?"

"Advil."

"Okay. So, go on back to bed. I'll get the heating pad for you. I'll lie down with you."

She headed out of the bathroom, saying

over her shoulder, "Mom? No offense, but could you, like, brush your teeth?"

I brushed my teeth, washed my face, took a couple of Advil myself, and then went to the linen closet for the heating pad. This is a sign, I was thinking. I can't go anywhere. My kids need me. This is a clear message: You're needed here more than there.

I plugged in the heating pad, gave it to Hannah, and lay down beside her. "Poor baby."

"What?" Her voice was muffled, miserable—her head was buried under her pillow.

"I said, 'Poor baby.' Ish a drag, huh?"

She lifted her pillow, looked over at me. "Are you drunk?"

I said nothing.

"Mom! Are you *drunk*?"

"Oh, not so much."

"I can't believe you're drunk! Gross!"

I sobered up to the best of my ability, concentrated mightily on my articulation. "I had too much to drink. That is true. But I am here to offer you comfort nonetheless. I know how much it can hurt when you get bad cramps."

She lay back down. I was marginally forgiven. "Yeah. What do boys get? They don't get *anything.*"

"Oh, of course they do."

"What?"

"They get . . . blamed for the sins of their fathers."

"What do you mean?"

"People still call men pigs, even though they're so much better than they used to be. You know. Think how it would feel to be called that."

She considered this. "It's better than cramps. I really get them bad, Mom."

"I know, sweetheart. I used to, too. Once, when I was your age, I got them in school and I took some Midol that a friend gave me. And I think I took too many or something, because I really flipped out."

"Why? What happened?"

"I don't know. I just got . . . weird. I went in the bathroom and was sitting on the floor—I remember I was wearing my Girls' Madrigals uniform, this awful green jumper, because we had a performance that afternoon. Anyway, I was sitting there and I was really hurting and someone went and got the nurse and I just went *nuts* on her. I was awful . . . wouldn't tell her my name, wouldn't let her help me."

"Why?" Hannah leaned up on an elbow, stared intently at me.

"I honestly don't know."

"So what happened?"

"The principal came. Then the nurse called my mother and told her I was not co-operating with her, I was behaving very oddly, and I had mistreated her, and Grandma came and got me."

"Was she mad?"

"No, she wasn't mad." I remembered her driving me home, silent. Not in anger but in a kind of complicity—she'd reached over and touched my knee, smiled. Tucked me in my bed when I got home, brought me a heating pad and a drink of blackberry brandy, which was her cure for cramps.

Hannah lay flat, the heels of her hands pushing against the heating pad. I used to do that too—as though it would push the heat through to displace the pain. "That's bizarre that you did that," she said, yawning.

"I know."

"Why'd you tell me that story?"

I laughed. "I don't know. I just remembered it."

"Okay, I'm going back to sleep. Don't wake me up even if I sleep till noon." She turned away from me.

I pulled the covers up over her shoulder. Then I lay back down and stared at the ceiling, too awake now to sleep any longer.

It is Steve and me, sitting cross-legged on the living room floor on a sunny afternoon, our heads bent together over a game of Monopoly. We are about six and ten, happily engrossed, both of us smiling, he because he's learning a "big kid" game, me because I am winning, no doubt—I almost never lost at Monopoly, no matter who I played. In the background, Caroline lies on the sofa in her pajamas. She has the chicken pox. She is clutching her big yellow teddy bear to her breast, craning her neck to try to see the game board. I remember that Caroline named the bear Hope, and we all thought it was so weird. Hope has the chicken pox too: red construction-paper dots, which Caroline carefully cut out and Scotch-taped onto him. While Steve and I sit playing the game with our backs to her, she takes what consolation she can from something she created. I remember her telling my mother that day that her throat hurt, the chicken pox were in her throat, and my *mother telling her not to be ridiculous. Years later, when Hannah got chicken pox and I took her to the pediatrician, he looked in her throat and said, "Yup."*

15

"You don't have to drive," I told my mother. "It's fine for you to fly. You won't need a car here. You don't like to drive long distances. You don't like to drive *short* distances!" Silently, I added, *And I am not going to come and get you and bring you here.*

"But I'll be there for a whole week," she said. "And you'll be working, and the kids are going to go back to school. . . . What if I want to go out somewhere? I don't want to leave you without a car."

"You can take it anytime. I don't really use it that much." I didn't want to tell her I was going to her house the day after she arrived here.

It was a rainy Monday morning. Just before I called my mother, I spoke to Caroline and Steve, both of whom agreed to meet me at our mother's house on Wednesday afternoon, presumably to talk about what to do with the place—Mom had always said she wouldn't want to live there alone. Whether she still felt that way, I didn't know, but I wasn't going to ask now. Steve had been a little put out. I'd awakened him from a sound sleep, and he had been intending to go home today. But he agreed, finally, after I convinced him he might as well take care of this now instead of having to fly back later. He had also agreed to pick me up at the airport. That way I could work on him a bit before he saw Caroline.

Thunder boomed so loudly I could feel it in my chest. The rain, coming in at an angle, fell in sheets against the windows. I couldn't believe the storm hadn't awakened the kids. I wanted to get off the phone—I'd heard you shouldn't use portables in such weather. I got a brief little vision of a cartoon death, a jagged bolt of lightning coming from the phone into my brain, my hair standing on end, my eyes turned spirally, and the toes of my shoes curled up. "I've got to go, Mom," I said. "I'll see you tomorrow."

I hung up the phone, went over to the coffeemaker to fill my mug, and sat at the table with Pete. "Here we go."

He looked up at me briefly and returned to the business section of the newspaper.

"I feel bad leaving when school's just starting."

"They'll be fine," Pete said. "They don't need us anymore."

"Yes, they do!"

"Not that way. Anyway, I'll be here. And Maggie always helps."

I reached for the front section of the paper, scanned the headlines. "Why don't they ever lead with good news?"

"Because people pay more attention to bad news."

"No, they don't. That's what you always say. It isn't true!"

He put down the newspaper. "You want to fight, Laura? Do you need to fight?"

I said nothing, blinked once, twice.

"What are you so mad about?"

"I'm not." I started reading the paper, then stopped. "I'm *not.* I just . . . don't want to do this. I want to stay home and work.

I've got work to do. A family to care for. I want to live my own life, not try to straighten out someone else's."

"She's your sister!"

"I don't even know what that means."

He stared at me, half smiling, *Are you kidding?*

"Well, I *don't* know. She wasn't normal. We didn't have a sisterly relationship, you know that. She . . . come on, this is a kid who used to tell me she could talk to dead people, okay? Not for creepy fun. She meant it."

Pete walked over to the sink, rinsed out his cup, and put it in the dishwasher. Pointedly remained silent.

"What?" I said, my back to him.

"Nothing."

I turned around. "Pete. What?"

"If it were Maggie having trouble . . ."

"Yeah? What, would I go out of my way to help her? Of course! But you know what? I don't know if I buy into the *It's your family, you've got to* thing. Maybe sometimes you make a family out of other people."

Pete came over to the table and sat down again. "You may have more in common with

other people, Laura. But you have your biological family for life, right or wrong."

"Well, I know that. But does that
mean—?"

"Yes." He looked at his watch and got up.
"I've got to go. I'll see you tonight."

"Wait!"

He turned around, a little impatient, I saw,
so I said, "Never mind." I stood at the window to watch him drive away and then I
went upstairs to shower. After that, I'd go
into the basement, to my sewing room, to
think about color and texture and patterns
that have nothing to do with personalities.
Only, of course they do. I remember Anthony once asking me, when he was maybe
six, "If you could understand *everything*
about just one thing, wouldn't you understand everything about everything? Because of how everything is all tied up
together? And that's why nobody understands anything all the way except
God?"

I turned on the fluorescent overhead in my
studio and looked around. What anticipa-
tory pleasure I was enjoying already! There

was my machine, recently cleaned and oiled and ready to go, all but transforming itself now into a metallic beckoning finger. There were my rotary cutters, lined up in order of size. There was the wooden multi-tiered riser holding all my spools of thread, over a hundred different colors, organized by hue and by type: cottons, metallics, silks, polyesters, quilting threads. I had drawers full of various notions: needles, thimbles, straight and safety pins, snaps in every size, tape measures and rulers, thin slivers of soap that I used to mark quilts, embroidery scissors, six- and eight- and ten-inch shears, a heavy silver pair of pinking shears, seam bindings and seam rippers, yards of elastics and Velcro. I had shelves of books on textiles, on buttons, on patterns, on every kind of quilt from antique Amish to contemporary, on hand and machine and sashiko quilting techniques. I even had volumes of poetry I read sometimes for a kind of oblique inspiration. I had patterns of my own design cut from sandpaper and stored carefully away in manila envelopes, endless varieties of beads and sequins, yarns and embroidery floss, fabric paint, tassels, and trims. I had graph paper and plastic templates in the shape of squares, triangles, and half circles.

And fabric! Big square wicker baskets lined up on deep wall shelves and full of solid or printed cottons, silks, batiks, woolens, blends—you name it, I had some. One of the many reasons I liked to be in fabric stores was that I was surrounded by people who shared the same benign illness as I. Once, waiting in line to pay for a nice selection of miniature florals, I'd heard the woman ahead of me say, "I have to hurry up and get home and hide this. If my husband sees me bringing in more fabric, he'll kill me." "Oh, I know," the woman she'd spoken to had answered. "I've been hiding mine for years. Try taking it home in a grocery bag. Just throw a box of Kotex on top and he won't go near it." That second woman had such a high pile of fabric in her arms she could hardly see over it. When the clerk who rang her up had asked what she was going to make with it, the woman answered with no sense of irony whatsoever, "Nothing." I smiled at the woman behind me, who shrugged and said, "You know what they say. Whoever dies with the most fabric wins."

Sometimes, a dinner guest will ask to see my studio—it's almost always a woman, although occasionally a man will want to see—and whenever they do, they stand still in appreciative wonder (the men with their hands in their pockets) and usually say just one word: *Wow.* It doesn't matter if they like to sew or not, they just appreciate seeing a room so completely stocked, so richly reflective of a person's passion. It's similar to the way a lot of people love hardware stores. Whether you know what the things are or not, they're *all there.*

On the flannel display board, a few vintage hankies were positioned *en pointe,* a suggestion for a quilt to be made from them. I'd been collecting these hankies for years. Such dainty imprints of social history were recorded there: florals from the twenties and thirties, Mr. and Mrs. hankies from the forties, whimsical patterns of floating toasters and Scottie dogs from the fifties. There were leaf designs for fall, reindeer and candy canes for Christmas, flocked velvet hearts for Valentine's Day, white-on-white embroidery with wide lace trim for weddings. One dark-red hankie had *Lipstick* embroidered on one corner. An ancient pale-blue one with an embroidered nosegay of violets was my favorite—I doubted I'd ever do anything but look at it. All the hankies were worn to a powderlike softness from washing, ironing, folding, holding; from tears. Sometimes I put the old hatbox I kept them in on my lap and just slowly sifted though them, looking to feel memories.

I was anxious to begin that hankie quilt, but first I needed to finish the one I'd been commissioned to do. I'd get the borders on, sew a scattering of seed pearls across it, and back, bind, and machine-quilt it today. Tomorrow morning, on the way to pick up my mother at the airport, I would mail it in the usual way, wrapped in a silk-lined storage bag made out of scraps of fabric that were used in the quilt. Customers went crazy for those bags. Some, it was the reflexive pleasure of receiving an unexpected gift. But I thought maybe it was also because we've become so unused to people doing anything beyond what they're paid to do.

The phone rang. I let it ring a few more times, thinking it was Pete calling to say he was sorry for having been so gruff, and

wanting to punish him a little in this pas-
sive-aggressive way. But it was not Pete, it
was Karen Benson, with whom I had made
an appointment for today and about which
I had forgotten completely. She was calling
to say she was going to be about forty-five
minutes late; was that okay? "Oh, don't
worry," I said. "I'll just be here, working."
After I hung up, I looked at my calendar to
see what kind of quilt she had called about.
I found her name next to the time she was
to arrive—ten minutes from now—and beneath that I saw a note for what she
wanted done: a dog quilt. For a dog? I
wondered. In honor of a dog? Using dog-
motif fabrics? I needed to be more thorough about taking information when I
made appointments. For one thing, I liked
to lay out samples of materials before people arrived.

I got out my basket of flannels, pulled
some green and brown plaids, and then
went through the novelty prints in case she
was a literal kind of customer. I had a cotton
print that was nothing but goofy-looking
cartoon dogs and one slightly more elegant
one featuring hunting dogs. I was digging

through my solids when I heard the back door open and Maggie calling my name.

"Down here!" I called back, and smiled at her when she came into the studio. "Hey."

"Guess what I have." She held out a bakery bag.

"Oh, God, Maggie, I just came back from the fair. And from a funeral, where you eat even more. Because . . . you know, you can."

"I only got two. And they're fat free!"

"Really?" I asked, looking in the bag.

"No. But I think if you tell yourself it is, your body processes it that way."

"No, thanks, Maggie."

She sat in my chair and started eating a Bismarck. "I just got in kind of a fight at the grocery store."

"Why? What happened?"

"Okay. I'm looking for Bisquick Light, right? For this recipe I found for chicken and dumplings? And I ask the stock guy do they have it. He's not sure. And then he says, in this really snotty tone of voice, 'I don't need that stuff to make pancakes.' I say, 'Well, I don't either.' He says, 'So why do you want it?'

"I'm thinking, *What is this?* and I say,

'That is none of your business!' He takes a look on the shelf and says, 'There isn't any. We're out of it. I guess *nobody* can figure out how to make pancakes,' and he walks off down the aisle. I yell after him, 'Hey! I make my pancakes from *scratch*! With *buttermilk*!' So here's my question: Am I cracking up?"

"I have Bisquick Light," I said, laying a solid tan flannel next to a green-and-black mini-check.

"Good. But am I? Cracking up?"

I stopped digging through fabric to look at her. "No. You just care too much about what other people think. That's a problem most of us have."

"I suppose." She licked off her fingers, then came to stand beside me. "What are you making?"

"I'm not sure yet. A client I'm meeting with wants a quilt having something to do with dogs."

"Hmmm. That could be fun."

"Yeah, it could."

"You could sew on real dog toys. Little squeaky ones."

I pulled out my gigantic clear-plastic box of buttons and handed it to her. "Look through here for anything having to do with dogs. In any way."

She rifled through the buttons while I looked at a few more fabrics, then said, "Voilà!"

I turned around.

"You have buttons with paw prints!"

"Well, see?" I said. "That's why I always buy anything that strikes my fancy. Whatever I get, I'll end up using eventually. Pull them out. I'll take them with me to Minnesota."

"So you're going, huh?"

"Yeah. I followed your advice. My mother's coming here tomorrow. Then the next day, I'll go there and meet with Steve and Caroline."

"Good."

"I guess. But I have to tell you, I wish I didn't have to do it."

"I know. But you do have to."

"I'm just too *busy.*"

Maggie scrunched up the bakery bag, tossed it in the trash.

"You ate *both*?"

She shrugged. "It's your fault."

"Right."

"I want to ask you something, Laura.

Don't take this the wrong way. But do you think the reason you don't want to go is because you're afraid you'll find out something you don't want to admit about yourself?"

"Oh, man."

"Okay, forget it. I dreamed I was Jenny Jones in my Maidenform bra. Sorry."

"No, *I'm* sorry. I guess there might be some truth to that; that's why I'm so jumpy about it. It's pretty awful to think you let someone suffer and did nothing about it. Kept yourself oblivious. I read this story once about a girl who watched a bully beat up another girl. She was in a ring of kids, all of them just watching the blood, the snot— it was kind of an awful thing to read. I remember thinking, I'd never do that, I'd never just watch. Easy to make yourself a hero in the abstract, huh?"

Maggie shrugged. "Well, it's also hard to leap in when there's a chance it will make the bully turn on you. And anyway, maybe you didn't keep yourself oblivious. Maybe you truly were unaware."

I started pulling out pieces of fabric. A nice red. A sunny yellow. Strong colors. Primary. Clear.

"You could put dog tags on that quilt too," Maggie said. "You can get them made at Petco—you engrave them yourself. You could get *Fido* and *Rex*. And *Spot*.

"That's a good idea. Can I steal it?"

"Of course. For five bucks."

I put down the fabric. "Come upstairs with me."

"Laura! You don't have to pay me! I was kidding!"

"I know. I'm going to give you the Bisquick and kick you out. I have to work."

"Me too. I'm working from home."

"Yes. I can see that."

When we were in the kitchen, Maggie saw a book I'd just finished lying on the kitchen table. She picked it up, leafed through it, then checked the spine. "*Lost Lake.* Mark Slouka. Is he any good?"

"It's actually one of the best books I've read."

"Can I borrow it?"

"Sure."

"Okay, I'll see you later then. Come over when you're finished working." I closed the door after her, started for my studio, and turned around when I heard Maggie come back in. "Bisquick," she said.

I was halfway down the stairs when I heard Anthony. "Mom? Are you making breakfast? Will you?"

Someday, I would miss this, I knew.

It is a photo taken at Christmastime, a picture of our tree. I look at how beautifully decorated it is, and I remember how the tinsel was painstakingly hung by my mother, one long strand at a time, so that the tree shimmered. Some ornaments are store-bought but many are homemade. I see a Santa I made from a lightbulb, an angel I made from a doily, a snowman out of cotton balls. There is a pair of felt mittens attached to each other by red yarn that Steve made in kindergarten and sprinkled liberally with glitter, and there are the red and green paper chains he loved to make because he got to use the stapler. There is a gingerbread man he made from Play-Doh. You can't see anything Caroline made because her things hang in the back. I told her to put them there because the tree was stationed in front of a window, and I said if she put them on the back, everyone would see her things first. Everyone outside. Years later, I told someone this, and we both laughed.

It seemed funny then, just a little Father Knows Best type of sibling upsmanship. I see it differently now. Which is to say, I see it.

16

"So how are you, mom?" I said, as we pulled away from the airport.

I hardly needed to ask. She looked awful: puffy bags under her eyes, her hair disheveled, her outfit appropriate for anyone else but alarming for my mother: a lightweight gray sweatsuit and sneakers.

She leaned back in her seat and sighed. Looked out the window. "As well as can be expected, I suppose. Such a shock. And you know, Laura, I think I see him *everywhere*. I mean that literally."

I looked quickly over at her. "You mean you're hallucinating?"

"No, it's . . . well, on the airporter, for example, I saw a man in the front of the bus, and it looked exactly like your father. Exactly. I stared at him the whole way. I thought about going up to him, but what would I have said? *Oh, Stan, is it you?* I see him walking down the sidewalk, in stores at the mall, even in the house—I come into a room and see him slip around the corner. Just . . . *zip*!" She laughed, a small sound.

I nodded, said nothing.

"Is that happening to you too?"

"No, but I've heard about it happening to other people. To other widows."

"Oh? And what else have you heard?"

"About widows?"

"Yes."

I pulled up at a stop sign, reached over to touch her shoulder. "Whatever you're feeling, it's normal. That's what I've heard."

"Well."

I started driving again, then said in as innocuous a way as I could, "You know, Mom, I was thinking I'd go back to Minnesota. I want to see Caroline again. And Steve, before he goes back home."

"What? Well, why didn't—"

"I mean see them alone. Just some

brother-and-sister time, without anyone else. Some time to talk. You know? When we were there, we didn't really get . . . well, you know, Dad died and . . ." It still felt strange to say it. I had an impulse to say, *Sorry, Dad,* as though this were some tasteless joke we were all playing on one another.

My mother stared straight ahead, eyebrows raised just the slightest bit.

"The truth is, Caroline's having some trouble, and—"

"Your sister is *always* having trouble. Always. It is the way she prefers to live."

I pulled up to a red light, looked over at her. "Yeah. Did you ever wonder about why?"

"She is that type of personality. She just is. You can let it drive you crazy, or you can just let her be. Green light." She reached in her purse and pulled out a Kleenex. Wiped at her nose. "Can we talk about something else?"

"Sure. Of course. Oh, listen, you'll love this. Hannah went out to buy some clothes the other day, for school? She came back with—"

"I don't see why you have to go back

there when I just arrived! Why can't you just stay here while I'm here and then we can go back together?"

I hesitated, then said, "Mom, I'm sorry this is upsetting to you. It's just something I have to do. Maybe I shouldn't have told you now, when you just got here. I guess I wanted to get it out of the way. Let's have a nice dinner tonight." I smiled over at her. "Okay? I'm glad you're here, Mom. Everyone's glad."

She closed her eyes briefly, opened them. "Maybe I should go back home. I don't know what to do."

I signaled for my exit off the freeway. "Almost there," I said. I meant it to be reassuring, even gay. It was neither.

Just before I was ready to put dinner on the table, the phone rang. It was Aunt Fran. "Hey, how are you?" I asked her.

"Oh, the same as always. Rich and famous. And you?"

"Just getting dinner. We're having your recipe for cucumber salad."

"Well, listen, can I talk to your mom

quickly? She called and left a message earlier."

"Oh! Sure." *When? What message?*

I went to the foot of the stairs and called up to my mother. She had spent some time in the guest room after she arrived, then came down in a better mood to help me make dinner. Now she was up in Hannah's room, going over her wardrobe with her.

"Aunt Fran's on the phone," I yelled. She answered that she'd take it in the guest room.

"Dinner's just about ready," I said.

Nothing.

"Mom?"

"Go ahead and get started; I'll be right down."

I went back into the kitchen, picked up the phone, heard my mother say breathlessly, "So I need you to—" and then, "Laura?" I hung up, flipped the turkey burgers for the last time, dumped the oven-baked French fries into a basket and salted them, sliced tomatoes, drained the water off the ears of corn, yelled up for Anthony and Hannah, and then went to the basement door to call Pete up out of his workroom. I once read an essay about a woman used to a large family making dinner for only herself, the oddity and awful stillness of it. I can imagine. There are random moments—tossing a salad, coming up the driveway to the house, ironing the seams flat on a quilt square, standing at the kitchen window and looking out at the delphiniums, hearing a burst of laughter from one of my children's rooms—when I feel a wavelike rush of joy. This is my true religion: arbitrary moments of nearly painful happiness for a life I feel privileged to lead. Think of the way you sometimes see a tiny shaft of sunlight burst through a gap between rocks, the way it then expands to illuminate a much larger space—it's like that. And it's like quilting, a thread surfacing and then disappearing into the fabric of ordinary days. It's not always visible, but it's what holds everything together.

"So you'll be at the house in a little over two hours?" my mother asked.

"Closer to three, probably." I turned around to look at her in the backseat. She'd come along with Pete to drop me off at the airport. "You know that, right? Why are you asking?"

"No reason. I guess I'm old enough that I'm still in awe of how quickly you can get somewhere."

"I guess I'm old, then," Pete said. "I'm amazed too."

"Wait until your *children* get old," my mother said. "Then you'll know what old is!"

I straightened in my seat. "I'm not old!"

"That's not what you tell me," Pete said.

I gave him a look, then pointed at the United sign up ahead.

"I see it," he said. "Now let's see if they'll actually let me stop long enough to let you out." He pulled up to the curb and I grabbed my suitcase, gave Pete a quick kiss, and then pecked my mother's cheek as she came out of the backseat to get into the front. "Say hello to Steve for me," she said.

"I will." And Caroline?

No message for her, apparently, unless it was in the way my mother slammed the car door. She waved, and then she and Pete drove off. I watched them go, wanting to go back home with them. Instead, I wheeled my bag inside to check the flight information board. ON TIME, it said. This, I have learned, is like a serving suggestion: what you see wasn't necessarily what you get. ON TIME usually means they haven't announced the delay yet. I grieve for the airlines, and I hate them.

I stopped at a kiosk before I headed for the gate. This is my deal: If I have to fly, I get a *People* magazine and a giant-size Snickers. I tell myself it's so that if there's one of those interminable stuck-on-the-tarmac delays and everyone is starving, I can say, "I have a candy bar. I'll share." But the truth is, the one time I was on a flight where there was a terrible delay, I ate the whole thing myself—one small secret bite at a time. I never tasted anything more delicious. I think my seatmate smelled the peanuts on my breath when I ate it; she snuck envious little glances at me while I looked out the window at the unchanging view on the runway. Half of me said, Would it kill you to give her some? The other half said, Did she not pass the same kiosk as I?

17

Steve was going to be a few minutes late picking me up because, unbelievably, the flight arrived more than half an hour early. I was sitting on a bench outside the airport, watching two young lovers kiss hello, when he pulled up and honked, then yelled my name.

"Sorry," I said, getting in the car. "I was distracted." I pointed to the rapturously kissing couple. "Are you and Tessa still like that?"

He looked at them in the rearview mirror. "Nah."

"How long were you like that?"

"I don't know; couple of hours."

I put on my seatbelt and pushed my hair back from my forehead. "How are you, sweetie?"

He shrugged. "I know what's up, in case you're wondering. There's no way in hell we'll be talking about what to do with the sideboard."

"Thanks for staying."

"I'm doing it for you, you know."

"And I'll bet Tessa asked you to."

Nothing.

"Didn't she?"

"Yeah, but I would have done it for you anyway."

"Uh-huh."

"I would! And anyway, what the hell, let Caroline get it out of her system. Whatever's *in* her system. Maybe then she'll stop her . . . stuff."

We rode in silence the rest of the way, but for the radio, the volume turned low. When we arrived, there was a car in the driveway. I wasn't sure, but I thought it was Aunt Fran's. Sure enough, when I stepped onto the porch and started to open the door, she opened it instead.

Her hand flew to her chest. "Oh! You're here!"

I laughed. "I was going to say the same thing! What are you doing?"

"I just came over to stock the fridge. You know how your mother is. God forbid you arrive and there's not enough to eat. I just put some things in there . . . a few things, you know, milk . . . So! How was the flight? Early, huh?"

"Yes," I said, thinking, *What is she so nervous about?* And then I realized my mother must have told her why we're here. Most sisters do talk, after all. That phone call last night. My mother must have told Aunt Fran about the Meeting.

Steve, after greeting Aunt Fran, disappeared into the den to check his messages. When he was through returning calls, we'd go to meet Caroline for an early dinner, then come back here for our talk.

"Call me if you need anything," Aunt Fran said, on the way out.

I closed the door after her and went to the kitchen to sit at the kitchen table and look out the window. The bird feeders were empty; it was my father who kept them filled. I saw that his vials of pills were still lined up. I picked up his antihypertensive, thought about how his were probably the last hands to touch it. *Stan Meyer. Take as directed.* My eyes filling, I put the pills back in place and went out into the yard. I was leaning over to admire the infrastructure of the tulips when I heard the screen door slam. Steve flopped down on one of the patio chairs, and I moved to sit next to him.

"Hot out here," he said. And then, "What do you think, Laura? Is this really necessary?"

"Seems to be. For her."

"But what are we supposed to do?"

"Just listen, for starters. Just let her say all she needs to say. And then . . . well, I don't know. Tell her the truth, I guess. Tell her what you saw or didn't see."

"I didn't see anything. I told her that."

"Well, maybe if we hear more, we'll remember something. She's just looking for some sort of validation. That's what she said."

He looked at his watch, leaned back, and closed his eyes. Then he raised his chin and opened a few buttons on his shirt.

"Tanning?" I asked.

"Might as well."

"It's bad for you."

"Yeah. I like things that are bad for me."

We sat in silence for a while, and then I said, "Do you miss Dad?"

"Aw, man." He sighed, shook his head. "I don't even have his death on my screen yet. You know? I haven't really realized he's gone. When I think about him dying I feel bad, but I haven't really missed him yet. But I will. I know I will."

I heard the phone ring inside, and ran in to answer it. When I came out, I told Steve, "Caroline. She wants to come over now. Forget about dinner. Or get dinner later. Whatever. I told her all right." I didn't tell Steve she was coming from her therapist's office. That made me nervous; it felt as though both of them would be showing up.

He stood. "Good. Let's get it over with."

We went inside and sat in the living room, both of us with our arms crossed, I noticed. Both of us silent. Finally, I laughed out loud. "We're so grim!"

"Well, this *is* grim."

"I suppose. But you know, I heard this couple on the plane arguing about whether or not world peace will ever be possible. He said no; she said yes. Finally he said, 'Do you *really* want world peace?' She said, 'Of *course*!' He said, 'Can you learn to get along with your mother?' And she said nothing. Maybe the guy's right. Maybe we all need to clean up our own backyards. Maybe it's as important for us to talk about this as it is for Caroline."

"I don't think *anything* is as *anything* as it is to Caroline."

"Whoa. *What?*"

"You know what I mean. She's such a fucking drama queen!"

"Well, maybe we'll find out why." I smoothed away a nonexistent wrinkle in my pants.

Steve looked at his watch again. "You want to watch TV till she gets here?"

"Sure." Together we went to the family room, where we debated over whether we should order a set of frying pans, the likes of which would apparently never be offered for this incredibly low price again. And then we heard the door opening and I reached for the remote, clicked off the TV.

Caroline walked in and leaned against the doorjamb, pushed her sunglasses up high on her head, crossed her arms. "Hi. Thanks for coming." She was wearing black pants and a beautiful turquoise top. I wanted to compliment her on it, but now wasn't the time, I supposed. Still, I secretly studied the intricate pattern of the trim running along the bottom of her blouse.

"Want something to drink?" I asked her. "Or eat?"

"No, thanks. Could we sit in the living room?"

We walked past her single file, Caroline bringing up the rear. I felt as though Steve and I were children being sent to the principal's office. I was overly aware of the back of my neck, sure my defensiveness showed there. I thought about a friend of mine whose parents never once said they loved her and never praised her, thinking it would go to her head. *"Who do you think you are?"* they liked to say. One day when she was in her forties, she was over there for something, sitting at the kitchen table, and her father came up behind her, put his hand on her shoulder, and said, "We love you." And it made her feel like vomiting. She said it was just like that, she could feel something rising in her throat, and she thought she might throw up. She had sat immobile, wanting him to just go away. Out of the corner of her eye, she could see his fingers, yellowed by nicotine, the nails too long. She wouldn't look at him; she had remained absolutely still until he took his hand away and shuffled out of the kitchen. She said she had wanted to scream after him *It's too late!* but of course she did not. She'd just sat there until he was out of the room, and then she went home. He'd never mentioned it again, nor did she. She wept the day he died, but she said she cried only for the waste in his life, for the shame there was in that.

Imagine a different scenario: She puts her own hand on top of her father's. How hard would that have been? How hard *would* it have been? Here's who knows: only the woman herself. And maybe her father. Maybe him.

"All right, I just want to say something," Steve told Caroline. He had been patiently listening to a litany of complaints, delivered in an odd, nearly detached way by our sister. But now he said, "We didn't have a family like some others. Our father didn't bounce us on his knee. Our mother didn't sit us at the kitchen table after school and give us homemade cookies. Neither one of them had heart-to-hearts with us. We didn't call good night to each other at bedtime, like the Waltons. But what we had, *we had,* you know? There were things you could depend on. I mean, remember that summer we went to camp? I got a letter from Mom or Dad every day. Every single day!"

Caroline said nothing, stared into the space before her.

"Didn't you?" Steve asked, and I could see his wariness, his regret at revealing yet another thing he got from our parents that Caroline might not have.

Still, she said nothing.

"Did *you*?" he asked me, and I shrugged and nodded: yes.

Finally, Caroline said, "I didn't go to summer camp."

"Yes, you did!" I said. "We all did, just that one summer; we all went to different camps, remember?"

"You and Steve went," she said. "I didn't. I went to a hospital."

"For what?" I asked. Now, this I would have to have known. Why would I not have known this?

A long silence. And then Caroline said,

"Because my mother came after me with a knife, and I was having a hard time dealing with it."

I sat wide-eyed and then felt a grin come on my face, an unfortunately misplaced expression of absolute astonishment, of horror. I covered my mouth.

"Okay, that's it," Steve said, and stood up. Then he sat back down. "Jesus, Caroline! I know you're lying! You went to summer camp! You came back with . . . I don't know, didn't you make a wallet or something?"

"Yes. At the hospital." She turned to Steve. "You and Laura weren't home. It was Sunday and we were going to have fried chicken for dinner. Mom was cutting up the chicken with a big butcher knife, and she got mad at something I said and raised it up over me. She said, "I swear . . . I *swear,*" and the knife was shaking in her hand. I was crouching on the floor, my arms over my head. The radio was on in the kitchen; I could hear some men talking and laughing. And then Dad came in the room and yelled her name and she spun around and said, "*What?* What do you expect me to *do* with her?"

I said, "But why, Caroline? Had you done anything to—" I stopped and wished I could grab back the words. Blame the victim. Great. I started again. "If this is true, why do you need us to verify anything? Why don't you just . . . I mean, there must be records."

"Remember the fire at St. Mary's?"

I did remember now: the summer of my junior year of high school. It was a spectacular fire; you could smell smoke miles away. "Yes," I said quietly.

"So. What I have is my memory of being there for a while. That's all. I don't remember the names of anyone who treated me. And no one but Dad knew I was there."

I saw my father in his hospital bed, almost telling me about someone being in the hospital and then deciding not to. Is this what he meant? *Oh, Dad,* I thought.

"It was after I came home that she finally stopped doing things to me. I think it scared her."

"But Caroline," I said, "how could they send you back home when you were in such danger? Why wasn't our whole family investigated by social services or something?"

"Because at a family meeting at the hospital, Mom denied everything. And the doctor believed her. And Dad said I had a tendency to exaggerate, a pretty wild imagination. That I seemed to gravitate toward the melancholy, the melodramatic—wink, wink." She leaned back in her chair, made a gesture of futility. "After that meeting, Mom went home and Dad took me to the hospital cafeteria to buy me an ice cream. Pretty cheap payoff, huh?"

"Oh, man." Steve rubbed his head. I thought I knew what he was thinking: *But you did gravitate toward those things.* It was, of course, what I was thinking as well.

Caroline smiled coolly. "I'm sorry this is so hard for you. And I'm not being sarcastic, I really mean it. But could you . . . I would like, finally, to feel that I can be supported by my brother. You are my brother."

"Well, what then, Caroline? What do you want me to do?"

She leaned forward. "Say you believe me. That's all."

He looked around the room, shaking his head. "You know, this is like—"

"Fine," she said. "If you can't, you can't. At least I tried."

"I didn't say I don't believe you!" Steve

said. "I just said . . . I'm just trying to tell you it's a shock, that's all!"

"It is, Caroline," I said. "I can say that I do believe you; but it's really hard to take in. We thought you were in camp. They told us we were all going to camp!"

Steve's cell phone rang. He reached instinctively for it but let it go. We all sat still, listening to it ring a few more times before it stopped.

"Well," Steve said, "I just want to say I'm sorry for anything I might have done to make it worse. I know I never paid much attention to you—or to Laura, either, actually. I guess I was off in my own world."

"I guess we all were." I asked Caroline, "Are you staying here tonight?" Maybe after a few hours, we'd be looser, better able to talk.

"No. Bill and I are trying—"

"Oh, good. I'm glad, Caroline."

"Let me finish. We're trying to work out the details of a divorce agreement."

Steve and I looked quickly at each other, and I assumed we were sharing the same thought: *Oh, no, not more!* I remembered seeing a film once where one bad thing happened after the other; things just kept getting worse and worse. "That would never happen in real life," I said to Pete afterward. "*Something* good would be in there *somewhere.*"

Fatigue in Caroline's face was mixed with a kind of relief. I supposed the good here was that she had finally revealed the abuse she endured to the people she needed to tell. Except for one: the person responsible for it.

It is a family photo that a stranger must have taken, somewhere around the mid-sixties. We are all outside, at a park. There is a big wicker basket on a picnic table behind us. I remember that basket. It had a wooden top and a lovely dark-green pattern of trim—little x's—all along the edges. It must have been a cool day; the sky is overcast, and we are all wearing light jackets. Steve and I stand smiling before my father, leaning back into him. Steve has a baseball bat at his feet; I hold a stick that I must have meant to use for roasting marshmallows. My father, smiling broadly, proudly, has one hand on each of our shoulders. Caroline stands before our mother, and it is one of the rare times she is smiling. Our mother stands straight-mouthed behind her, arms crossed tightly across her chest, like a little kid in a store who's been told, Don't touch.

18

Steve and I went for dinner to a fast-food burger joint at the airport. It was Tessa who'd tried to call him earlier—she'd come down with something, and although she didn't feel sick enough to go the doctor, she was in need of some caretaking. Steve was only too willing to fly home and tend to her. He finished his hamburger, scrunched the wrapping into a tight ball, fired it at the nearby wastebasket, missed. He laughed and went to pick up his trash and deposit it from closer range. "About my yearbook aspiration to be a basketball star?" He sat back down, looked at his watch. "I should get to the gate pretty soon. God, what a trip this has been! You come home for a simple family visit, and all hell breaks loose. How are you doing with all this?"

"Oh, I'm fine. I've got Pete and the kids, and . . . you know, my life at home." I folded my napkin in half, then in fourths, offered a quick smile. "So." Not the real answer. The real answer was, I didn't know how I was doing. I felt numbed by all I'd been told, and I went back and forth about what to believe, sometimes minute to minute.

"How can you suffer abuse like that and not tell someone—a teacher or a minister—a friend? Not that she had many friends. But you could tell *someone*. What about you and me? If we couldn't see what was happening, why didn't she just *tell* us?"

"You heard how much help she got from Dad and the doctor. And the three of us weren't exactly close. Anyway, she told me she actually believed it was her fault, that she caused that behavior in Mom."

He shook his head. "Even so. I just don't see how you can keep being around a person who treats you that way and not say something. It doesn't make any sense."

"I know." I stared at the table next to us, at the three little children sitting with their parents and eating their hamburgers. They were remarkably quiet and well behaved. One of them held a sock monkey, and she offered it a bite of her burger. Seeing this, something suddenly occurred to me.

"Steve? I wonder. Maybe what happens in these situations is the opposite of what we think."

"What do you mean?"

"Did you ever read about those monkeys they used in an experiment to measure love?"

"You can't measure love."

"Well, I know; I don't think so either. But this was . . . *did* you read about them?"

"Not that I recall."

"I saw it in the newspaper. What happened is that researchers in a primate lab put baby monkeys in with crazy mothers—cloth mother monkeys that had soft bodies so they could cuddle, but they were all booby-trapped. They would unexpectedly do something awful when the babies clung to them. One shook the baby violently, and one blew air out really hard on top of the baby's head, and one had brass spikes embedded in her chest that would all of a sudden pop out. You know what the babies did when those things happened? Clung tighter, if they possibly could. Or if they were thrust off by the force of what was done to them, they got up and ran right back."

Steve stared at me. "How can anyone work in a place like that?"

"Steve. The point is, the babies *clung tighter* when they were abused!"

"Caroline didn't cling tighter. She's really cold with Mom."

"*Now* she is. But remember when she used to idolize her? When she used to buy her all those presents and—"

"We're not monkeys, Laura."

"Sure we are."

He stood, pushed in his chair. "I've got to go. Want to walk with me to security?"

I walked beside him quietly, and then, just before we reached the line, I told him about a woman I once lived next door to who was sexually abused by her father in ways too horrible ever to repeat. And yet when I went over one day to borrow some coffee from her, there the man was—sitting on the sofa, reading a book to his two-year-old granddaughter. And the woman introduced me to her smiling father like she adored him. "So there you are," I said.

And Steve said, "Okay, I'll call you soon." He hadn't heard a word I'd said. Too full of things to listen anymore. Or too tired. Or something. And I didn't blame him.

I went out to the rental car I'd taken over from Steve, put the key in, and then sat there, thinking. I remembered something else about those monkeys. The abused babies were so preoccupied with reaching their mothers, they had no energy for friends, no time for trying to bond with anyone else. They were on a kind of psychological island, stuck with something that would never give them what they needed. The article ended by saying that every mother has the assurance that her baby will love her. But a baby has no assurance at all of being loved in return.

Tomorrow I would buy a cell phone. Times like this, I really did need one. I would call Pete, and when I heard his familiar voice, I would close my eyes and listen only to him.

* * *

Back at my mother's house, I wandered around the quiet rooms, looking at the place in a way I hadn't for a long time. When I lived there, I saw it one way: home. It was a fact as irrefutable as the nose on my face. It was a personalized haven where I could get my needs met, though surely I didn't think of it that way. Rather, I thought of it as a repository for my things, a place where Velveeta cheese was kept on the refrigerator door and extra bottles of Pepsi in the laundry room. There was a big metal box of Band-Aids in the medicine chest, a never-ending supply of clean towels stacked in the linen closet. There was a desk in my room at which I did my homework, a living room where, in the evenings, my father sat in his chair under deep yellow lamp light with a library book, his shirtsleeves rolled up, his legs crossed in a way I came to find effeminate.

After I left home, I saw my parents' house another way: a place full of memories that dimmed year by year if not month by month, a place decorated in a way I would never consider, and then a place where I needed to be overly mindful of what my children were doing even after they were no longer young.

Now I stood in my parents' bedroom, thinking about what their life together was really like. I recalled various things we kids witnessed—the kisses hello and goodbye, the stereotypical sharing of household tasks—and I wondered about what we didn't see.

I moved over to their bed and sat down on it. What did they talk about before they went to sleep? Did they share corny rituals, as Pete and I do? Did they argue in hushed tones more often than we knew, turn angrily away from each other and pretend to be asleep until they actually were, then awaken in the morning with the psychic hangover that such resentment brings?

I took off my shoes and lay down on the bed, on my father's side. His nightstand still held the things he had kept there: the brown alarm clock, a "man-sized" box of Kleenex, an ashtray in which he kept not ashes but pennies. I closed my eyes, whispered *Daddy?* Nothing but a silence so profound I could feel it pressing against my ears.

I went to my mother's dresser and stared

at myself in her mirror. This is what she looked into when she got up every morning. And what did she see now? Herself, alone, fifty years older than the time she bought this dresser. What a difficult transition she would have, going from a woman who was openly and exuberantly adored to one who lived in echoing silence. No one would be constantly complimenting, reassuring, and supporting her, as my father had. Or protecting her—perhaps egregiously. He was forever giving everything to her, and she was forever taking it with a kind of entitlement that used to make me furious. *Give something back!* I would think, but she did not, not really. She washed his underwear; she prepared meals; she stacked his mail on the dining room table. And she stayed beautiful.

I pulled open one of the top drawers. Bras and panties, folded neatly. In the drawer below that, negligees. This surprised me. I'd never seen her in one. I lifted the top one up, a light blue, with a matching peignoir. It looked brand new. Which accounted, I supposed, for my never having seen it. I was pulling out another drawer when the phone rang. I jumped, slid the drawer back in quickly, and went to the kitchen to answer it.

"What are you doing?" Maggie asked.

"You want the truth?" I sat down, smiling, grateful to hear her voice.

"Of course!"

"I was snooping in my mother's drawers."

"Find anything good?"

"Only a negligee. Matching peignoir."

"Excellent score."

"I think she just bought it. Isn't that weird?"

"Nothing's weird about what people do when someone close to them dies. And anyway, if she's like *my* mother, it's not new. It's just that she never wore it. 'Too good to wear.'"

"That wouldn't be my mother's problem. Speaking of which, what's happening at my house?"

"Well, your mother made her famous coconut cookies today. Anthony brought me some. He said they're famous because it's the only thing she makes that tastes good."

"That's pretty much right."

"And Hannah came home with a posse of girlfriends—I saw them all traipsing in as Anthony was heading out. So life over there is pretty normal, I'd say. How are *you* doing?"

I contemplated telling her everything but decided against it. "I'll tell you about it when I come home. Another couple of days here ought to do it."

"Well, I just wanted to check in."

"I'm glad you did."

"I wanted to know if you were all right. Are you—really?"

I hesitated, then said, "Yes."

"Just don't want to talk about it?"

"I guess not, Maggie. Not yet."

"Okay. Well, I'll see you soon. Call me anytime you want. Any time."

As soon as I hung up, the phone rang again. I picked it up, laughing, said, *"What?"*

"Hello?"

Steve. "Oh, hi!" I said. "I thought you were Maggie. Are you home?"

"Yeah, I am."

"How's Tessa?"

"She's got the flu, but it's the dry variety."

"What's that mean?"

"You know. No body fluids."

"Oh. *That's* good."

"Listen, Laura, I want to tell you something. I took a nap on the plane, and when I woke up, maybe even before I woke up, I was thinking about . . . well, I remembered something. And I wanted to tell you to tell Caroline."

"Me? Why, what is it?"

"Okay, this was . . . I don't know, I guess I was about five, because I remember Caroline was in first grade, and Mom got a call from the school nurse, and she had to go to school to get Caroline. And she was really mad. I went along, of course, and all the way she was muttering about how she guessed she knew her own child. But we picked up Caroline and she really *was* sick, so pale, and she just lay on the backseat of the car all the way home, didn't say a word. I remember thinking there was something kind of *off,* but I didn't know what. Now I think . . . you know what I think it was? I think maybe Caroline told Mom she was sick that morning, and Mom made her go to school anyway. And I think the nurse must have yelled at Mom."

"But Steve, why don't you tell Caroline all this?"

"Aren't you going to see her again tomorrow afternoon?"

"Yeah, but—"

"Just . . . tell her I remembered those things, okay? For what it's worth. Tell her I don't think she's crazy. I don't want to get into some huge—I just want her to know I don't *disbelieve* her. Would you tell her?"

"All right."

"And I'll . . . you know, I'll call her sometime soon. I will."

"Okay. Give my love to Tessa."

I hung up the phone and went outside, sat on the back steps, and looked up into the night sky. He wouldn't call her. He was out of it now. I knew him. He'd be at his bar tonight, slapping the backs of his male patrons, charming the females. Talking about the White Sox and Daley. Not for him the mess of all this. I have a personal theory about why most men walk away from difficult emotional situations: It's because they don't have babies. It is bred in them to leave the dwelling place to hunt and gather, to be outward-oriented; it is bred in women to lie down and give birth and stay home in order to care for the small world they have delivered into the larger one. Men conk things on the head or are conked themselves; women work out the kinks of the inner life.

I wished the fair weren't over. I wished I could sit outside and watch fireworks, blossoms of light in the darkness that would carry me up and away from myself. Instead, I thought of Caroline, of the life she had lived in this house: murderous rages and then a pork-chop dinner that night, with a mother whose face gave away nothing, with a father blinded by love, and with two siblings focused on anything but her. After such a dinner, days of relative peace, perhaps weeks. But I wondered if those peaceful times were any easier to bear, since she must always have been waiting for the next thing to happen.

I needed out of there. I looked at my watch—still early. I'd drive over to the huge bookstore a few blocks away, have an iced coffee, and look at some science books. There was a client who wanted a quilt made into linking chains, "kind of like DNA," she'd said. "You know what DNA looks like?" What it looks like is interesting. What it does is fathomless. But it is only a part of what makes us into who we become.

* * *

In the coffee shop of the bookstore, two women about my age sat at the table next to me. "I think it's hormones," one of them said. "I'm just feeling so emotional. On the way here, I saw a blind man trying to cross the street. I wanted to help, but I didn't want to offend him if he didn't need me. So I just watched him for a while. He was listening to the traffic so carefully, his head cocked, and—anyway, finally I just took his arm and said, 'It's okay to cross now,' and he smiled at me—this radiant smile—and it made me feel like bawling. I don't know why."

"It *is* hormones," her friend said. "I have days like that, when my skin feels peeled back, when I feel completely exposed. And on those days, I cry over everything: Hallmark commercials, dropping a dish . . . it's those damn hormones."

But I wondered if it wasn't something else. Maybe it was the tender irony of the way that we, blind ourselves, offer our arm to others, hoping to ease the crossing. Maybe it was the odd surges of love one can feel for an absolute stranger. Or maybe it was the way we give so little when it's in us always to give so much more. Thomas Merton wrote about feeling a sudden awareness of a profound connection to others, understanding that "they were mine and I theirs." I always loved reading things like that, things that pointed to our oneness and, by extension, our responsibility to others. It's the execution of anything specific that's the problem. It's kneeling down to meet the eyes of someone slouched on a sidewalk that you'd so much rather walk past. It's bothering to listen with an open heart to someone who smells bad. It's hard.

The three of us kids are in a bathtub piled high with soapsuds. In the background Steve and I are grinning happily. I have made a lavish up-sweep, using the thick lather of White Rain shampoo. Steve has made devil horns. My knees are up against my chest, my arms spread out wide—I remember I was being Dinah Shore, singing "See the USA in your Chevrolet." Steve has his hands behind his head, "wewaxing." In the foreground sits Caroline, solemn-faced, wide-eyed, dry-headed. Her eyes are raised as though in silent appeal to the person above her. She wants to be lifted up. She does not want to be there.

19

In the morning, I made a pot of coffee. I'd have a cup, and then do some handwork on the quilt I'd brought along, the one for the woman I met with just before I left. It was *for* a dog, as it turned out. That would eliminate any sew-ons, which the dog could eat. Instead, everything would be incorporated into the design of the quilt. I'd suggested some appliquéing, which would lessen the cost, but the woman thought appliqué was tacky.

I'm always amazed at how much people spend on their animals. I've never understood that kind of love, though I don't denigrate it. Maggie has a mutt that looks like a poodle in the front and an extraterrestrial in the back, and she worships him. Every Friday night he gets an Italian beef sandwich from Johnny B's.

When the coffee was ready, I went to the refrigerator for milk. I didn't see any—where did Aunt Fran put it? I saw a carton of cottage cheese, a package of English muffins that, though unopened, had passed its expiration date. Some Tupperware dishes holding leftovers. And that was it. I looked in the freezer, thinking she might have absentmindedly put it there. Nope.

I searched the cupboards for fake creamer, found none. It might be Dunkin' Donuts time. But first I'd call Aunt Fran.

When she answered the phone, I said, "Hey, you! Where's the milk?"

"Who is this?"

"It's me, Laura. I thought you brought us some milk. I don't see any."

"Well, yes, that's . . . listen, honey, is Caroline there with you?"

"No. I'm going to see her for lunch today. Why?"

"I wonder if I could ask you to come here first."

"Sure. Is something wrong?"

"Well, I just want to . . . I think there's something you should see."

"Okay. I'll be there in half an hour."

I dressed and got in the car, headed for the drive-through window of Dunkin' Donuts. If I didn't go in, I wouldn't be tempted to get a doughnut. When I spoke my order into the silver box, I requested a large regular coffee, skim milk, light, no sugar. "Anything else?" a voice asked, and I paused, then said, "A bowtie?"

On the way to Aunt Fran's, I passed a sign for a backyard play posted to a telephone pole. Aunt Fran once had a role in one of our backyard plays (to which Steve sold tickets, ten cents for a show and a paper cup of Kool-Aid), and she played a wicked witch so convincingly that one of the little kids in the audience went home crying and the mother called my mother to complain. I tried to remember the last time I stayed over at Aunt Fran's. I believe it was a summer night when I was fourteen. She helped my cousins and me write letters to stars that night. Gregory Peck was her choice, Paul McCartney was mine. Everyone I knew loved either Paul or John, except for Caroline, who preferred Ringo.

When I knocked at the door, it took a long time for Aunt Fran to answer, but then there she was, in her bathrobe. "I was just getting out of my gardening clothes," she said. "I'll be with you in a minute. Go in the kitchen, there's a big plate of chocolate chip cookies."

"Did you bake this morning?" I asked.

"No," she called, from her bedroom. "Brunderman's Bakery."

"I'm disappointed," I said.

"Eat one," she answered. "You won't be disappointed anymore."

Since I had already ruined my "diet," I ate two. Then, as I was pouring myself another glass of milk, Aunt Fran came into the room, carrying something under her arm. A small photo album, it looked like.

"*Here's* the milk," I said, holding up the carton and smiling at her.

"Sit down, Laura."

"Okay." I put the milk back in the refrigerator and sat down at her little kitchen table. There was a pitcher of flowers in the center, a beautiful arrangement from her garden: hydrangeas, lilies, small roses, all in shades of pink, a little baby's breath here and there, not the nearly yellow, defeated kind sold in grocery stores but bright little white blossoms, full as miniature petticoats.

She sat opposite me and put the photo album between us. "I didn't go over to bring you food the other day. I went over to get this out of the house. Your mother asked me to."

I recalled the brief bit of conversation I heard between the two of them. No wonder my mother hadn't wanted me listening in; she must have been talking to Aunt Fran about Caroline making trouble again. And she must have wanted her sister to remove anything that could get Caroline going.

"What is it?" I reached for the album, but Aunt Fran pulled it closer to herself.

"Your mother does not want you to know about this. But I've decided you should. I hope it's the right thing to do. She just never wanted you to know."

"About what?"

She opened the album to the first page, to a photo of a newborn in a crib. "Is that me?" I asked.

"It's your sister."

"Caroline."

"No. It's your sister who died. Her name was Claire."

I looked up quickly at Aunt Fran and then back at the baby. She was remarkably thin.

"She died when she was only nine weeks old."

"From what?"

"A heart defect. She never had a chance, really. It just about killed your mother."

I looked at the photo again. The baby was so young, it was hard to see much in her face. And her eyes were closed, her fist close to her face. I turned the page: more photos, the old-fashioned kind with jagged edges. There were only about twelve in all, some with my mother or father, one with another baby. "That's me, right?" I said, pointing to a picture with an older baby, staring in a direction opposite my sister.

"Yes, that's you. I wonder—I've always wondered, really—do you have any memory of that child?"

I shook my head. "No."

"You weren't even two when she died."

"I don't remember anything."

"Well, I wouldn't expect you to. And that's certainly the way your mother wanted it."

"Why?"

"The only way she could get past it, finally, was to deny it. But then when Caroline was born—too soon, really; it was much too soon for your mother to have another baby—she . . . well, it made all the sorrow come back. She saw Caroline healthy, and it reminded her of Claire, dead. And I think it affected the way she treated Caroline."

I nodded my head slowly, though I didn't really buy this explanation. It seemed to me that if you lost a baby you'd be overjoyed to have another one.

"At first it was just that she was afraid to get close, thinking it could happen again. Or maybe it was postpartum depression, which everybody talks about now. We didn't know about it then. But Laura, despite the way things were between them, you must know she does love Caroline."

"Pretty long time for a postpartum depression to last, Aunt Fran. And pretty selective behavior on my mother's part." I stared into the open face of a lily, all its parts exposed. Then I said, "Do you know that Caroline was in the hospital when she was a kid? She was there because—"

"I know," Aunt Fran said. "Your father and

I both knew, though your father thought he was the only one. It was a terrible thing. But at least Caroline got some help. Things got better after that."

"But . . . what about my *mother*? What about help for *her*?"

"Things were very different then. People relied more on their own resources. I think your mother felt that if Caroline got help, she would be helped too."

"That makes no sense at all."

"It was a long time ago." Aunt Fran turned the photo album toward herself to look at the pictures. "She was a beautiful baby. And smile? That baby smiled from the day she was born. I swear, she was the happiest little thing you ever saw. And then came Caroline, such a sad little girl. Always so sad. I think your mother saw that sadness and it bothered her, that the one who lived would be so—"

"But Aunt Fran, my God! Caroline had reason to be sad!"

"Oh, I know. I know. But I often wonder which came first. Who caused what in whom. She closed the photo album. "Anyway. May I ask you to keep this a secret?"

"I . . . don't think I can. I'm sorry."

"Well, Laura, I showed you this so that when Caroline complains about her life, you know part of the reason that your mother had difficulty with her. And the other part, I must tell you, was Caroline herself. She was a difficult child. Surely you remember that! She remains difficult today; that woman cannot settle down inside herself. I love her, truly, but she is a tortured soul. It is not easy to be around her—not then, not now. You've had good luck with your children, Laura. I don't know if you've ever thought about what it would be like to have a child like Caroline.

"I really don't think your telling others about Claire will help anything. It might make things worse. Your mother made mistakes, but she tried her best to take care of all of you. That's all a parent can do."

I stood. "I've got to go."

She took hold of my arm. "I will ask you again to keep this a secret, Laura. It was your mother's wish that you kids never know. Not only so that she could try to forget about it, but so that you children wouldn't have to know about such a sad event. She wanted to protect you; she still tries to protect you. Don't remind her of things she tried so hard to forget and then, on top of that, tell her that her sister betrayed her—not when her husband has just died. Please, Laura."

"I won't say anything right now. That's all I can promise."

What I meant was, I wouldn't say anything to Caroline. But I was going back to my mother's house, and I was going to make a few calls. One to Pete for consolation; one to Maggie for advice. And then I would call Caroline, to tell her I was on the way to see her for lunch.

I drove home mindlessly, mechanically. The only thing I seemed to take in was a cemetery, which I noticed as I sat at a stoplight. Was Claire there? I wondered. I looked at one of the markers: a stone angel, bent at one knee, head hanging low, hands clasped over her heart, weeping tears of stone.

20

Naturally, I got advice from Pete and consolation from Maggie. Pete thought I shouldn't say anything to Caroline; she was in such a fragile state that hearing what I'd learned might harm her further.

"But it might help her too," I said.

Pete said, "Well, it's hard to know how she would interpret it. So why take the risk?" I supposed he was right. I'd often been surprised by Caroline's reactions to things. And this was a delicate time.

Maggie told me she felt bad for me, handling all this alone. Which I realized I was, at least at this point. I told her to tell me something funny, to give me a yang for the yin. She said, "Hmm. Something funny. How about an Amazing Fact instead?"

"Fine."

"I used to be able to bounce a quarter off my stomach. Now I can hide an all-terrain vehicle in there."

"Sorry," I said. "I don't find that amazing. I find that funny. Also convenient. Next time we get tired on one of our walks, we'll just pull out your Hummer."

"Next time we take a walk, we'll be too old to walk."

"No, we really are going to start walking regularly."

"I know we are, sweetheart."

"As soon as I get back. I mean it."

"Hey. I'm lacing up my sneakers."

A few miles from Caroline's, I turned off the radio and listened to the sound of the rain that had begun. I turned on the windshield wipers and remembered, suddenly, a cabdriver I once had on a rainy night when I was visiting New York City. His wipers weren't working very well, the traffic was heavy, and he was in a terrible mood. I wanted to put a daisy down his rifle barrel, so I said, "Pretty bad traffic on Friday nights, huh?" "*Every* night!" he said, speaking from between clenched teeth. I looked across the backseat of the cab, as though seeking some sort of rolled-eye affirmation from an invisible ally. Then, in the warmest voice I could muster, I said "I guess it can be pretty hard to live here." We were at a stoplight, and I thought he might turn around and crack a smile. But he did not turn around. Rather, he began pounding his steering wheel. One fist, pounding steadily but slowly, terrible little intervals of silence in between. *Bam! . . . Bam! . . . Bam!* I got out then, said this was close enough, thank you very much, and gave the guy a really good tip, though he did not deserve one at all. I walked away thinking, What happened to this man? Why is he not like the cabbie I had earlier, who had a picture of his daughter on his dashboard, who pointed out tourist attractions in his thickly accented English, who sang a little song to himself as we waited for the light to change, who waved at and then laughed with another cabbie who pulled up beside him? Surely the angry man did not emerge from the womb shaking his fist. Who did this to him?

Pretty obvious memory to have pop into my head, as I drew closer to the house where my sister lived. Though of course what she pounded was not the steering wheel but herself.

Caroline was sitting at her drafting board, looking at blueprints for an addition she was doing to someone's house. I looked at the finely drawn lines on the big white pages and said, "Funny how we both ended up doing kind of the same thing."

"What do you mean?" Caroline erased something, penciled in a correction.

"I mean, you know . . . making things out of raw materials. I use cloth, you use wood."

She looked up. "You know what I think? I think it's very different. I think I focus on seeing the actual substructure. You take things as they are and chop them up to re-create a new whole. And then you say, 'See? *That's* what it is!' "

"Meaning?"

"Meaning I want to know the truth of

what's beneath. You want to transform things into something comfortable and beautiful, but not what they *are.*" She stared at me, a little smile on her face. And then her smile faded and she said, "I'm sorry."

"It's all right."

"No, it's not. It's just . . . I'm in such a bad mood. I'm sorry."

"Maybe it's good for you to be in a bad mood."

She moved from her desk to sprawl out in a chair. "I'm so sick of this. I am. I am so sick of myself. You know what happened this morning? I toasted half a bagel. So far so good, huh?"

I smiled.

"And then I wanted to have it on a beautiful dish, I just wanted to have something beautiful to eat on because I'm trying to do what my therapist says and *nurture and reward myself.* So I have these cute little saucers I bought in an antiques store, cherries all over them, and I took one down from the cupboard, and here comes the big finger from the sky, pointing at me. *Put that back! That's a saucer! You can't eat a bagel on a saucer!* She looked up at me, sighed. "All the time, this voice: *Wrong. Stupid.*

That is not for you. It is for everyone else, not you. And Laura, I want you to know, I really want you to be clear about this: It's not how I want to be. I look up at the night sky and see the same beauty you do. I mean . . . torch singers, little red potatoes, the sight of a kid running down the street with her tongue sticking out of her mouth . . . I *get* that.

"I want you to know that whenever I go to a museum, everything in my head gets pushed away. It doesn't matter what I look at: ancient pottery bowls, period rooms, sculptures—doesn't matter. The whole time I'm there, everything pecking away at my soul bows to greater considerations. I stand in front of a little French oil of a woman at a food market and all you can see is one slice of her cheek and her coat and hat and her shoes, and everything about her comes to me: where she lives, her little overheated apartment, the half circle of camembert wrapped in butcher paper in her refrigerator, the split in the lining of her shoe, the water level when she takes a bath, the little pink roses on her teacup, how she'll buy the lemons and the peaches—I see it all! I feel like I'm lost in the Wheel, only a part of some larger whole, and I can *breathe.* It's such a relief. But then I have to come out. I have to come back.

"What's wrong with me is what always intrudes. It overlies everything, that shadow. It's what never, ever, ever goes away. *No! You can't do that, you can't do that, shame on you, shame!* And I have had enough. I have had enough! I am going to give it a real try here, I am by God going to try everything I can, and I am . . . I am . . . *No fear,* okay?" She pounded the arm of her chair at this last. Then she stopped, deeply embarrassed. "Jesus. Oscar clip. I'm sorry."

"Don't be sorry," I said, moving over to her, touching her am. "I'm glad you told me that. It makes me . . . well, it makes me know you." I looked at my watch. "Let's go out to lunch, want to? My treat. You can eat anything you want from anywhere you want it. I need to tell you something from Steve. And then I need you to tell me how I can help." *And then I want to go home.*

"I *was,* sick," Caroline said. "And Steve's right. When I was lying on the cot in the nurse's office, I heard her kind of yelling at

Mom. *Didn't you notice she had a fever, Mrs. Meyer?* I remember wanting to come home because I felt so bad and yet dreading it because I knew I'd be in trouble again."

I played with the few strands of pasta left on my plate. In it, I suddenly saw a kind of filigree design that was actually very beautiful. I started to say, "I'm listening to you, Caroline. But I just saw something here that I want to get down." I could feel heat rising at the back of my neck at the thought, at how close I came to pulling out my sketch pad, knowing that she would have said, in one way or another, "It's okay. I don't mind."

Instead I said, "I . . . it must have been so hard for you." I cleared my throat. D+, I gave myself for that attempt at an empathic response. Beneath the table, my free hand curled into a fist.

Caroline smiled sympathetically. She could see I was ready to jump out of my skin. "Look. I know you've been trying very hard to . . . in the midst of . . ." She put her hand over mine. It was such an awkward gesture; I could feel the clamminess. Were we friends, were we real sisters, I could comment on this, say something funny, and it would be fine. As it was, I ignored what surely both of us were aware of, making the moment even more awkward than it already was. "I'm trying to say thank you. It means so much that you listened to me. And that you said you believe me." She took her hand away, put it in her lap. "So."

I moved closer to her. "So. What now? Do you still feel like you need to talk to Mom?"

"I know it's not the right time, with Dad . . ."

"Probably not."

"And I've got lots of work to do in the meantime, God knows."

"I guess we all do."

"Thank you for coming back here, Laura. You can . . . why don't you go back home? I know it's hard for you to be away. But could I call you sometime?"

That she needed to ask. "Any time," I said, and a small black part of my heart singsonged, *You don't mean it.* "Any time," I said again, overcoming it.

I decided to pay the extra cost and fly home that evening. Before I left for the airport, I called Aunt Fran. "I've been thinking," I said. "I would really like permission from you to tell Caroline and Steve what you told me."

"Oh, Laura."

"I think it might help. I think it might help everyone."

"She trusted me to never let you kids know."

"But look at what's happening. Caroline is having a lot of trouble right now, dealing with the way she grew up. I mean, she had a mother who attacked her with a knife, and she—"

"What?"

"Well, Aunt Fran . . . you know that. You said you knew. You said you knew! Mom attacked—or very nearly attacked—Caroline with a knife! That's why Caroline was hospitalized."

"Oh, honey. Oh my goodness. That's not true. It was the other way around! She came after your mother!"

"That's what my mother told you?"

"It was the other way *around*! Oh my goodness. Caroline said your mother attacked *her*? No, sweetheart, I swear to you, it was the other way around! Ask—oh, I was going to say ask your father. But he knew. It was Caroline who tried to attack your mother!"

There sat the spider, beautiful in her web, drops of dew shining like diamonds all around her. I spoke very carefully. "Aunt Fran. Do you honestly believe that?" I picked up a pencil from the kitchen table, balanced it along the knuckles of one hand while I waited for her answer. *Come on, Aunt Fran, you were my favorite. You in a yellow sundress, holding two of your own kids, one under each arm, laughing.*

"Well, of course I do! It's the truth!"

I let the pencil fall; it rolled under the table. I would not bother to retrieve it. My mother had Aunt Fran, just like she had my dad. There was no more to say. I held on to the phone and stared out the window at the sunset. Beautiful pinks. Dusty rose. Mauve. Wonderful next to sage green.

"Laura?"

"I have to go." I hung up the phone, locked my mother's house, and headed to the car to go to the airport. Enough. I turned on the radio, turned it up loud. Then louder still.

*It is a travel advertisment in a news-
paper, a half-page picture of an older
couple in their late seventies or early
eighties, floating in a pool on rubber
rafts with built-in pillows. The water
is crystal clear and shot through with
jagged lines of sunlight. The man
wears black bathing trunks that
come almost to his knees, funny, in
their way. The woman wears a beautifully designed swimsuit in a Hawai-
ian print with a plunging neckline
that—unbelievably—looks sexy. Her
necklace is made of shells that coor-
dinate with the bathing suit. She
wears a bathing cap covered with
flowers but has left uncovered one
perfect wave of streaked hair. Her
husband holds her hand—it is he
who has reached out to her; it feels
somehow that it is always he who
reaches for her. Her face is a study in
pride: eyebrows plucked in a grace-
ful arch, cheekbones high and
rouged, lipstick perfectly applied.
She has a smile on her face; his expression is more serious, nearly anxious.*

When I came across this picture, I had an odd reaction to it. "Look at this," I told Pete, and he looked over and said, "Huh. Cute."

"It's not cute!" I said angrily.

Pete looked up, surprised.

"It's not! Look at her! This is a woman whose been overly cared for all her life. She's a user; she thinks only of herself. Look at her eyes!"

He looked again. "You can't even see her eyes."

He was right. Both people in the photograph wore dark sunglasses.

"Well, I know what they look like," I said.

"How?" Pete asked, and I did not answer, because I could not say.

21

Pete picked me up at the airport. He leaned over to give me a quick kiss before we pulled away from the curb. I wondered what he'd ask me and what I'd say. I realized I'd fallen once again into uncertainty. I was beginning to think I understood battered wife syndrome: seeing someone as a monster, then as someone not so bad, then as someone familiar and loved. "Damn it!" I said.

"What happened?" He slowed the car, checked the rearview.

"Nothing," I said, waving my hand. "Sorry. It's okay, don't stop. I'll tell you later. I don't even know what I'm feeling." I began to cry, which only made me angrier.

"Are you okay?"

"Yes. No. Oh, I don't know." I wiped away the few tears I'd shed. "Listen, can we go get a drink somewhere? Are the kids okay?"

"The kids are fine. Your mother's there. And . . . well, surprise, my parents are too."

I stared at him, open-mouthed. "When . . . ?"

"They didn't tell me. They were on their way back from somewhere, and they were only fifty miles away. . . . They arrived just after your flight took off from Minnesota."

I leaned back against the seat and closed my eyes. "Pete. You know I love them. But so much is going on!"

"Let's go somewhere and talk."

"Somewhere close. I don't know why I'm angry. I'm not angry. I really am not angry."

The crowded bar was in an airport hotel, and many of the patrons had their carry-ons beside them. I had to squeeze past a large black overnighter to get into my seat. "Oh, sorry," a young woman said, pulling it in closer to her.

"No problem." I said this, though what I wanted to say was *Move it!*

Pete ordered wine at the bar and brought it back to the table. I said nothing until he reached over and rubbed my shoulder.

"What a mess!" I shook my head.

"Did something else happen?"

"You won't believe this. Aunt Fran told me—" I stopped talking, aware that the young woman I squeezed past was listening intently. "I'll tell you in a minute," I said. And then, pointedly, "Maybe we should switch tables."

With that, the young woman rose, put money down on the table, and stalked off.

Pete watched her go. "What was that all about?"

"She was eavesdropping."

"Ah."

"I hate it when people do that."

He said nothing, but in his silence I could hear his all-too-correct accusation: *You do it constantly.*

"Anyway, Aunt Fran told me it was Caroline who attacked my mother, not the other way around."

Pete sat back. "Wow. So what do you think?"

"At first, I was absolutely convinced that Fran was taken in by my mother in the same way Dad always was. But now I don't know. I can't think straight. I feel like I need to be doing something, and I have no idea what to do. I mean, I feel weird going home to see my mother, when I don't know if she . . . I don't know what to believe, Pete. I honestly don't."

"Maybe you just have to let things sit for a while. It's not like you have to make any decisions about anything right away. Whoever did what, it happened a long time ago. Caroline's said what she needed to say, and she's getting help. Your mother's okay for the time being. I think . . . well, I might as well tell you now, I think she wants to stay with us for a while. Lots of hints about how she feels glad to have company, how she can help with this and help with that."

"Help with what?"

"Oh, babysitting—"

"We don't need a babysitter. We finally don't need one!"

"Shopping, she mentioned grocery shopping."

"I like to pick out my own things."

"Laura?"

"What!"

"It's not *my* idea. She's not *my* mother. You know?"

"I know that!" I stared at him. "Oh, I'm sorry. I'm just mad. I want to go home and just have it be normal again. I don't want her there. That's the truth. And I miss my dad, and I haven't even been able to take the time to mourn him." I sighed. "I don't know, I guess you're right. There's nothing to do now but let some time go by. Let's just go home."

In the car, with the radio off, the quiet and the darkness and the presence of Pete began to soothe me. "I'm not going back *there* for a while!"

"You don't have to." He took my hand. "So. You want to know my thing that happened today?"

"What?" I turned toward him, nearly giddy with relief.

Rosa, Subby, my mother, Pete, and I were seated at the kitchen table, and the kids were upstairs in their rooms. We were hav-

ing coffee and the excellent pistachio biscotti that Rosa baked this afternoon, probably fifteen seconds after she set foot in the
house. We were all in our pajamas, and despite the strain of everything that had been
happening, I felt happy. It was as though I'd
awakened from a bad dream, had left behind a pulling darkness to join these familiar faces in this most familiar of settings.
Our voices overlapped as we talked; we
laughed frequently. What was notable, of
course, was my father's absence, that per-
sistent raw spot: my mother's smile fading
as she rubbed the familiar bump of bone on
the outside of her wrist the way she used to
rub the knuckles of his hand.

Rosa's short gray hair was in pin curls,
and she wore a black hairnet over them.
She was talking about her father, how he
used to stuff a sock and call it a cat. "He
would hold it in his arms and pet it,
Goooood kitty, goooood kitty, and then—
MEOW!—he'd make it jump out of his
arms. Oh, I'm telling you, we loved it. We
used to laugh till we peed our pants."

"Today, these kids need cyberspace to
be entertained," my mother said.

"They use it for their schoolwork too,

though," Rosa said. "It's all right. They all find new things; every generation has its own new things."

From upstairs, I heard Hannah calling me, so I excused myself and went up to her room. She had the phone pressed to her chest. "Can I babysit for the Pearsons Saturday night? Their regular sitter canceled."

Hannah had never done this, though she did take a Red Cross course in babysitting. And the Pearsons lived just down the block and their children weren't all that young— maybe five and seven. "Sure," I told her.

Hannah held up a finger, asking me to wait, and said into the phone, "That will be fine. . . . Okay, seven o'clock. Thank you."

She hung up and beamed at me. "My first job. I'll get six dollars an hour!"

"That's great!"

"So . . . what do I do?"

"Do for what?"

"To babysit!'

"Oh! Well, you know, first and foremost, just make sure they're safe. That's why people hire babysitters, to make sure their children are safe. You remember what it was like, having babysitters."

"Yeah, I don't want to be like them, though."

"What do you mean?"

"They were boring. I'm going to be a fun one, like Mary Poppins."

"Okay," I said. "That's a noble goal."

"Did you babysit a lot, Mom?"

"I did." I went over to her bed, motioning for her to move so I could sit beside her. "I have to tell you, though, I was not one of the fun ones."

"Why not?"

"I don't know. I guess I thought I had to be a tough boss."

"Well, I'll be the boss, but I'll be a fun boss. Do you think I could take some things over to show them?"

"What things?"

"I don't know. Books. Maybe a game or two?"

Of course they would have their own. But I loved her enthusiasm. "I think that would be great."

"Okay. So . . . would you close my door?"

Dismissed.

I went out into the hall and then stood for a while at the head of the stairs. I could hear my mother talking about my father, describ-

ing the way he used to make shadow pup-
pets on the walls for us. How much we
used to love that. How none of us would
ever agree on what he was making, and he
would never tell, so that all of us could be
right.

The next morning, I was standing at the
cutting table in my studio when Rosa appeared. "We're going to take off in a little
while."

I put down my rotary cutter and started
upstairs.

"Oh, no, keep working; I just wanted to sit
with you for a while."

"Good." I slid a chair over to her and returned to the mat, to slicing off three-
quarter-inch strips from a bright yellow cotton print.

"Well, it's official: Subby is on the last
hole of his belt. He's going to have to get
suspenders."

I laughed. "That's what you get for being
such a good cook. Anyway, I like suspenders."

"Oh, but he doesn't!"

"Why not?"

"Because his Uncle Yaya wore suspenders and he was such a mess! His pants wouldn't button anymore and his zipper was always a little bit open. Little bits of saliva always at the corners of his mouth. He had a banged-up hat he would never take off, and his shirts always had stains on them. He was the kind of man, seemed like flies were always buzzing around him. They weren't, but it *seemed* like they were. And you know Subby, he likes to be so neat. Every day, with his hair cream and his cologne."

"Well, he doesn't have to look like his uncle just because he wears suspenders!"

"You know how it is. You have associations with things. But today I'm going to get him a nice pair of yellow suspenders; he'll love them. I saw them in Brooks Brothers. He doesn't know. I told him we had to go to the mall on the way out of town. He'll wait in the RV for me; he takes naps while I shop."

"You still like driving around in that thing?"

"Oh, it's wonderful. You make a lot of friends."

I smiled, sliced through more fabric, stacked the strips I'd cut into a pile.

"Laura? I want to ask you something. How are you doing with . . . how are you feeling?"

"I'm okay, Rosa. Thanks." I looked over at her, smiled.

"I remember when my father died, it was . . . I felt suddenly so alone in the world."

"Yes."

"It will take time, sweetheart."

"I know."

"So! I made you some sauce—it's in the freezer. Red gold."

"Thanks. I love your red sauce. I still can't make it like you."

"You have your own way. You're a wonderful cook."

"Rosa? I want to ask you something. If you heard something from a reliable source about someone else—" I looked at her, her wide gray eyes. "Okay. Suppose your sister told you something about your mother that you had a hard time believing. Would you—"

She held up her hand. "I think I know what you're going to say."

"You do?"

"Your mother and I have talked over the

years about your sister. Not a lot, but enough so I know it isn't good between them. And of course I've been with Caroline a few times, and she's . . . well, she's—"

"I know. She's kind of hard. But Rosa, can I tell you something in confidence?"

I looked upstairs, guiltily, and Rosa said, "Your mother is sitting outside with Subby."

"Well, here's the thing. My sister told me about some things that happened between her and my mother, really terrible things."

"Show me a parent who says she hasn't made mistakes, and I'll show you a liar."

"But these were big mistakes, Rosa. Damaging mistakes. I don't know . . . well, the truth is, I don't know who to believe or how to handle this."

She sighed. "Okay. Show me a parent who hasn't made *damaging* mistakes."

"My sister says my mother came after her with a knife."

Rosa sat very still, then breathed out. "*Madonna.* Somebody is in big trouble."

It is someone's birthday party, I can't tell whose. There is a big cake in the middle of the kitchen table. My mother has cut a huge piece, the first piece, and is offering it to Caroline. There are butter-cream flowers on the slice she holds; a candle too—it is a prime piece of birthday cake. My mother's back is to the camera, her hand on her hip. Without seeing her face, you can guess at her expression. That is because you can clearly see Caroline's face, taut and unsmiling. Refusing what is offered her. It must be my father taking the picture; he is the only one not at the table. What he was attempting to document, I don't know. For Steve's and my part, we are tossing a balloon back and forth, over Caroline's head. For a long time, we have known that sometimes it serves you best simply to work around an obstacle, to make invisible what you are tired of seeing or don't understand.

22

It was a crowded Saturday morning at Fabric World, and Gregory was spending too much time searching out a fabric for me. He'd vaguely remembered seeing a dog-bone print in novelty fabrics, but now it was nowhere in sight. He looked through all the juvenile fabrics, then searched the back room. "Maybe somebody put it in with the black-and-whites," he said. "Let's go see."

I slogged along behind him, carrying an armload of bolts of fabric that had nothing whatsoever to do with what I was working on. "Put those *down,*" he told me—again—and again I told him no. "What do you think, someone's going to come along and buy a whole bolt?"

"It could happen."

He bent down over a row of black-and-white prints and started going through them. "You know, my partner does that in bookstores. He always buys a lot of books at once, and he carries them around the whole time, this big stack of books. I tell him to put them *down,* and he says no, somebody might buy them. Like there's not more. Like he's holding on to the last copies. And even if he were, like he couldn't order others."

"I understand completely," I said. "That is the way things should be done."

He looked disapprovingly over his shoulder at me. "Hmmm. I suppose you're a first-born."

"I am!"

"So is Raymond. You all are so bossy." He pulled out a bolt of fabric, a white printed with tiny black dog bones. "Voilà!"

I snatched it from him. "Oh, perfect! Thank you!"

"Come over to the table, I'll cut it for you myself."

"To what do I owe this great honor?"

He shrugged. "Friendship."

It was true. We were friends. And yet I'd never exactly thought of it that way. I sought out Gregory every time I came to Fabric World; I was disappointed when he wasn't there; we sat in his office and talked fabric and gossiped, yet until now I'd never really thought of him as a friend. It felt vaguely greedy to think of him that way, as though one were appropriated a certain number of friends and should not cultivate relationships beyond that. But that was ridiculous! And so, "Hey, Gregory," I said. "Would you and Raymond ever like to come to my house for dinner?"

"Ever? Is this a tentative invitation?" He whispered this last.

"No. It's a definite invitation."

"What night?" He began unwinding one of the bolts of fabric. "How much?"

"Three yards of each. And . . . I don't know. Any night."

"How's tonight? Because I know we couldn't do it otherwise for a couple of weeks. We're very popular, as you can imagine."

"I can."

He looked over the top of his glasses at me. "You're so easy. Actually, it's that we're going on vacation tomorrow. Two weeks in San Francisco, and I can't wait."

"Tonight? . . . Well, sure, why not? I have to warn you, though, my mother is staying with us."

He folded up the fabric he'd cut for me, leaned forward to say, "She'll love me."

"I'm not worried about that part."

"I'm sure I'll love her too."

I said nothing. Finally, he laughed and said, "Oh, so what?"

"Seven o'clock?" I said and he nodded, then rolled his eyes as he heard himself paged. "I hate it when you're at work and they make you work!" he said. "It's so un-fair!"

At four o'clock, I called Maggie and asked her if she and Doug wanted to come to din-ner as well. "Can't," she said. "We're al-ready going out—with Doug's boss. I have to wear nylons and everything."

"Sorry."

"Has to be done."

"So tell me," I said. "If I use my mother-in-law's red sauce, do I have to confess it's not mine?"

"Who'll ask?"

"Gregory will. I can feel it in my bones."

"What's so wrong with saying it's not yours?"

"I don't know. I feel like if you invite people to dinner, you should make it yourself."

"That was in the olden days."

"Okay. Thanks for the reality check." I hung up and the phone rang immediately. It was Caroline.

"Hey," I said. "How are you doing?" I looked at the clock on the kitchen wall; I had to get busy on the lasagna. I should have let the machine pick up.

"I'm okay," she said. And waited.

I waited too, then finally asked, "So . . . things are going well?" I could hear the tension in my voice; I hoped she could not.

"Have you . . . do you know when she's coming home?"

"Mom?"

"Yeah."

"I don't. Soon, I would expect. I think she just felt like she needed to have people around her for a while. Why?"

"Oh, just—"

"Are you thinking you need to . . . do something with her?"

"I'm thinking I need to spend some time with her, yes."

"I don't know, Caroline. She hasn't said much about when she's going back. Listen, I'm sorry, but this is a really bad time. I'm having company for dinner, and—"

"Oh! Why didn't you say so? Never mind."

"Don't do that."

"What?"

"Look, I'm sorry, I just don't have time right now."

"Yes, I know. You told me. I heard." She hung up.

I stood for a while with the receiver in my hand, then put it back in the cradle. *Not this time,* I was thinking.

I took out the things I needed from the refrigerator and began chopping onion and garlic. Maggie was wrong; I had to make my own sauce. The door burst open and Anthony came in, followed by Hannah and my mother. In a way, my mother had moved from being my mother to another one of the kids. I kind of liked her like this. "Where have you guys been?" I asked.

"We took Grandma to Sam Goody's," Hannah said. "She got us CDs."

My mother leaned on the kitchen counter, watching me chop the onions. "What's for dinner?"

"Lasagna," I said. "We're having guests."

"Who?" Hannah asked, and when I told her, she wailed, "Nooo! I can't be here! I have to babysit!"

I'd forgotten, but I didn't want to admit this, so I said, "Well, there'll be another time."

"How do you know? You've never had Gregory here!"

"There will be," I said. And then, as the phone rang yet again, "Answer that, will you?"

Hannah picked up the phone, listened, and then said, "Oh, hi, I'm so happy you're coming!" Then, listening more, she said, "Oh, no! Really? Well, tell him he'll get better if he comes here!"

I wiped my hands on a dish towel and reached out for the phone. "Here's my mom," Hannah said. She grabbed her CDs and ran toward the stairs and her room.

"Who's Gregory?" I heard my mother ask

Anthony at the same time that Gregory told me, "I'm going to kill Raymond. Don't tell anyone I did it. I'll try to be humane."

"What's up?" I said.

"He is *such* a hypochondriac! He's convinced he's having some *respiratory* problem. I have to take him to the ER, his home away from home."

"But *is* something wrong?" I asked, alarmed, and Gregory said, "No, no. It's nothing. It's never anything. He always does this before we go on trips. He gets anxious when we leave home. It is never anything, and it won't be this time either. He's always got something. And it's always something with a very grim prognosis." I hear him cover the phone with his hand and then he shouts, "I'm coming! Just start the car." He lowered his voice. "Last time the doctor said, 'Mr. Haley, why don't you just go home and get on with your life?' Listen, I'm so sorry to cancel at the last minute. . . . Although I also invited myself at the last minute."

"It's okay," I said. "We'll do it another time."

"Can we?"

"Of course. Call me when you get back from vacation. We'll set something up."

"His real problem," Gregory said, "is that he just quit his job and now he's *between.* He doesn't know what to do with himself. He runs around vacuuming all the time. I mean, I'm gone all day and then I come home and I'm returning phone calls and he has to go and *vacuum.* I say to him, "Uh, Raymond? Can you see that I'm—*Hold on, I'm coming!*"

"You'd better go."

"Yes, on to macaroni surprise at the hospital cafeteria. I can't wait."

I hung up the phone, crossed my arms, stared at the lasagna pan. "Well, that's that."

"What? He can't come?" Anthony asked. "But can't you make it anyway?" Lasagna was Anthony's favorite food. He could easily put away half a pan for a single serving.

"I'll make it," my mother said. "Why don't you and Pete go out to dinner? You two could use a night out."

The idea of going out with Pete was very appealing—a dress-up date with my husband. Time alone.

"Go ahead, I'll feed the kids," my mother said. "Pick Pete up at work and surprise him."

I looked at my watch, then at her.

"Go!" she said.

Anthony stood and raised his arms up high, stretching. "Okay with me," he said. Fewer people equaled more lasagna.

I went upstairs and into Hannah's room. She was listening to her new CD with her headphones on, her eyes closed. I lifted up the headphones and told her, "I'm going to go out to dinner with Dad, okay? I know I said I'd be here when you babysat, in case you needed anything."

"I'm fine," she said. "I've got everything planned—they're going to love me, they're going to want me all the time. And anyway, Grandma will be here."

I changed clothes and all but skipped down the steps. I wouldn't tell Pete anything except that he had to come with me. Then I'd take him for a steak the size of Russia. We would talk about everything but the stone in my shoe.

On the way home from the restaurant, Pete turned off the radio and looked over at me. "Hey. Want to go make out?"

"I knew you'd like this outfit." I'd worn a

red dress with a low neckline that I still looked pretty good in, and heels high enough to cause pain. All through dinner, I'd left them off my feet.

"I mean it. I know a place right near here."

"How do *you* know a place?"

"Watch." He made a few turns, and we pulled into the back lot of a grocery store.

"Very romantic," I said, gazing over at rows of wooden crates stacked up against a concrete wall, at a massive-sized Dumpster, the lid yawning open, heads of what looked like cabbage strewn across the top of a small mountain of garbage.

"This is what constitutes romance at our stage of the game: It's dark, and there are no other people." He tuned the radio to what passed as a jazz station and raised an eyebrow. "There will be absolutely no interruptions."

"You must have had more wine than I thought."

He pulled me to him. "I love my wife."

"Well. That's very nice."

Very slowly, he ran his hand up my leg. I started to laugh, to say, We're too old, this is ridiculous! But we weren't, and it wasn't.

When I was in grade school, I, along with

the other girls, wrote boys' names on my notebook paper, wrote myself as *Mrs.* a hundred times in a dreamy script. But I did that in the same way that I wore whatever clothes were in style—I had no real belief that I would ever meet in the middle with someone. And indeed it did take a long time for me to find someone I wanted to marry. But I'm so glad I waited. What I know about Pete and me is that the flame will never go out. I do not look up from tossing the salad and think, *Oh, God, how the hell did I ever get here?* I do not look at the back of his head and think, *I don't know you at all.* I wake up with my pal, and go to sleep with my lover. He still thrills me, not only sexually but because of the way he regards the life that unfolds around him. I am interested in what he says about me and the children and our respective jobs, but I am also interested in what he says about the Middle East and the migratory patterns of monarchs and the amount of nutmeg that should be grated into the mashed potatoes and the impact that being a thwarted artist had on the life of Hitler. I believe Pete is a truly honest and awake and kind individual. If we live more than once, I want to find him again. The family I have made with him are my bunker and my sword. They are another form of oxygen: Without them, everything in me would shut down. It is terrifying to know that love can have such power. It is also gratifying.

As we turned down our street, I saw the spastic flash of ambulance lights. I sat up straight and leaned forward, alarmed. "What's that?"

"It's not our house," Pete said. And then, "It's the Pearsons! Isn't Hannah babysitting for them?" Reflexively, a little drama played out in my head: me, telling Maggie, *Pete said, Isn't Hannah . . .*

We pulled up outside of the Pearsons and ran out of the car. There on the lawn were Hannah, the Pearson boy, and my mother. My mother was kneeling beside Tyler, talking to him. The ambulance attendants were putting a gurney with a small figure—Nicki—strapped in place into the back. There was a big bandage on her forehead. I ran over to them and asked breathlessly, "What happened?" The attendant who climbed in with Nicki leaned forward to close the door. "Not as bad as it looks, but we've got to go." The door slammed shut and the ambulance took off, siren wailing.

Hannah wept loudly, and Pete stood beside her, speaking quietly to her. I went over and put my arms around her. "Hannah, what happened?"

"I was giving Nicki a piggyback ride to bed," she gulped. "She leaned back, trying to reach for her stuffed animal, and I dropped her and she fell and cut her eye on the coffee table."

"She cut her eye?"

"Right beside her right eye," my mother said.

"Oh, Hannah." I pulled her closer, rubbed her back. She was crying so hard she was hiccuping. I looked over at Pete, who nodded at me, meaning he'd stay. I took her hand. "Come on, let's go home."

"I'll stay here," I heard my mother tell Pete. "You go with them."

Hannah cried until she exhausted herself. Nothing Pete or I said seemed to console her. Finally, leaving her in her room, Pete and I went downstairs. Just as we were collapsing into the sofa, the door slammed and my mother came into the room. "Mrs. Pearson is at the hospital; Mr. Pearson just came home. They said the girl will be all right. She can come home tomorrow." She sank into a chair.

"Do you think we should go over and talk to Jim?" I asked Pete.

"Wait till tomorrow," he said. "I think that will be better. I'll go with you first thing in the morning."

"What was he like?" I asked my mother. "Was he really upset?"

"Well, of course he was! Wouldn't you be?"

"Well, *yes,* but . . . what did he say?"

"Not much, really. Just listened to what happened and made sure his son was all right. I told him it was all Hannah's fault and apologized for her."

For a moment, I sat very still. Then I said, "What?"

She cocked her head brightly. A woman at a bridge table, her hand in the peanut bowl. Charms on her bracelet tinkling.

"What did you say?" I asked, my voice rising.

Confused, she looked over at Pete, who said, "Laura—"

"No!" I told him. And then, to my mother, "You told him it was all Hannah's fault?"

"It was!" She was angry now; twin patches of color appeared in her cheeks.

"It was an accident, Mom! She didn't mean to do it!"

"Well, I know that. But it was her *fault*!"

"Did you tell her that?"

She opened her mouth, closed it.

"Did you, Mom?"

"I may have said something like that. I mean, it was very confusing at first. I got a call; I went over there; the child was bleeding badly."

I stood, started to say something, but went instead upstairs to Hannah's room. I turned on her bedside light and saw her lying there, her eyes wide. "Honey? Listen. I know you feel so, so bad."

"Grandma's right; it's all my fault."

So she'd heard everything. "It was an accident, Hannah. You never anticipated such a thing would happen."

"I made her get a scar!"

"How do you know? They do things now that—"

"Grandma said. She said she'll have a big scar on her face her whole life!"

"Hannah, Grandma—she didn't really know what she was saying. She just said the first thing that came into her head. She was frightened, and she—"

"No, Mom! She's right! Don't you think I know that?"

Again, she began to sob, and I lay beside her and wrapped my arms around her. I was remembering the time she was four years old and I took her to a Kmart, telling her she could have any toy she wanted. She'd decided she wanted a doll, and we looked for a long time at all the options available: the long-haired high-breasted Barbies; the fancy baby dolls that talked and ate and wet; the ones that came with high chairs and playpens and dishes and toys; the delicate porcelain dolls with dresses made of lace and velvet, with prim, painted lips. And then Hannah found a doll lying along the bottom of a bin. She was not in a box, and she had a rip in her cloth body. "This is not a good one," I'd told Hannah. "This one is damaged." The doll was cheaply made; her eyes did not open and close, the fabric used to cover her body was thin and shiny, her plastic toes were more grotesque than endearing, and she came with not so much as a diaper. But Hannah pulled the doll to her breast. "I will call her Baby Annie," she'd said.

I remembered, too, a time when she was about the same age and Anthony had a play date, so Hannah and I decided to have a play date of our own. We were walking to the bus stop, on our way downtown, when we passed a tiny turquoise-colored egg on the sidewalk, not far from a tree. "What's that?" Hannah asked, squatting down to inspect it, and I told her it was a robin's egg. I did not say that it appeared that a cat had gotten at the nest or that perhaps the wind had knocked it down. I did not point out the fine crack running along its side. "Where's its mother?" Hannah asked, and I said, Oh, the mother would be back soon. We went downtown and bought new clothes at Hannah's favorite store. We had lunch and ice-cream floats at the dime-store lunch counter. We went to the library and spent over an hour selecting just the right books to bring home.

That evening, I'd sat her on a high stool to help me wash potatoes for dinner. The sun was setting; I remember admiring the red highlights it brought out in her still baby-fine hair. "Now, you scrub all the dirt off the potatoes," I'd said. "And then we will bake them." "Okay," she said. And then, "Mommy? Did the mother come yet?" It took me a moment to remember what she was talking about. But then I kissed the top of her head and said, "Yes, she did. She's putting the egg to bed now." "How do you know?" Hannah asked, and I took a breath in, and then, with all the nonchalant authority I could muster, I said, "Well, because it's *sunset,* silly." "Oh," she said, and began scrubbing the potato, which was twice the length of her hand. It must have felt heavy for her to hold but she scrubbed it uncomplainingly.

I saw Hannah as made of bamboo, light in the wind. She was still just a child, un-formed and questioning, guileless and gullible, her psyche wet clay. She was tak-ing in what was around her and it would help make her what she would be. I realized what I needed to do. I would stay here until Hannah fell asleep, and then I would tell my mother that I wanted her out of here. That I knew who she was. That I knew everything.

* * *

After I heard the deep and regular sounds of Hannah breathing, I crawled into bed beside Pete. "Are you awake?" I whispered.

"Yeah. How's Hannah?" He didn't open his eyes, but he turned onto his side, facing me.

"She feels terrible, but she finally fell asleep. Pete, tomorrow I'm telling my mother she has to leave."

Now his eyes opened. "Laura—"

"She ruined one of her own children. She's not going to ruin ours."

"She didn't ruin Hannah. She said something at the time that—"

"She's diabolical, Pete!"

"Shhhhhhhh!" He turned on the light.

"I don't care if she hears!" But I did lower my voice to say, "Why do you defend her? Why are you so easy on her when you know what she did to my sister?"

"I *don't* know everything that happened between your sister and your mother. I don't know yet! And neither do you. We might never know."

"Well, I know this. If she can make a kid who already feels terrible feel worse, if she can *on purpose* do such a thing, she's capable of more."

"But Laura, think of what else she's done. Think of how the kids feel about her, how Hannah loves her!"

"So did Caroline, Pete. Caroline adored her. Until she woke up. I'm telling you, I am throwing her out. She cannot be around my children."

"Maybe you need to just . . . sleep on it."

"Nothing will change my mind, Pete. If you don't want to see, don't see. But nothing will change my mind."

"Laura, if Hannah can forgive your mother for overreacting one time, can't you?"

"Hannah forgives her because she doesn't know what's coming next."

"Neither do you! Laura, people make mistakes, sometimes they make terrible mistakes. Forgive us our trespasses, you know?"

"Yeah, right. Directed at Our Father, who art in heaven. On earth is not like heaven."

He was quiet for a moment, and then he said, "Well, here's what I believe. Sometimes it is. I guess it's up to us to try to make it so. At any rate, at least make sure your mother was the one at fault before you blame her entirely for the way Caroline is."

"How?" But then I knew how. I would do what Caroline had been asking me to do. I would sit with the two of them while Caroline opened that big black bag.

It is by itself, barely adhering to the center of the page with Scotch tape turned butterscotch yellow and brittle to the touch. The photo is small in size and the image is blurred, evidence of the imperfect skills of the photographer. But there is a loveliness about it, a kind of peace. In the center is a large tree, leaves in the barely budding phase. There are a few high clouds in the sky, the cirrus variety that look like stretched cotton candy. There is an oblique slant to them; they look as though a giant hand has brushed over them, urging them ever upward. The land is empty-looking; in early spring, not much would have been growing yet. But there are low hills in the background, and a far-off line of evergreens lends the picture a softness, a kind of promise. Beneath the picture, in labored child's writing, is this:
BY: CAROLINE. THIS IS NUMBER ONE!
There are no more.

23

In the morning, I dressed and came into the kitchen to find Pete at the table, eating breakfast. "I'm going to call Jim Pearson," he said.

"Why don't we just go over there? He'll be up—he's an early riser."

"Okay. All right." He got up, shoved his hands in his pockets, cleared his throat. "Ready?"

Together we crossed the street to go to the Pearsons' door. I rang the bell, then looked over at Pete. I was as nervous as he. Anything could happen. A lawsuit.

The door opened, and Jim said, "Oh, hey, I was just going to call you two. Come on in."

We entered the hallway and followed Jim into the living room. "Have a seat," he told us, and we moved to the sofa, sitting close to each other. On the floor, I saw a pile of books I remembered reading to Hannah when she was a little girl; she must have brought them over. I looked away from them.

"I just want you to know we're so sorry about what happened," Pete said. "How is Nicki?"

"She's *fine.* She'll have a tiny little scar that will all but disappear when she gets older. She's being released this morning. I'm getting ready to go and get her and my wife. How about Hannah? Is she okay?"

I had an impulse to turn triumphantly to Pete and say, *See?* Instead, I said, "She feels pretty terrible."

"I was afraid of that," Jim said. "When I was in fifth grade, I accidentally hit a kid in the head with a baseball bat. It ended up that he was all right, but man! I had some sleepless nights." He reached into his pocket and pulled out his billfold. "I never paid her."

"It's all right," I said, and felt Pete lightly

touch my arm. He thought I should take it for her.

"I'd like her to have it," Jim said. "And I'd like you to tell her that almost the first thing Nicki said when I saw her is that she'd like to have Hannah sit again. Up until the time of the accident, they were having a great time. Hannah helped Nicki make a coat for her doll, and she and Tyler made a picture using popcorn kernels. He's got it on his wall."

"I'll tell her," I said.

"If we don't call her right away, it's because we do have a regular sitter—"

"I understand."

Pete rose and offered his hand to Jim. "I know you must be eager to go. Thanks so much for understanding. I really appreciate it."

"It's fine, Pete. Let's go out for a beer soon."

When we walked back home, I said, "That's the kind of compassion I would have hoped for from my mother."

"He's had a day to get used to it, Laura. And he had a doctor tell him his daughter was going to be fine. He didn't see her standing there screaming with blood all over her."

I said nothing until we arrived home. When we came into the kitchen, my mother was at the stove, fussing with something in a frying pan. "I'm serving Hannah breakfast in bed," she said.

Pete looked at me. "I'm going to the store and catch up on some paperwork," he said. Meaning, *It's all yours.*

I sat at the table, watching my mother. It was still familiar to me, the movement of her back in a robe, fixing breakfast at a stove. I knew precisely how high she would hold the spatula, how briskly she would scramble the eggs. "Hannah's up already?" I asked.

"She is. I heard her calling for you, and I—"

"I'll be right back." I went up into Hannah's room and found her leaning back against her pillows, reading a book.

"Hey." I sat beside her.

She marked her place, put the book down. "Where were you?"

"Dad and I went to talk to Mr. Pearson." Her expression changed, and I said, "Don't worry, he's fine. And Nicki's fine too—she's coming home today, and she'll have a very, very small scar that will end up disappearing completely. And you know what she wants?"

"What?" She wouldn't look at me.

"She wants you to babysit again. She really liked you. And Mr. Pearson did too. He sent over the money you earned."

She looked up, her eyes full of tears. "I don't want it. And I don't ever want to babysit again."

"Oh, Hannah. I know how bad you feel, honey. I really do. But if you never babysit again, you'll deprive a lot of kids of some really wonderful experiences. It was an accident. Nobody blames you. In fact, Jim told us about a kid he once hit accidentally with a baseball bat!"

Half a smile. "Really?"

"Yes!"

"Was he okay?"

"Yes! He was!"

"Well, I think I'll wait awhile. But I'll tell Mr. and Mrs. Pearson I'm sorry. I'll write them a note."

"Okay." I kissed her forehead. "So you're having breakfast in bed, are you?"

"Yeah, I woke Grandma up but she was

really nice. She said she'd make me breakfast. And she said she was sorry for yelling
at me."

"Did she? Well, I'm glad she did." I waited
for a moment, then said, "Hannah? I'm going to take Grandma home today."

"You are?"

"Uh-huh. I think I'll drive her back."

"Does she want to go home?"

I stood and straightened Hannah's covers. "Yeah, I think she's probably ready to
go back. It's hard to be away from home for
too long. You know."

"But . . . she said she wished she could
live here."

"When? When did she say that?"

Hannah tilted her head, looked deeply
into my eyes. "Are you *mad*?"

"No! When did she say that?"

Hannah shrugged. "A lot of times. To me,
and to Anthony too. Didn't she tell you?"

"Here we are," my mother said, and
walked into the room with a tray. Hannah
and I exchanged glances, and I said, "You
go ahead and eat, honey. I'll talk to you
later." Then to my mother, "Mom? Can we
go downstairs and talk for a minute?"

"Wait!" Hannah said.

I turned around, and Hannah said to my mother, "Could I . . . I need to talk to my mom alone, Grandma. Okay?"

"That's fine," my mother said lightly. "My goodness, I don't mind. A person has to have privacy sometimes. You enjoy your breakfast."

She closed the door in as pointed a way as it was possible to do. I sat down again, at the foot of Hannah's bed.

"Don't make her leave, Mom."

"It's time for her to go home."

"Why?"

"Hannah, I can't explain everything right now. But"—I lowered my voice—"there are some things I need to find out. I don't feel I can really trust her. She's capable of bad things. I think she—"

Hannah dropped her fork and covered her ears. "She's my *grandma*!"

I wanted to say, *Yes, and you are my daughter.* Instead, I uncovered her ears and said, "Okay. Okay. Don't worry. Eat your breakfast, okay? Don't worry."

Downstairs, my mother sat at the kitchen table with a toasted English muffin covered with her usual slathering of butter. She loved butter, and she used to put it on my sandwiches when she made my school lunches. I would tell her every day not to, and the next day she would put it on again, because that was the way she liked *her* sandwiches. She had just begun to take a bite, but when she saw me she stopped and put the muffin back on her plate.

"Eat," I said, and surprised myself by the nasty tone of my voice. I moved to sit across from her, reached out to touch her hand. "I'm sorry. I didn't mean that the way it sounded. I just meant, don't stop eating on my account."

She said nothing. I could see her heart beating in her throat, saw sleep in the corner of one of her eyes, something I was sure I'd never seen before. I didn't know if my mother was becoming less meticulous or simply couldn't see well anymore. Whatever the reason, I could feel my resolve weakening. Should I really ask her to leave my house, insist that she do so, when everyone else in the family seemed so much against it, or at least deeply ambivalent? Was I making too much out of what she said to Hannah because it was the only way I could think of to support my sister? Was I now going to start cataloging my own slights, punishing my mother for putting butter on sandwiches forty years ago?

My mother is the one who took us kids out one hot summer afternoon to pick up pizza at a parlor where the temperature was truly unbearable. It wasn't the temperature outside or the blasting ovens on the inside; the air-conditioning had gone out in the place. The woman who waited on us had sweat pouring off her; yet she smiled pleasantly and wished us a happy picnic—we were going to a park across the street. After we ate lunch, my mother took us into the florist next to the pizza parlor, bought the woman a lovely bouquet, and then asked me to give it to her. "But what should I tell her?" I asked my mother, a little angry that she wouldn't deliver it herself. "You don't have to tell her anything," my mother said. "She'll know we just appreciate her being so pleasant under the circumstances." I think she wanted me to do it so I could enjoy the reaction, so I could see it was possible to bring joy to a stranger and take away more for yourself.

And once, when I whimsically suggested that I wanted my teddy bears to get married, my mother immediately manufactured

a wedding between two stuffed animals.
She made a paper-towel runner in the upstairs hall, put a white cake in the oven,
and, while it baked, ran to a nearby party
store for supplies. She bought napkins with
a wedding motif, and silver and white crepe
paper, and a plastic bride and groom to put
atop the cake. She made Steve, then eight,
be the minister; she made me the matron of
honor, and she made herself the "guests."
Caroline was supposed to be the soloist,
but at the last minute she refused to sing.
"There's no music," she said petulantly, and
she sat off to the side, watching the ridiculous but tender ceremony and picking at
one of her toes. You could look up her
faded red shorts and see her underwear,
which to my mind ruined the ceremony entirely.

But. There was also everything Caroline
had told me. There were the brief flashes of
memory and understanding that I was beginning to have. If one's life was about anything, it was about making choices, taking
risks, deciding what was worthwhile and
what was not. I could not have my mother
with my children when so much was still in
doubt.

My mother pushed her plate away and sat up straighter. "What do you want to talk about, Laura?"

"This is hard for me to say, Mom, so bear with me. But things are kind of . . . well, I need a little time to be alone with my family. I think it might be best if I drive you home."

"When?"

"Today."

She drew in a sharp breath, started to say something, and then rose abruptly to carry her dishes to the sink. "You can take me to the airport right now." She turned on the water hard to rinse out her cup and ended up splattering herself. She jumped back and dropped the cup, shattering it, then put her hands to her face and began to weep. I walked slowly over to her, stepped past the shards of china, and put my arms around her. She hugged me back abruptly, tightly, and then whispered into my ear, "You know, don't you?"

I nodded. "Yes."

"Caroline told you everything?"

"Yes. And I know it was you who came after Caroline with the knife that day, Mom."

Inside myself, a frayed string on which hung a last hope: *Say no. Say you never did that, it never happened.* But what she said was, "Yes."

I closed my eyes, swallowed. "And . . . I know about Claire. Aunt Fran told me."

She stepped away from me, sighed deeply. There passed a long moment during which she would not look at me. Then she said, "I'll go and pack. And then I would like to be driven to the airport."

I wanted to say, You know what? Your days of dictating are over. Your needs coming first? That's over. But all I said was, "I'm going to pack too, Mom. I'll drive you home."

It took two hours of driving before either of us said anything. While my mother packed, I rather abruptly told my children what I was going to do, then called Pete at the store to tell him the same. When we left, I looked away when my mother hugged Anthony and Hannah and tried not to mind their stiffness when I hugged them too. When I spoke privately to Anthony, telling him I was taking Grandma home because I wasn't comfortable with her behavior during the babysitting incident, he said, "God, Mom, you're pretty hard on people." I wanted to argue my case, but I remembered Hannah's reaction when I tried to tell her more. In the end, I just told him I'd see him in a few days and left. At the right time, I hoped I'd find the words.

It was odd, having my mother beside me in front. I couldn't remember a time when I drove her for any length of time. It didn't compute, somehow, to see her knee in my peripheral vision, to feel the small moves she made adjusting herself on the seat.

I was still full of such a mix of conflicting emotions. Not the least of these was still a kind of anger at Caroline, for bringing all this on. I recognized it was unfair, this lack of love and support one should have for a sister. But I didn't have it. We grew up virtual strangers to each other. It was hard, at this age, to try to create a natural bond I never had, to feel for someone who so often made me impatient. If I were to meet Caroline as someone other than my sister, could I feel sympathy for her? If what she was saying was true, I could. And it was true.

So here beside me, in the form of my mother, was the woman who did all those terrible things to her child. How did one begin a dialogue with such a person? Especially when she was such a different mother to Steve and me. Did she deserve a last chance to defend herself? Did the fact that she was such a recent widow entitle her to more consideration? Should I begin by telling her that things would be different between us from now on, I wondered, and that for one thing she would not be left alone with my children? Or should I not worry about it at the moment and instead start figuring out how I was going to get her and Caroline and me together, thus putting Caroline's concerns first? Wasn't it time Caroline came first?

I turned off the radio. "Mom?"

"Don't let's talk now," she said. "Let me just get home first." I thought I understood her need for the anchoring influence of one's own things.

"Okay. But I want to tell you, we're going to meet with Caroline as soon as we get there, you and I. It's something she asked for, and we're going to give it to her."

"All right."

I was shocked. I had expected anything but matter-of-fact cooperation. I snuck a look over at her: a faded beauty. A woman staring straight ahead seeing nothing. A woman whose hands were in her lap, fists clenched, waiting out the miles.

I turned on the radio again. Then I said, "I'm going to stop for gas soon. I'll get us some sandwiches."

"All right."

"And I'm going to call Caroline to say we're on the way."

"Yes, I know. I know you will." Her hand to her earlobe, checking for the diamond there. Her only ally on this her judgment day.

24

I once went to a photo exhibit at a museum of modern art. Included in it was a display of school photos taken in the early sixties, children mostly around the age of eleven who had been hauled out of class to line up and then sit on a chair before a school photographer, one of those skinny men with bad breath and a defeated attitude who ask kids over and over to smile without caring, particularly, if they smile or not. The pictures at the museum were framed, and there were yards of foil silver stars on wire wrapped around them and pinned up on the wall be-

tween them. There were tiny white lights
everywhere, too, the kind you put on Christmas trees. Otherwise, the room was dark
and the walls were painted black. I remember thinking that this worked well to con-
tribute to the mood of going back in time, of
feeling encapsulated. You felt yourself disappearing before all these photos of kids
you didn't know, yet did.

Most of the photos were funny, the kind
of thing you point to and giggle: the goofy
expressions, the cowlicks, the braces, the
glasses, the collars with one side up and
one side down. But there was one photo
that stopped me in my tracks, that had me
standing unsmiling before it for a long time.
After I left the exhibit to go and look at other
things, I went back to stand before that
photo again. Then, as I was putting my coat
on, getting ready to go home, I went to go
and look at it for a third time. It was a little
girl, straight-mouthed and clear-eyed. There
was something so compelling in her expression, so deep in her eyes. Looking at
her photo had a kind of pulling effect:
Standing still, I felt as though I moved into
her, then felt inside my own chest the
weight of her great sorrow.

I know now—knew then too, probably—that that photo was Caroline to me. And now, years away from what happened to her and what I contributed to, I was ready to move forward in a way that might make a real difference. I felt a little—a *little*—like I did the time I signed up for tap-dancing lessons at age forty-seven. Not that I saw my intentions as trivial. It was just that I was so late, and I had so much doubt about my abilities.

About ten minutes from Caroline's house, my mother began to speak. "I read once about how anxiety on behalf of a child can transform itself into aggression against a child."

I said nothing, but what I was thinking was, *I read once about how the weakest of a litter is sometimes destroyed by its siblings. We are all guilty.*

She said, "I don't mean this as an excuse. But I was so brokenhearted after the baby died! I felt her every minute of every day for so long. Reaching for me. I couldn't climb out of this terrible despair. Aunt Fran used to come and take you, and I would

just sit in the rocking chair in Claire's bedroom and cry and cry and cry. I don't think I
knew my own mind for a long time. Then,
after Caroline was born, I told your father I
thought I was going crazy. I told him I didn't
love her, that sometimes I felt I hated her,
and he said, No, no, you're fine, you've just
had a shock, you'll be fine, of course you
love your baby, everybody can see that.
And then Caroline was so difficult from the
very beginning, such a dark child, so oversensitive and demanding, really, you might
not realize this, but she was very demanding. Maybe I had Steve in part to prove to
myself that I wasn't a monster. Maybe—"

"Mom. I think Caroline needs to hear this
too. Let's wait till we get there." Somewhere, a pinprick of sympathy for her. A
memory of her lifting me up, pointing at
something she wanted me to see, kissing
my cheek, and then gently wiping away the
marks of her red lipstick. A memory of her
deteriorating handwriting on the tags of the
gifts she sent for my last birthday. Finally,
oddly, perhaps, a memory of a scene in a
movie about Mary Kay, of Mary Kay Cos-
metics, where she is sitting on her bed
as an old woman, wigless and without

makeup, putting blusher on her rapt young granddaughter, telling her in a soft voice why it's "*verrrry* important to put it on your chin and forehead as well as your cheeks. Right?" Her old bones and sunken chest. The tenets on which she built her life now outdated and irrelevant, almost foolish. Though not to her granddaughter. Her granddaughter had her own way of seeing her, and her own relationship to her.

I have a friend from college—Anne—who was recently cleaning out her daughter's room after her daughter left home to move to her first apartment. I'd always thought they had a terrific relationship, and I told Anne that day how much I admired it. But she said, "You know, I was moving some books off my daughter's shelf and I was looking at all the titles and it was such a wonderful mix of literature: novels in French, texts on physics and Dutch art, poetry by Neruda, and then—the killer—*My Goodnight Book.*" This was a picture book Anne used to read to her daughter over and over when she was a little girl. She'd had no idea her daughter had kept it. She started bawling, not only because of the engulfing nostalgia but because she had no idea her daughter had read those *other* books; they'd never talked about a single one. "I always vowed that I would really know my children—and they me," she said. "You just can't do all you intend. Every mother fails."

I felt the quick sting of tears; one rolled down my cheek. Out of the corner of my eye, I saw my mother handing something over to me. A folded handkerchief, a floral one, lace around the edges, perfumed. "You might need this yourself," I said, not looking at her.

"I have another," she said. "I'm never without them. Don't you know that?"

When we knocked on Caroline's door, I was prepared for anything. I accepted that she might carry on for hours, or refuse to talk, or have white bandages wrapped around her wrists that she waved accusingly in front of us. She was completely unreadable when I called and told her we were coming, when I told her about Claire, when I told her that Mom knew I knew everything.

The door opened. Caroline was wearing black pants and a red top, no makeup. She had her hair pulled back, some small hoop earrings on. There were dark circles under her eyes, but her face was blank, noncommittal. From inside, I smelled something chocolaty.

"Come in," she said, and stepped aside while we went down the hall and into the living room. When we were all seated, Caroline said, "I needed to tell, Mom."

My mother nodded. She had not yet looked at Caroline.

"It would have been worse to not tell."

Silence.

It went on and on. I thought of Pete and the kids. I wondered what the dog outside was barking at. I thought of all that might happen after this encounter, wondered whether Caroline would finally free herself from all of us, for which I certainly would not blame her. I wondered how many years it would take for this to settle.

Finally, my mother spoke, her voice low and tentative. "Caroline? Can you tell me about a time in your childhood when you were happy? One time?"

I sat up straighter, ready to hear the onslaught my mother deserved. The selfishness! The cruelty—again! To focus on what was not even the point of this meeting, to make a wounded person turn away from her own vital needs to take care of you!

My sister quietly cleared her throat. "There was a time shortly after . . . It was that summer, a few days before Steve and Laura were going to come home from camp. You and I went for a walk. We were going to buy some groceries, I think. But on the walk, you told me about when you had to get glasses, and Aunt Fran didn't, and how mad you were. And how ugly the glasses you got were. You said they were so heavy and black, you used to hide them all the time, and one time Grandma sat on them because you hid them under a sofa cushion, and she sat on them and broke them and she was really angry. You hid from her for hours in the lilac bushes and Aunt Fran brought you sandwiches, though you didn't deserve them, you said, you didn't deserve them at all. You laughed and you looked so pretty; you were wearing a sky-blue skirt and a white blouse. And then you looked at me and took my hand, and you held it all the way to the store and you tried very hard not to let me see that you were crying. I remember that."

My mother sat still as a painting; it was

hard to see her breathing. Then she said, "And . . . if you could please tell me what you would like me to do now. What I should do."

"Well, I made some brownies," Caroline said. "I thought we could all have some, and then maybe we could go shopping together." I looked over at her, incredulous. That's *it*? But when she looked back at me, something in the clarity of her gaze made me feel as though I understood. The conversation I had just witnessed was between the two of them and had nothing to do with me or my expectations of how things should go. Also, it had nothing to do with bitterness or blame or retribution. This was what my sister was saying: Start here.

25

Next to my bed, I used to keep a photograph of two little girls I didn't know—sisters, judging from the way they closely resembled each other. They were sitting on a porch swing, laughing. They were barefoot, and they wore baggy shorts and sleeveless T-shirts; they had soda-pop mustaches. Their foreheads were nearly touching and their hands were moving toward each other. It was a movement signifying love and ease, as well as a certain sense of belonging. I kept it there because I liked looking at it; for me, it signified the way families ought to be. People who saw it always said, "Oh, this is you and your sister." And I always laughed and said, "No, I have no *idea* who that is." This begged another question, of course, about why I would keep a photo of strangers next to my bed, which was never asked and so never answered.

But Hannah, who just started sixth grade, was recently told to write an essay defining what *family* meant. She described this assignment, uncharacteristically, as impossible. When I asked her why, she said, "Because it's too slippery to say what a family is. It always changes." But she did write the assignment, and in it she said what I thought was a wise thing. She said that you are born into your family and your family is born into you. No returns. No exchanges.

It was reading Hannah's words that prompted me to replace the photo of the little girls I never knew with something else.

It is winter, and Caroline and I are lying outside on the ground, making snow angels. We are head to head, and the photo was snapped when our arms were stretched up, our fingers touching. Our eyes are closed, and we are smiling.

I remember how carefully we stepped away from our imprints, how very much we wanted to leave behind a flawless image. And I remember standing beside her after we got up and seeing that we had done it: There in the snow before us were two perfect angels. But more snow was on the way; already tiny flakes were beginning to swirl around us. All the evidence of our little success would vanish.

Caroline looked up at the gathering clouds, heavy and gray, and shrugged. She said, "We can make another one. We have a lot of days left to go."

ABOUT THE AUTHOR

Elizabeth Berg is the author of twelve previous novels, including the *New York Times* bestsellers *Say When, True to Form, Never Change,* and *Open House,* which was an Oprah's Book Club Selection in 2000. *Durable Goods* and *Joy School* were selected as ALA Best Books of the Year, and *Talk Before Sleep* was short-listed for the ABBY Award in 1996. The winner of the 1997 New England Booksellers Award for her body of work, she is also the author of a nonfiction work, *Escaping into the Open: The Art of Writing True.* She lives in Chicago.